GUARDING
CANADA'S HEALTH SYSTEM

The History of the Canadian Healthcare Association

1931 to 2006

by
Eleanor Sawyer

with the
Working Group on the
History of CHA

CHA Press
Presses de l'ACS
Ottawa, Ontario

Published by CHA Press, 17 York Street, Ottawa, ON K1N 9J6
Tel. 613-241-8005, ext. 264; Fax 613-241-5055; chapress@cha.ca

Cover photo shows delegates at the Canadian Hospital Council General Assembly in 1943 at the Chateau Laurier in Ottawa. All photos in this book are under the copyright of the Canadian Healthcare Association or the author.

Library and Archives Canada Cataloguing in Publication

Sawyer, Eleanor
        Guarding Canada's health system : the history of the Canadian Healthcare Association, 1931 to 2006 / by Eleanor Sawyer ; with the working group on the history of the CHA.

Includes bibliographical references and index.
ISBN 1-896151-23-X

        1. Canadian Healthcare Association—History. 2. Medical care—Canada—History.   I. Canadian Healthcare Association
II. Title.

RA395.C3S29 2006   362.1'06071   C2006-905579-3

Desktop publishing and cover design by Evelyn Budd, Budd Graphics Inc., Ottawa, Ontario

Printed by Marquis book printing inc., Montreal and Cap-Saint-Ignace, Quebec

PRINTED IN CANADA

CONTENTS

FOREWORD

While the idea of writing a history of the Canadian Healthcare Association (CHA) has been considered many times over the years, there never seemed to be a good time to undertake such a project. However, when we were reminded more than two years ago that CHA would celebrate its seventy-fifth anniversary in 2006, this seemed like the appropriate occasion to publish a history of CHA. The board of directors is pleased to see the completion of this book under the title *Guarding Canada's Health System: The History of the Canadian Healthcare Association, 1931 to 2006.*

We believe there is much for CHA to celebrate during this seventy-fifth-anniversary year. From a small ad hoc group of hospital superintendents and physicians in 1931, CHA can rightly be called the voice of Canada's health system today. We speak on behalf of our provincial and territorial health and hospital organizations to ensure that the concerns of the health system are heard at the federal level. How we arrived at such a place today is essentially the story of our association and its journey between 1931 and 2006.

The board of directors would like to extend its congratulations to the members of the Working Group on the History of CHA. This project has taken more than two years and considerable work on their part—both the volunteers and the staff in CHA Press—in order to write this book. Without their commitment and resolve to see this project completed for our anniversary, it is unlikely that there would be a written record of our association available today.

For those who do not know very much about CHA, we hope this book provides you with an historical picture on how and why our association was set up, its evolution as a national organization and the changes it has undergone over the course of its history. For those who have been associated with CHA for some time now—either as board members, member CEOs, past and current staff or associates, partners and opponents—we believe this book will add to your current knowledge and help you to discover many things about the organization that you didn't know. For everyone, we hope it is an enjoyable read—at the very least, an informative one.

GARNET BURNS, CHAIR
CHA Board of Directors
September 2006

PREFACE

In February 2004, the board of directors agreed that a history of the Canadian Healthcare Association (CHA) should be written as part of its seventy-fifth anniversary celebrations in 2006. A draft manuscript already existed, so a Working Group was set up to determine how much of this manuscript could be used for the book and where revisions and more research were needed. Members of the group selected chapters that they would write or revise and a schedule and budget were approved. The first meeting of the group was held in June 2004 to determine how to proceed with this project. In early August 2006, the members met to approve the final manuscript for publication. This book, titled *Guarding Canada's Health System: The History of the Canadian Healthcare Association, 1931 to 2006*, is the end result of more than two years of work by the members.

The Working Group decided at the initial meeting to divide the book into separate parts, each of which would look at a specific aspect of the association. Each part would be introduced by a descriptive overview, followed by specific chapters that provided more detail and outlined CHA's development and growth in these particular areas. Each part of the book would be linked to four key periods in CHA's history as set out in the first section of the book. This initial section also describes some key historical events in the development of Canada's health care system and ties these to developments in the association's evolution.

Part one presents an overview of the four key time frames in CHA's history. These have been divided into the early development of hospitals and associations in Canada from 1899 to 1930, the establishment of the Canadian Hospital Council from 1931 to 1952, the activities of the Canadian Hospital Association from 1953 to 1977 and, finally, the association in Ottawa from 1978 up to 2004. These various periods are covered in chapters one to four in this section of the book. The other five parts of the book focus on specific areas in which CHA has been involved over the course of its history and follow the timeline and format of part one and its chapters as much as possible.

Part two describes the development of the association's governance structure and the evolution of its membership. Chapter 5 discusses governance from the establishment of a powerful executive committee in 1931 to its current board of thirteen members which represents CHA's member organizations on a regional and provincial/territorial basis. Chapter 6 provides an overview of CHA's relationship with its members and how this has changed over the years. The chapter ends with brief historical descriptions of each provincial and territorial health and hospital member association, several of which were provided by the member organizations themselves.

In part four, the book focuses on the programs and services that the organization has developed during its history. Chapter 11 looks at CHA's oldest service, which is journal publishing, and describes CHA's various efforts in other areas in this field. In chapter 12, information is provided on the association's distance learning programs, which have added considerable credibility and both national and international recognition to the organization. This section ends with chapter 13, which looks at CHA's entrance into the conference business and notes some of the key conferences that have been offered over the years.

Part five of the book outlines CHA's activities in the areas of policy development, research and advocacy. Chapter 14 describes the association's research and policy development agenda. While these activities were not part of the early hospital council mandate initially, they came to occupy much of the organization's focus in the late 1970s onward. The last section, chapter 15, describes CHA's early advocacy efforts and moves forward to present in detail how the association has become one of the major national organizations speaking on behalf of Canada's health system today.

In part six, chapter 16 presents a brief look at several major projects that CHA undertook to position both itself and Canada's health system for the future. It describes those that succeeded, as well as those that did not, and shows the various phases of some of these projects over the course of the association's history.

The book ends with a summary of CHA's successes and describes where the organization has played a key role or been most effective for the country's hospitals and for Canada's health care system during its history.

In setting up the format for this book, there were two areas where it was not possible to follow the historical time frame set out in part one. The biographical sketches of the women and men, who were CHA's presidents or chairs, are decribed in chapter 7. In chapter 8, brief outlines of the ten chief executive officers are provided. These are presented on an individual basis, starting with the first person to hold the office and moving forward to 2006. These chapters are in part two. Similarly, it was not possible to discuss CHA's historical partnerships in chapter 9, or the relationships it forged with new partners in chapter 10, by following the historical framework. Again, these two chapters identify the specific organization and present an overview of its relationship with CHA throughout the years. They constitute part three.

Except for special events that have occurred, the Working Group decided that the content of the book would focus on CHA's history up to 2004. Occasionally, it has been necessary to record events in 2005 and 2006, if they became a significant part of the history. But, for the most part, the cutoff year is 2004.

The title of this book is based on a summary of the work that Dr. Harvey Agnew had done over the course of his long involvement with the association. At one point, his actions on behalf of the hospital council were described as guarding the interests of Canada's hospitals to various federal officials. Given his impact on this organization, it seemed appropriate to use words in the title of this book that paid tribute to this man's remarkable contributions to both Canada's hospitals and to CHA. What he started has been carried on over the course of CHA's history, as it too has focused on guarding Canada's health care system over these past seventy-five years.

WORKING GROUP ON THE HISTORY OF CHA
September 2006

ACKNOWLEDGMENTS

As members of the Working Group on the History of CHA, we are entirely responsible for completing this project. As such, we also accept responsibility for the final content in *Guarding Canada's Health System*. However, we would like to acknowledge several other groups or individuals who have contributed to this book and supported the Working Group members either directly or indirectly.

First, we would like to thank the members of the 2004 CHA board of directors for agreeing that this was a worthwhile project to undertake. Several times over the past years, the idea of publishing a history of the association has been discussed by both former and current CHA staff. It is a credit to these board members that they believed this was a worthwhile project to undertake and agreed to commit CHA resources to ensuring that it was finally completed.

Second, we would like to express our appreciation to the chief executive officers (CEOs) of our member provincial and territorial health and hospital organizations who assisted in completing chapter 6 in this book. Their help in undertaking the research and providing historical material about their provincial associations has added valuable information to this book that might not otherwise have come to light.

Third, we want to express our appreciation to four major organizations that generously agreed to provide sponsorship money for this project. Their donations have enabled the members of the Working Group to meet in Ottawa to review various drafts of the manuscript as it progressed between June 2004 and August 2006. These contributions have also supported the editorial production, design, layout, desktop publishing and printing of the final stages of the book.

The Canadian Medical Association (CMA) provided a donation of $5,000 and agreed to support desktop publishing services in the amount of $5,000 for the book.

As one of the initial members of the Canadian Hospital Council, when it was founded in 1931, the CMA remained an active member of CHA until 1981. Periodically, throughout our history, CMA has often supported the association in other ways. These have been described throughout this book. We are most appreciative that CMA's support of CHA has continued for our celebratory history book.

Sun Life Financial was equally generous in contributing $10,000 for this book. Beginning in 1928, this organization funded the work of CMA's Department of Hospital Service. Their annual funding was transferred to the Canadian Hospital Council in 1945 and Sun Life provided an annual grant to CHA for its programs well into the late 1960s. The Working Group would like to thank Sun Life Financial for its sponsorship of this book.

The Canadian Institute for Health Information (CIHI) also donated $5,000 to this publishing project. The institute shares a unique bond with CHA in that our initial Management Information System (M.I.S.) Project, set up in the 1980s, eventually merged with several other organizations to create CIHI. The Working Group wishes to acknowledge and thank the Canadian Institute for its support of this project.

We also want to thank Merck Frosst Canada Ltd. for their $5,000 donation to this celebratory history. Merck Frosst has been most generous in the past in providing sponsorship for other CHA Press projects, especially our long-term care textbook. We are grateful to them for considering this a worthwhile project to which they were also willing to contribute.

The Working Group would also like to thank Sharon Sholzberg-Gray, CHA's president, for her assistance in helping to find sponsors for this book. She has been very understanding and supportive of the Working Group and its efforts and has enabled CHA Press staff to concentrate their time and energy on this project, so that the Working Group members could complete this book for the anniversary celebrations.

We also owe a considerable debt of gratitude to past CHA staff who had the foresight to save CHA's archival records. The association has retained a considerable number of board and committee minutes, some dating back to the early 1900s, as well as journals that date from the early 1920s to 1996. By accessing these historical records, we have been able to accurately record CHA's development and progress over these past seventy-five years. We trust that current and future staff will continue to maintain this record for posterity and for the eventual update of CHA's history when it celebrates its next milestone.

MEMBERS OF THE WORKING GROUP

The Working Group on the History of CHA was set up in June 2004 on the approval of CHA's board of directors, to research and write the history of the Canadian Healthcare Association. The group was made up of six people, who brought a combination of more than 125 years of knowledge and experience through their respective connections to CHA. Each member of the group has made their own unique contribution over the more than two years during which they have worked on this book.

JEAN CROFT has been the Administrative Assistant to the director of CHA's Publishing Department, where she provided administrative, technical and editorial support for title production and maintained the CHA Press offices. She has also assisted in supporting the tenants at 17 York Street. Prior to joining CHA Press in June 1994, she was hired as secretary to the vice-president of conferences in 1985. From 1988 to 1993, she was secretary to a program director and later a senior coordinator for Education programs.

Based on her more than 21 years at CHA, she has provided administrative support to the Working Group. She has also assisted in the research and writing of chapters 12 and 13 on CHA's conferences and distance education programs. With her considerable knowledge of the association, she has researched other chapters for the Director, helped with the selection of photographs for the book and organized meetings for the Working Group. She has also been responsible for keeping track of each member's chapters and maintaining the various drafts of the manuscript as it has progressed. She also prepared the final manuscript for desktop publishing.

Although Jean retired from CHA at the end of 2005, she has remained committed throughout 2006 to ensuring that this book was completed and continues to provide contractual services to CHA Press. Her experience, knowledge of CHA and commitment to the completion of this project has been invaluable to the Working Group.

KENNETH (KEN) EZEARD joined CHA's board of directors in 1990 and has served almost continuously on it as a representative from Prince Edward Island in one capacity or another to this day. He was the chair of the board in 2001 through 2002. He initially approached CHA staff in November 2003 with the idea of publishing a book on CHA's history to celebrate its 75th anniversary in 2006. He agreed to chair the Working Group on the History of CHA. He has researched and written several sections in various chapters, particularly on CHA's history between 1990 and 2006, and provided the historical overview for Prince Edward Island in chapter 6. Ken is also the board liaison between the Working Group on the History and the board Working Group on the 75th Anniversary Celebrations. Although he is retired today, he continues to serve as the executive director of the Health Association of PEI and is CHA's board member from that province. (For more information on his contributions to CHA, *see* chapter 7.)

JEAN-CLAUDE MARTIN was president of CHA from 1977 until 1989. He was also the Director of Development for the CHA Foundation until it was dissolved by the board in 1990. He enthusiastically agreed to join the Working Group in 2004. It was his framework and revised table of contents, based on an original draft manuscript completed in 1991, that was adopted by the Working Group for this book. He has provided research and background from his personal files, and from his own considerable knowledge of CHA and its operations during the period from 1977 to 1989. He has also been particularly helpful in researching, reviewing and writing content for various chapters, particularly chapter 5 on governance and management. And he was most supportive of the Working Group's chief writer during the final months to the completion of this book.

In June 2006, he was awarded CHA's Award of Excellence for Service and Leadership in Canada's health system at the board dinner in Victoria where CHA's celebratory activities for its 75th anniversary were launched. (For more details about his presidency, *see* chapter 8 specifically and several other chapters throughout the book.)

JOAN ROCHE joined CHA in 1964 and provided secretarial and administrative support to the executive director's office and to the board of directors. In 1977, she was one of three CHA staff in Toronto who chose to move to Ottawa where she became the Director of Administration. In 1982, she became CHA's Corporate Secretary, a position she held until 1989. She also worked very closely during these years with the Canadian Association of Health-Care Auxiliaries to help rebuild its membership. In 1995, Joan retired from CHA. She agreed to become a member of the Working Group in 2004. Unfortunately, Joan died in June 2005 before this book was completed. CHA and the members of the Working Group owe much to her for the work she did in writing a draft history of the association between 1990 and 1991. In fact, her original draft manuscript provided a major starting point for this project. Much of her original material remains in parts of chapters 7 and 8. Where it has been possible to do so, we have incorporated other material she wrote into various parts of this book.

ELEANOR SAWYER is the Director of Publishing and Property Management at CHA, a position she has held since 1996. She has worked for the association for more than 31 years in a number of publishing positions. She was Managing Editor of the *Canadian Hospital Directory* for ten years (1977 to 1986) and Editor-in-Chief of the Publications Department until 1989, when CHA Press was launched as a stand-alone publisher. In 1996, she became responsible for CHA's heritage building at 17 York Street. For the last ten years, she has also been a member of the CHA senior management team.

When the board approved the project to publish CHA's history in June 2004, she was responsible for setting up the Working Group, finding a chair and selecting its members, as well as managing its activities over the next two years. She has reviewed chapter content for each member, provided feedback, revised and redrafted chapters and written several others. Eleanor also worked closely with CHA's president to draft the sponsorship letters that eventually led to funding for the book. She also undertook much of the research, writing and revision of major parts of the manuscript, particularly CHA's history between the early 1900s to its move to Ottawa in 1978. As the book's publisher, she has also overseen the completion of all editorial production, including finding and selecting appropriate photographs for the book. She has also been the CHA staff liaison between the Working Group on the History and the board's Working Group on the 75th Anniversary Celebrations.

MARION L. STEPHENSON worked for CHA for 18 years as Assistant Director of Education and Program Director of two distance education courses—health record technicians and long term care organization and management. She was responsible for curriculum development of the long-term care program and she coordinated the revision and expansion of the program from a one- to two-year course. Prior to joining CHA, she directed several health record departments in Saskatchewan, Manitoba and Ontario. For many years, she was a member of the provincial and national associations for health record administrators.

She is a graduate of St. Michael's Hospital School for Medical Record Librarians. She successfully completed CHA's Hospital Organization and Management program and holds a bachelor of administration (health services) degree from Northland Open University. In 1995, the Canadian Long Term Care Association (CLS) presented her with the first President's Award for Outstanding Contribution to Long Term Care. The following year CLS renamed the award the Marion Stephenson Award to be presented to an individual recognized for their outstanding contribution to long-term/community care. For many years, she volunteered her time to the Canadian Association for Community Care and to CHA. She worked closely with CHA Press staff to develop the first textbook on long-term care in Canada, published in 1995, and on the revised edition released in 2002. She was responsible for researching and writing chapters 12 and 13 on CHA's distance education programs and conferences. Based on her association with CHA, she has provided valuable feedback on various aspects of the book.

Part I

THE HISTORICAL EVOLUTION

Part one of this book sets the historical framework for the development of the Canadian Healthcare Association over the course of its existence between 1931 and 2006. The framework is divided into four key time frames that parallel major historical developments in the evolution of Canada's health system. The intent of this historical overview is to provide the reader with a way to measure the evolution of CHA against the larger national health care story. What was happening across Canada's health system was reflected by CHA and its member organizations through major periods of growth and expansion, followed by a slowdown and, then, a period of downsizing and reassessment.

As the book progresses, each of the following parts and the chapters within them will be organized around these four key historical periods in the history of CHA. This section of the book is not intended as a definitive history of Canada's health system but rather as a guide to highlight key events that impacted on the various stages in the evolution of our national health care organization. There are several textbooks that have been written over the years which provide considerably more detail about the history of Canada's health system.

Chapter 1 covers the period between 1899 and 1930. It outlines the conditions under which hospitals were founded in Canada and presents a brief description of their growth and that of the earliest national hospital organization in 1899. Surprisingly, there was an early Canadian Hospital Association during the first part of the twentieth century. The chapter describes what happened after its demise and why the Canadian Medical Association decided to become involved in hospital affairs in the mid-1920s. This led to the establishment of the Department of Hospital Service and the hiring of Dr. George Harvey Agnew, no doubt one of the most influential leaders in Canada's health care system in the twentieth century.

Chapter 2 covers the difficult years of 1931 to 1952 from the depression, through World War II and into the beginning of the 1950s. It picks up on Dr. Agnew's decision to invite Canadian hospital superintendents to set up a national hospital organization. The chapter describes the decisions of these early hospital council delegates to found an organization and what this council would be expected to do on their behalf. It also outlines what was happening across the country during the depression years, how Canada's health system—and hospitals in particular—were coping during this time, and the council's struggle to survive. This chapter ends in 1952 just as the period of intense hospital building is about to get underway in Canada.

Chapter 3 covers the Toronto years from 1953 to 1977 at the end of which the hospital association packed up and moved to Ottawa. This period is one of the most dynamic times in Canada's health care system as the federal government increased its involvement in health delivery through the passage of two key pieces of legislation. The chapter looks at the impact this had on the health system and, most particularly, what it meant for the Canadian Hospital Association and its members. Explosive growth in the health system was usually reflected among CHA's provincial members and, thus, at the national hospital association. For CHA, this was a time of considerable expansion of its activities, its staff and its role as a permanent player on the health care scene.

The last chapter in this section, chapter 4, focuses on CHA in Ottawa from 1978 to 2006. It presents a decidedly more political picture as the association improved its relations with the federal government and with sister health organizations. The chapter also describes how the impact of restructuring and downsizing of Canada's health system throughout the late 1980s to the mid-1990s ricochetted through the system to affect CHA. Most of the events in this chapter end around 2004, although a major event that had significant ramifications for CHA during 2005 and into mid-2006 may be mentioned or referenced at the end of the chapter.

1

THE EARLY HOSPITAL ASSOCIATIONS, 1899 TO 1930

"The first hospital associations were not established until the first decade of [the twentieth] century and even these faded into inactivity after a few years."

(AGNEW 1974, 2)

In his history of hospitals in Canada from 1920 to 1970, Dr. Harvey Agnew writes that ". . . until the end of the nineteenth century, hospitals in Canada, as elsewhere, were little more than refuges for critically ill indigents and immigrants" (1974, 1). The very earliest hospitals in Canada were set up by religious orders such as the Grey Nuns and the Sisters of St. Joseph, usually to provide care to the native peoples. Some of these religious orders also built hospitals in the Maritimes and in the western provinces as the population grew during the early twentieth century. Many of the hospitals in Canada were established as charitable institutions by wealthy philanthropists and humanitarians to provide care to those who could not afford a physician. Most of them were operated without any government funding by untrained staff and conditions in them were appalling. There were no sanitary standards, sterilization was unheard of and patients were left pretty much on their own to look after themselves.

Being admitted to a hospital at the turn of the century was considered tantamount to a death sentence. It was during the period 1870 to 1920, with the introduction of a more scientific practice of medicine and the Nightingale nursing system, that hospitals gradually came to be viewed by the public as acceptable institutions in which to receive care. This led to the growth of more and better hospitals and also to the need to finance and manage them more effectively.

Hospital administrators, known as superintendents during this time, had very little contact with governments at any level, with professional associations or even with each other. It was only when their institutions became increasingly more complex to manage that they realized the need to consult with each other to discuss mutual problems and to become informed about new, scientific technologies (Agnew 1974, 58).

The Earliest Association

Canada is a very large country, stretching some four thousand miles from the Atlantic to the Pacific Oceans and northward from the American border to the Arctic Ocean. Yet, at the beginning of the twentieth century, only five million Canadians lived in the country, most of them close to the Canadian-American border. Transportation such as the train, and later the automobile, had made access somewhat easier across the country. But mass transportation also exposed the Canadian population to contamination, diseases and more accidents as a result of their increased mobility. One advantage stemming from these improvements in transportation, however, was the ability for people to meet more frequently to discuss problems and identify solutions. Canadians could now travel more frequently and greater distances to meet colleagues.

A number of Canadians were active in the Association of Hospital Superintendents, which was formed in the United States in 1899. The 1900 records of the American Hospital Association (AHA) show that Dr. Charles O'Reilly, the medical superintendent of the Toronto General Hospital, became one of the thirty-one founding members of this association. By 1905, there were over three hundred representatives in attendance at the AHA's annual convention in Boston and the association "had developed, up to this time, into an association international in scope, including the best known hospital administrators in the United States and Canada" (Fifield 1933, 14).

At the AHA's Eighth Annual Convention in 1906, a new constitution and bylaws were adopted and the name of the organization was changed to The American Hospital Association of United States and Canada. W.W. Kenney from Victoria General Hospital in Halifax was elected as a vice-president. By the time of the Tenth Annual Conference of the association, which was held in Toronto in 1908, there were 350 delegates in attendance.

While Canadian hospital superintendents were joining the American association, the need for a Canadian association began to surface. In 1907, a group of Toronto hospital superintendents met to consider whether they would continue to affiliate with the American association or whether a Canadian organization should be formed. On 1 April 1907, the inaugural meeting of the first Canadian Hospital Association was held in the parliament buildings in Toronto with about forty-five people in attendance. Among the guests were Dr. Renwick R. Ross from General Hospital in Buffalo, New York, who was the president of the American Hospital Association. There were also several Ontario cabinet members at the meeting, and the first elected president was a woman, Louise Brent, from the Hospital for Sick Children in Toronto.

The handwritten minutes of these early meetings, which were held over two days, report mostly about who attended the meetings and what papers were presented. In 1908, a resolution was approved to amend the constitution to admit board trustees to active membership and extended associate membership "to include anyone connected with Hospitals or who is particularly interested in Hospital work" (CHA 1908, 12). The members also set up nominating, membership and audit committees, and a committee on the constitution and bylaws. A further resolution was approved regarding the treatment of diseases:

> Whereas, tuberculosis and other diseases are very prevalent among the children of our country and that from researches it appears that not a few of the cases of tuberculosis developing later on in life are due to early infection, therefore,

> Resolved, that the members of the Canadian Hospital Association feel it desirable to put forward prophylactic measures to prevent these disastrous results by instituting more thorough and systematic means of education among the young along the lines of health-measures, which, when once learned, and practiced will within this generation protect the home and household from tuberculosis and other diseases; . . . (Ibid., 9).

Following this resolution, Dr. Helen MacMurchy gave a paper on the "Milk Supply" and Dr. A.D. MacIntyre read one on "Fumigation." (What the exact content of these papers included is not known, as they have long since disappeared from the early record book.) Dr. W.L. Babcock, secretary of the American Hospital Association, was introduced and extended ". . . a hearty invitation to the members of the Canadian Hospital Association to become members of the American Association, the next meeting of which will be held in Toronto next September" (Ibid., 10).

The minutes of the 1909 Executive Committee meeting recorded the members' decision ". . . to accept Dr. Dobbie's offer to provide an automobile drive to take place about 4 o'clock . . ., the trip being to visit the King Edward Tuberculosis Sanitorium at Weston" (CHA 1909, 14). This appeared to be the most pressing business for this particular meeting. But the members did request that letters be written to several superintendents inviting them to prepare and read papers for the next meeting of the executive.

These presentations, which may seem unusual for today's health care organizations, were of major significance in the early twentieth century health system in Canada. Outbreaks of infectious diseases such as typhoid, malaria, cholera and influenza could wipe out significant parts of a population. There was little that health professionals of the day could do to care for people who acquired these diseases except comfort them as they died. With the discoveries in immunology and bacteriology and the application of better local health practices, the emphasis through these pre-World War I years was on municipalities to look after their local populations. Thus, the focus of the early CHA on the milk supply.

In 1910, the Fourth Annual Meeting of the association was held at the Royal Victoria Hospital in Montreal, most probably because H. E. Webster, who was its superintendent, was also the president of the association at the time. Papers were given on "The Relation of the Training School to the Hospital Deficit Problem" and on "Hospital Accounting." A committee was appointed at this meeting to develop some system of hospital accounting suitable for smaller hospitals and to report back to the next annual meeting.

At the fifth annual meeting, held in Niagara Falls, Ontario, from 23 to 24 May 1911, a trustees' section was instituted. The members also discussed amalgamation and passed a motion that ". . . a Committee made up from the Canadian Hospital Association, the Association of Superintendents of Training Schools, and the Graduate Nurses' Association . . . consider and arrange a Constitution as a working basis for some national organization" (CHA 1911, 33-34). Even then, hospital superintendents were looking for ways to establish a truly national hospital organization.

In 1912, a committee was appointed by the membership to appear before the dominion Tariff Commission to press for the abolition of duties on hospital supplies. The minutes also recorded that the journal, *Hospital World*, published by Dr. G.A. Young of Toronto, had become the official organ of the Canadian Hospital

Association. The precedent for the hospital association to lobby the federal government on behalf of hospitals, as well as affiliate with a journal to communicate its message across the country, was set very early in CHA's history.

Throughout this period, Canadians were heavily involved in the American Hospital Association but continued to support this struggling Canadian organization. At the 1913 CHA annual meeting, the membership once again urged the committee, which had been set up the previous year, to meet with the federal government to discuss the revision of tariffs for hospitals.

The minutes of the Executive Committee of 20 February 1914 are the last record of this active, but short-lived, association. The president at the time was Dr. E.H. Young of Kingston. Members of the committee selected 20 to 22 October as the date of the next annual meeting, set up the program and suggested that a noncommercial exhibit be provided. This meeting was suspended, however, because of the outbreak of World War I. In his book, Dr. Agnew indicates that there was no further activity conducted by this early association after 1914.

The members of the first Canadian Hospital Association were mainly based in Toronto and other parts of Ontario. But later minutes do record that there was some representation from Quebec and the east and west coasts, indicating a growing interest in some kind of national organization to represent hospitals. This early version of the association remained inactive until 1924, when it ceased to exist. But it was only a matter of time before someone would come forward to spearhead a uniquely Canadian hospital organization once again.

From the record of this early CHA, the members envisioned a national organization composed of hospital superintendents, trustees and others in the hospital field. They drafted a constitution and bylaws, very quickly focused the organization as a lobby group to represent hospital interests to the dominion government and opened up discussions with other organizations on issues of mutual interest.

Canada's Post-World War I Health System

By the end of World War I, new methods of treating disease, injury and infection—often tested on the battlefields in Europe—were being adopted as standard practice by physicians. Returning physicians and nurses, who had served in the war, required additional hospital training in order to prepare for specialization and to adapt their skills and knowledge to work in a hospital.

The postwar period, and especially the early 1920s, was a time of considerable hospital construction. A 1924 issue of *Hospital Buying* reported that hospital construction was expanding at a great rate, and diagnostic and other equipment was being developed at a rapid pace. In fact, between 1923 and 1924, almost a hundred new hospitals had been built in Canada ("Hospital" 1924, 7). With this rapid expansion, there were ongoing concerns about the quality of care being provided and the need for standards for everything from medical internships in hospitals to standards for construction and the training of hospital superintendents.

Provincial Special Hospital, 1929, in Edmonton, Alberta, for the Treatment of Infantile Paralysis. Shows the Flat and Elongated Structure of Hospital Architecture at the Time.

Dr. Agnew describes conditions in these hospitals in the early 1920s as being extremely crude relative to care in our modern sanitized facilities almost a hundred years later. A general hospital in 1920 did not have an intensive care unit, a coronary care unit or a recovery room in surgery. There was no blood transfusion service available, or sterile saline or other intravenous solutions, although some hospitals did prepare their own sterile solutions. There were no antibiotics or anticoagulants and insulin had just been discovered in 1921 by two Canadian physicians (Agnew 1974, 11–12).

Hospital anesthetics consisted of either ethyl chloride or chloroform or a mixture of both dropped on a cloth, which covered the surgical patient's face. Any member of the medical staff could do their own surgery and administer anesthesia. Nurses, usually graduates of the hospital's training school, worked long hours, were often in short supply, and were as likely to perform housekeeping tasks as to deliver care to patients.

Sanitation and hygiene were crude, if there was any such environment at all. As laboratories and surgical units increased in number, they were often equipped with hazardous and flammable substances, which were equally as dangerous to hospital personnel as to patients on the wards and in private rooms (Ibid., 14–15).

The primary funder of health care by the early 1920s was the federal government. Although the British North America Act of 1867 relegated the delivery of health care to the provinces, it designated the power to tax and to borrow money to the federal government. It was this spending power that had allowed the federal government to enter into the health field shortly after World War I.

Returning soldiers were suffering from tuberculosis and venereal disease, and they also required hospital care for their wartime injuries and rehabilitation back into society. As Dr. Agnew noted: "At the conclusion of the First World War the federal government was faced with the duty to build and maintain hospitals for a large number of wounded veterans, all entitled to government care" (1974, 53). To deliver this care, the government established the Department of Health in 1919, which oversaw the building and operation of hospitals mainly concerned with delivery of care to veterans and members of the armed services. In 1928, the health department merged with another to become the Department of Pensions and National Health.

Through such acts as Food and Drug, Narcotics Control and Tobacco Products Control, the federal government also protected the public health of Canadians. These acts had evolved over the years to inspect and regulate the food and drug supply in Canada.

The federal government also began to use its significant spending power to assist the provinces in setting up their health care infrastructures. Through a series of conditional health grants, it provided funds to the provinces to set up venereal disease prevention and treatment programs and to assist them in developing other public health programs (Ostry 2006). Between 1919 and 1931, federal dollars were transferred to the provinces and then severely cut back during the depression of the 1930s.

The provinces used much of the federal money to set up their own health care systems. They also established their own health departments throughout the 1920s in response to the new federal department set up in 1919. In turn, the provinces took on a greater role in coordinating municipal public health operations such as free tuberculosis clinics, child and maternal health services and even cancer clinics.

As more and more investment was put into provincial and municipal health delivery systems, the need to regulate the quality of care and set standards became a major concern. Leading the drive to set up standards, Dr. Malcolm T. MacEachern, a Canadian and president of the American Hospital Association in 1923, pressed for more advanced education for hospital superintendents, better training for medical interns and standards for hospitals at every level. He was successful in getting the American College of Surgeons to implement the hospital standardization program, a program that would also be applicable to Canadian hospitals. But Canadian physicians were not so enthusiastic about adopting an American-based standards program.

Thomas Clarence Routley, MD, General Secretary of the Canadian Medical Association. 1922-1954. Instrumental in Setting Up the Department of Hospital Service.

Canadian Medical Association Involvement

World War I had not only brought an end to the young Canadian Hospital Association it had also created financial problems for other organizations such as the Canadian Medical Association (CMA). Although it was already a well-established organization in its own right, with fifty years of history and experience, CMA was struggling to survive after the war. Membership had fallen considerably during the war years and ". . . the association was perennially afflicted with difficulties in persuading potential members of the desirability of a national medical organization" (Agnew 1974, 62). There was also growing resentment on the part of Canadian physicians about implementing the American standards program in Canadian hospitals.

The 1921 annual meeting of the CMA helped to turn around the fortunes of the association and also set the direction for the creation of a hospital department within the organization. Dr. Thomas Clarence Routley was elected as the full-time secretary of the CMA and effectively persuaded the members to adopt a resolution that expressed the ". . .'unqualified approval' of a plan to standardize Canadian hospitals" ("C.H.A.", 1). CMA was well aware of physicians' suspicions about applying the American hospital standards program in Canada. The association also vigorously promoted postgraduate education for physicians and sought financial support from Sun Life Assurance Company of Canada for tours across Canada for medical educators.

The CMA's next focus was to improve hospital standards across the country, having now persuaded its membership to accept the American standards program. In 1926, at its meeting in Victoria, the CMA agreed to set up a Committee on Hospital Efficiency and held a conference detailing how an organization could be set up and funded to improve standards at both the provincial and national levels.

Establishing the Department of Hospital Service

The CMA formally approved creating the Department of Hospital Service in 1927 with funding from Sun Life. A small committee was formed to determine the activities for this new department. In turn, this group suggested that an advisory committee for the department be set up. As Dr. Harvey Agnew acknowledged in his book, the hospitals of Canada owe much to the early steps taken by the CMA to improve hospital standards and to create an independent organization to represent Canadian hospitals (1974, 62–63.).

In 1927, forty delegates, representing some of the largest hospitals in Canada, attended the annual meeting of the American Hospital Association in Minneapolis. At a special meeting, these delegates decided to cooperate with the CMA by employing a hospital secretary, who would devote his entire time to resolving problems of national concern and unique to Canadian hospitals.

Until this time, the CMA's main interest in hospitals had been to develop postgraduate education in medical practice. This new department would look into such hospital issues as choosing new equipment, purchasing supplies, methods of organization, and the relations of hospitals to their communities and to each other. It would provide a clearinghouse of information for Canada's hospitals and a library for hospital administration, visit hospitals to consult about issues and help found provincial associations where these did not exist (Agnew 1974, 66).

At this time, T. B. Macaulay, president of the Sun Life Assurance Company, which had already funded a series of postgraduate medical lectures in the amount of $212,000, was looking to fund another CMA project. The result was that Sun Life offered a grant of $15,000 a year to finance the Department of Hospital Service, which began in January 1928. In March, Dr. G. Harvey Agnew was appointed associate secretary of the CMA in charge of administering this new department.

In his address to the Ontario Hospital Association annual meeting on 18 October 1928, Dr. Agnew described some of the activities in which the CMA hospital department had been involved:

> . . . This Department of Hospital Service is really a consulting bureau and reference library and is studying all manner of hospital problems, especially those problems which are perplexing the smaller hospitals. We are really trying to pool the experiences of all of our hospitals, make them readily available for others and, in short, endeavour by every means possible to make our Canadian hospitals the most efficient in the world (1929, 15).

The department's first report clearly showed the energetic and capable way in which Dr. Agnew had already begun to deal with hospital problems. He pointed out that there was no national hospital organization and, in some provinces, not even a provincial group.[1] Hospitals were being built and equipped without proper guidance. There was a shortage of interns and no adequate list of Canadian hospitals. In the short time since its creation, the department had received more than 150 requests for advice and assistance from hospitals across Canada.

One of the department's first activities was to develop a reference library on hospital topics. The library was named after Dr. A. D. Blackader, who made an annual contribution toward the purchase of books and journals. After he and his wife died, the CMA received a bequest to maintain a hospital collection from their estate in memory of their son, Captain Gordon H. Blackader, who had died during World War I.[2]

The Department of Hospital Service also made arrangements to work in conjunction with the American Hospital Association and other national organizations in the United States such as the Department of Hospital Activities of the American College of Surgeons, under Dr. Malcolm MacEachern. This department was responsible for setting standards and inspecting Canadian hospitals to ensure they were meeting minimum requirements.[3]

One of the CMA department's earliest achievements was the successful negotiation with the federal government in 1930 for the removal of all tariff duties on various types of hospital equipment. This resulted in considerable savings for hospitals. Later, the task of approving hospitals for intern training was undertaken. Previously, this had been done by the Council on Medical Education and Hospitals of the American Medical Association.

In December 1930, Dr. Agnew wrote to the secretary and president of each of the existing provincial hospital associations about the need for a Canadian hospital council. In his letter, he stated that the comment had often been made that Canada was big enough to have its own national hospital organization and that hospitals were one of the few components of the health care system without a national body. However, he did state that there seemed to be unanimous agreement that ". . . the time does not seem ripe to organize a Canadian Hospital Association" (Agnew 1929, 15). Hospitals could not overcome the four-thousand-mile geographic handicap that was Canada; the smaller hospitals preferred to attend conventions organized by the American Hospital Association, the hospital section of the American College of Surgeons or the Catholic Hospital Association of the United States and Canada.

Dr. Agnew suggested the formation of a national hospital council. It would be composed of the various provincial organizations, with one or two delegates from each, who would meet annually for several days to discuss hospital issues of national or interprovincial interest and concern. Among the issues identified by Dr. Agnew were custom tariffs, the closer alignment of the various provincial hospital acts, reciprocal recognition of indigent claims by the various provinces and the outlook of hospitals in any impending national hospital insurance scheme.

Dr. Agnew promised that the existing Department of Hospital Service would provide secretarial services and underwrite the printing of bulletins, reports and pamphlets arising out of the activities of the council. The expense to the provincial associations would be restricted to the travel costs of their delegates. Dr. Agnew concluded his letter by suggesting that a first session be held in Toronto in September 1931 at the same time as the American Hospital Association convention. He wrote: "This would prove a good gathering point as it is likely that most provinces will send delegates to this convention."

Summary

Hospital superintendents successfully launched a uniquely Canadian hospital organization at the turn of the twentieth century. But World War I disrupted the activities of this early Canadian Hospital Association and it had ceased to exist by 1924. While the Canadian Medical Association took hospitals under its wing, by the beginning of the 1930s, hospital superintendents were being asked to consider whether the time was now right to set up an independent organization to represent their interests.

Endnotes

1. The following provincial hospital associations were listed on the masthead of the January 1930 edition of *The Canadian Hospital*: Alberta Hospital Association, British Columbia Hospitals Association, Manitoba Hospital Association, Maritime Catholic Hospital Association, New Brunswick Hospital Association, Nova Scotia Hospital Association, Ontario Hospital Association and Saskatchewan Hospital Association. The nature of their involvement with the Department of Hospital Service of the CMA is unknown.

2. Dr. Blackader was, at one time, the editor of the CMA journal. The library collection was named the Blackader Library and eventually permanently loaned to CHA. (*See* chapter 12 for more information on CHA's library service.)

3. Although the standards program was voluntary, those who actually conducted the survey were referred to as inspectors, not surveyors as they are called today.

2

THE CANADIAN HOSPITAL COUNCIL, 1931 TO 1952

"What the Council will accomplish in the nature of hospital welfare only time will tell, but we predict great things."

(BURCHER 1931, 12)

In order to set the framework for the founding of the Canadian Hospital Council, it's important to understand the health care setting in Canada as hospitals entered the decade of the 1930s. The Great Depression was settling in across the country, displacing thousands of Canadians and placing millions on unemployment relief. Looking after the poor and the indigent was left to the municipalities, including paying the hospital for their care, based on taxes collected from local property owners. As the depression deepened, there were fewer and fewer of these taxpayers.

For the hospitals of Canada, the depression was just as difficult a time. Although they had seen some good years in the 1920s, with considerable expansion, new technologies, many scientific and medical treatment discoveries and the growth of nurse training schools, which added more free staff to their departments, the financially tough times were putting the long-term existence of many hospitals in jeopardy. As the depression years continued in the early 1930s, ". . . many hospitals had a hard time surviving . . . because individual fee payers, . . . and tax payers had less money to spend. Hospitals cut back their staffs and supplies as much as possible, but some were reduced to bartering . . . to continue to operate through these difficult times" (Crichton et al. 1994, 185).

Hospital funding for the most part fell to the private-pay patient, philanthropists or municipal tax schemes which provided mostly partial payment for the indigent sick

15

on public wards. By the 1930s, the number of indigents on the wards of public hospitals was growing to the point where hospitals faced financial ruin. Municipalities were bankrupt or carrying massive debt loads, and the provinces were also facing bankruptcy unless the federal government could be persuaded to step in to help ease the burden of unemployment relief being carried by provincial and local governments.

Nor was this an easy time for the physician. He was also dependent on the patient to pay for medical treatment and, frequently, there was no money to do so. Throughout the 1930s, physicians also required some assistance with unemployment relief to support themselves during these hard economic times. Health insurance plans for physicians and hospitals sprang up across the country to offer support for the unemployed and to pay for physician and hospital services. Increasingly, the attitude across all parts of society was that the country needed some type of government-sponsored public health insurance.

By the middle of the depression, Saskatchewan had developed municipal-based insurance plans through its union hospital districts. The rural areas of Saskatchewan had already developed municipal doctor systems in 1914 to hire and pay for a physician's services from local taxes, and there were some similar schemes in other provinces.

Often hospitals owed large debts to banks, couldn't pay their suppliers or were forced to go bankrupt because of the lack of payments from patients receiving care. Municipalities were unable to pay their share of the indigent poor cost of care to hospitals because they didn't have any money. Their unemployment relief systems were bankrupt and the provinces couldn't bail them out because they were in similar straights. It was during this environment that the Department of Hospital Service and its secretary determined the greater need for a national hospital association to look after the common needs of Canada's hospitals.

Dr. Agnew's exploratory letter in December 1930 had obviously elicited a number of responses and requests for further information about the proposed council because a follow-up letter was sent to the provincial secretaries and presidents of various provincial hospital associations on 14 April 1931. Dr. Agnew outlined the objectives in more detail. That is, the council will "act as a connecting link between the various provincial organizations and . . . on behalf of the hospitals of Canada in any matter of national importance."

Dr. Agnew believed that a main focus for the council would be to target federal legislation that impacted on Canadian hospitals. For example, he cited the following:

> The proposed increase in the Sales Tax to 4% or 5% will be a heavy blow to hospitals unless they are exempted. Again, our D.H.S. has initiated the recent nationwide request to Ottawa for Hospital exemptions, but a National Council could have done still more. If imposed, this Tax may cost the hospitals of Canada half a million dollars or more annually, depending upon the sales covered. Various Federal matters are of general concern to hospitals—the care of returned soldiers, narcotic addicts and sailors, for instance (Source unknown).

Dr. Agnew also suggested that the council should have no executive or legislative power. It would express policy and exert influence by means of formal resolutions and the publication of the reports of various study committees.

The Founding Meeting of 1931

The founding meeting of the Canadian Hospital Council took place at the Royal York Hotel in Toronto on 28 and 29 September 1931, immediately preceding the American Hospital Association Convention. It was a wise choice to hold the inaugural meeting of the council in conjunction with the AHA meeting because eleven of the provincial and other hospital associations were represented. The federal Department of Pensions and National Health, the Ontario Department of Health and the Canadian Tuberculosis Association also sent representatives. One of the main attractions for Canadian delegates to this convention was the naming of Dr. George Findlay Stephens, general superintendent of Winnipeg General Hospital, as president-elect of the American Hospital Association.

Dr. Alf K. Haywood of Vancouver was asked to preside over the meeting, with Dr. Agnew as the secretary. He asked Dr. Agnew to explain to the delegates the reasons that had prompted him and others to call a meeting to form a national council. Dr. Agnew spoke of Canada's geographic handicap, with hospitals stretched out for four thousand miles, and how the small hospitals that needed help could not afford to send delegates to a large annual convention. The best solution therefore seemed to be a council or conference that would represent all the hospital associations and other bodies that took an active part in hospital work. The council could coordinate activities in the various provinces and study hospital problems peculiar to Canada.

Whether the council would supersede the CMA Department of Hospital Service was discussed. Dr. Agnew noted that the department had become so much a part of the hospital life of Canada that it should not drop its work under any circumstances. Yet the council would be an autonomous body distinct and separate from the CMA department. The two organizations would work closely together in the best interests of both the hospitals and physicians of Canada. To do this, the council would be headquartered in the CMA offices in Toronto.

Delegates and Guests Attending the Inaugural Meeting of the Canadian Hospital Council, Toronto, 28-29 September 1931.

After some discussion about the relationship between the two bodies, it was moved by Dr. A.L.C. Gilday, representing the Montreal Hospital Council—there was no Quebec association at that time—and seconded by Dr. R.J. Collins of the New Brunswick Hospital Association that the Canadian Hospital Council be formed. The motion was carried unanimously on 29 September 1931.

One of the most interesting discussions at this founding meeting was determining who should be the council's members. (*See also* chapter 6.) Proposals for an institutional versus a personal membership organization were debated and rejected, as was the notion of an organization similar to the American Hospital Association with which the newly formed council would have to compete. Dr. Agnew wanted the membership to extend beyond general hospitals to include other groups such as tuberculosis sanatoria. There were also many hospital superintendents opposed to a national organization of any type because of their fears that local (or provincial) concerns would become lost at the national level (Agnew 1974, 68).

There seemed to be no way around the problem until Dr. Haywood, the chairman, wisely suggested that "a certain number of organizations be specifically named today, to be charter members of this Canadian Hospital Council." Dr. Agnew then read the list of proposed members which included the Hospital Association of Nova Scotia and Prince Edward Island, the Maritime Conference of the Catholic Hospital Association, the New Brunswick Hospital Association, the Montreal Hospital Council, the Ontario Hospital Association, the Ontario Conference of the Catholic Hospital Association, the Manitoba Hospital Association, the Saskatchewan Hospital Association, the Alberta Hospital Association, the British Columbia Hospitals Association and the Department of Hospital Service of the Canadian Medical Association. The Department of Pensions and National Health and the provincial departments of health would also be included as nonvoting members.

Next came the thorny subject of financing and whether the council should, as Dr. Haywood said "pay our own way or hitch our wagon to the Canadian Medical Association." In the end and in spite of some remarks to the contrary, it was agreed to accept the generous offer of the CMA to set aside a sufficient portion of its annual budget to cover office space, stenographic costs and the printing of pamphlets and bulletins for the council. This apparently ended the discussion. Dr. George F. Stephens of Winnipeg noted that the CMA Department of Hospital Service was maintained by an annual grant of $15,000 from the Sun Life Assurance Company of Canada, with no strings attached.

On the following day, 29 September 1931, the redrafted constitution and bylaws, apparently rewritten overnight by Dr. Agnew, were considered and approved by the membership. The following officers were then elected: Dr. Fred W. Routley as president. Dr. G. Harvey Agnew became the secretary-treasurer and continued in his role as associate secretary of the CMA. Walter R. Chenoweth, general superintendent of the Royal Victoria Hospital, was elected first vice-president and Reverend Mother Audet, sister superior of the Hotel-Dieu of St. Joseph in Chatham, New Brunswick, became second vice-president. The Honorable R.B. Bennett, prime minister of Canada, was named honorary president, and the Honorable Dr. Murray MacLaren, minister of the Department of Pensions and National Health, was elected as honorary vice-president.

The members also appointed the executive of the council which would carry out much of its business in between biennial meetings. The executive was composed of Dr. Fred W. Routley, W.R. Chenoweth, Dr. Harvey Agnew, Dr. George F. Stephens, and L.D. Currie, who was president of the Hospital Association of Nova Scotia and Prince Edward Island.

Dr. Fred W. Routley, the First President of the Canadian Hospital Council, 1931-1933.

Dr. G. Harvey Agnew, Secretary-Treasurer, Canadian Hospital Council, 1931-1947; Executive Secretary, 1947-1950.

In his presidential remarks, Dr. Routley spoke somewhat prophetically about the future of the council: "I recognize very fully that this Council has a great future ahead of it in the hospital world of Canada. In the days to come we will find it developing into a great Canadian hospital association." Finally, the delegates thanked the federal government for the recent sales tax exemptions and the Sun Life Assurance Company for their continued interest in the welfare of Canadian hospitals.

T.B. MacAuley, President of Sun Life Assurance Company of Canada. Agreed to Provide Funding to the Department of Hospital Service of the CMA in 1928.

The council created a number of committees—construction and equipment, public relations, administration and statistics, legislation, finance, medical relations, research, nursing and small hospital problems. These committees were charged with preparing studies on all these subjects. Eventually, the reports would be published in issues of *The Canadian Hospital*. In its first year of operation, the council was well on its way to providing a valuable service to Canadian hospitals.

The Pre-War Years for the Council

The Second Biennial Convention of the Canadian Hospital Council, held at the Fort Garry Hotel in Winnipeg from 7 to 9 September 1933, was historic in that it brought ". . . together for the first time in Canadian history representatives of the various hospital associations and of the provincial and federal governments" ("Canadian" 1933, 27). The program was very ambitious for such a new organization. Beside the routine affairs of a biennial meeting, sessions were held on hospital legislation, including comparisons of provincial legislation; and on special problems such as indigency and sales tax exemptions; construction and equipment; public relations; finance on issues such as collection methods and group hospital insurance; administration and statistics covering standardization of accounting, nomenclature and possible economies. A report of the Committee on Research, which dealt largely with the problem of tuberculosis in nurses, was briefly described and a session was held specifically on relations between the medical profession and hospitals. Finally, there was a roundtable on medical staff problems.

The 1933 biennial meeting approved a resolution of appreciation to the prime minister, the minister of finance and the government of Canada for the exemption from sales tax which "has been of considerable assistance in permitting our hospitals to carry on their ministrations to the sick poor under extremely adverse conditions." Another resolution urged the National Research Council to set up a bureau to study the quality of building materials and equipment. And, for the first time, the need for standardized accounting practices among hospitals was mentioned, with the objective of adopting uniform accounting forms throughout Canada. Of particular interest was a resolution that recommended the formation of local hospital councils wherever two, three or more hospitals were located in the same area. It is clear that the council was already demonstrating national leadership and beginning to exert pressure on and influence government whenever it was deemed necessary.

The establishment of a national council to speak on behalf of the hospitals of Canada and its member associations had come at a very critical time. By 1933, Canada was deep in the midst of the Great Depression which was having a severe impact on hospitals throughout the country. Still a relatively rural country, with a small population spread over a considerable geographic area, hospitals were struggling to provide care to more and more homeless and unemployed, many of whom were without the very basics of life—food and shelter—let alone a job and money to pay for treatment when they fell ill.

By the mid-1930s, the vast majority of hospitals in Canada—whether voluntary, religious or municipal—were dependent on revenues from three basic areas: 1) patients in public and private wards who could pay, 2) fees from municipalities (from taxes) to pay for indigents or provincial agencies such as Worker's Compensation to pay for workers injured during the course of work and 3) philanthropic donations or endowments with a specific request not to be used to pay for patient care. Federal government assistance was unheard of except for veterans or First Nations people on reserves. The provinces picked up medical costs only for the mentally disturbed, epileptics and for those suffering from tuberculosis and other contagious diseases.

The biggest problem for hospitals, which were providing free medical care to indigents on public wards, was to recover the costs of their care. As the depression continued and men moved across the country seeking work wherever they could find it, the number of indigents throughout the country continued to increase and burden hospitals financially. Hospital deficits continued to grow at alarming rates and some municipally owned hospitals in the Prairie provinces actually traded for goods such as cord wood and beef to settle accounts (Agnew 1974, 150).

While some prepayment plans had been available for hospital care, mainly in industry and mining in Canada, by 1934, a CMA survey documented that twenty-five other insurance plans had been set up in the country. These had been established by hospitals, service clubs or mutual benefit societies (Agnew 1974, 156). British Columbia had even passed a medical care insurance act in 1937 but had failed to get the approval of the medical profession and the legislation died on the books.

At the 1935 Third Biennial Meeting, the Canadian Hospital Council urged the federal government to take a leadership role in the development of a health program for Canadians. It endorsed the recent decision of the Conference of Health Ministers to form a Cabinet of Health for Canada under the chairmanship of the minister of the Department of Pensions and National Health. The council delegates approved a resolution "that the hospital is the logical and necessary centre of the health activities of its community and wherever feasible should take leadership in all health problems and should supply services designed as fully as possible, to meet all the health needs of its community" ("Canadian" 1935, 6). An extremely important issue was a uniform system of statistical returns for Canada and the council endorsed "the adoption of these forms . . ., as being sound and conforming in principle to other plans internationally used, . . ." (Ibid.). A special committee was also set up to study the various types of health insurance, an issue that was beginning to appear on both the provincial and federal agendas.

The depression years were also difficult for physicians whose services could not be paid for during these lean years. They, too, were forced to barter for payment of their fees through goods or waive their bills entirely. In fact, several voluntary medical insurance plans were set up across the country during the 1930s, beginning with Associated Medical Services in Toronto in 1937. With the proliferation of hospital and medical plans, it was only a matter of time before more and more pressure was mounted on the federal government to use its spending power to cover the rising costs of care, especially in hospitals, through some form of national health insurance.

To provide some relief to the provinces, the Conservative government under R.B. Bennett had passed the Employment and Social Insurance Act in 1935. But the legislation was ruled as beyond the powers of the federal government because of constitutional issues. (It was eventually passed in 1940 [Crichton et al. 1994, 186].)

As the depression continued, more provinces, as well as the federal government, began to consider national health insurance as one way to deal with the growing costs of delivering health services to an impoverished population. The Canadian Hospital Council and its members also had to deal with the issue of a compulsory health insurance plan. At its Fourth Biennial Convention held in Ottawa on 8 and 9 September 1937, the issue was discussed at some length The question for the council was: What should the attitude of the hospitals be toward compulsory health insurance? Dr. J. K. Holbrook, who represented the Ontario Hospital Association at the meeting, spoke eloquently about the issue and noted that hospital support would depend on "the length to which health insurance goes" (CHC, 66). He was adamant that the hospital had to be fully involved and that physicians' services, that is, medical treatment, which was provided chiefly by the physician in the hospital, needed to be given every consideration in such a plan. The final resolution on health insurance approved by the membership, among other items, stated the following:

> THEREFORE BE IT RESOLVED: (a) That all hospital associations and hospital workers be urged to make a careful and intimate study of the whole field of health insurance and the effect such a system would have upon hospital development in Canada; . . .

> (e) That any form of health insurance which would interfere with the autonomy of our voluntary institutions . . . , or which would destroy the spirit of freedom and charity or would place hospitals under political control, should be strongly opposed. CARRIED (CHC 1937, 101).

During this key meeting, the issue of the council's incorporation was also presented to the membership, a move that was necessary to protect the council which had taken over the operation of the hospital journal (*see* chapter 11 for more details). The question of more financial aid for the council was also raised, given the demands that were being placed at the time on Dr. Agnew and his small staff. The president of the council, Walter R. Chenoweth, reminded the members that ". . . up to the present time [1937] the cost to the hospital associations of maintaining the Council has been very nominal . . ." (Ibid., 11). This would not be the first time that finances would be discussed.

Hospital construction was also undergoing major change in the 1930s. Patient wards were being reduced from ten to thirty-bed units to those of four to ten beds only. Hospitals needed to be altered in order to accommodate "the tremendous development of the elevator service with the consequent saving of time . . . a material factor in hospital planning . . ." (Stevens 1932, 24). The hospital physical plant required renovation to accommodate new methods of heating and ventilation, lighting and sanitation, as well as alterations to meet new standards of fireproof materials.

Hospital facilities were being built upward because "in the cities the higher building has the advantage of getting better light and air. Also a higher building [was] relatively less expensive to construct than a group of low buildings" (Ibid., 24), which was the common design and layout used for buildings during the early twentieth century. Nurses' residences, add-ons such as garages to accommodate cars (the first such garage having been built by the Ottawa Civic Hospital in 1932), and expanded outpatient and emergency departments all required more space in order to make the changeover to the modern hospital facility.

More and better equipment for laundry, housekeeping and dietetic services, for sterilization and operating rooms, as well as laboratory equipment, was placing considerable demands on the limited floor space in the older hospital physical plants. There was also the requirement to meet the standards of construction and equipment being developed and recommended by the American College of Surgeons and its Hospital Research and Information Department, which was now responsible for setting standards in North American hospitals. The Canadian Hospital Council's membership had passed a resolution at its 1935 biennial meeting to support a study of building codes and regulations, and to eliminate any obsolete requirements in this area.

With the new and increasing technologies, there was also the expectation that hospital personnel would continue to develop their skills and knowledge to keep pace with this growing field. Training programs were being developed for janitors, porters and maids, because these new buildings required new caretakers. Nurses needed to improve their skills for use in the more modern operating rooms and in order to take on more supervisory responsibilities. Physicians, occupational therapists, physical therapists, librarians, record keepers, stenographers and many other health personnel were now required to staff the ever-growing and new modern hospital.

The addition of new services and technologies placed increasing demands on hospital staff not only to learn new techniques but also added more hours on-site, so that work days became longer ("Should" 1932, 20) The hospital superintendent, increasingly referred to as an administrator, was also expected to manage the new, more scientifically oriented hospital and its more highly trained staff through better management skills. He had to find ways to ensure that all employees within the hospital were well-functioning and committed staff, whose primary objective was the care of the patient, as well as cope with changing workers' expectations and unionization.

The first move to form unions occurred in Toronto hospitals in 1934. Although hospital workers had formed various associations and other organizations, ". . . in all instances the objective behind these societies or bodies has been to further the scientific features of their work or to improve the efficiency or economy of their particular activities; . . ." ("Should" 1932, 20). The issue of unions was debated across the country by hospital administrators, boards of trustees and in the pages of hospital journals. Unionization was also raised at the 1937 biennial meeting of the council under the debate about hospital administration. Both A. J. Swanson, superintendent of Toronto Western Hospital, and Dr. J. C. Mackenzie, Montreal General Hospital, spoke of the inevitability of unions in hospitals. However, Dr. A. F. Anderson, the medical superintendent of the Royal Alexandra Hospital in Edmonton, believed that the way to address the issue was to form an agreement with the labor unions. He stated categorically: "I would prefer to have a union in my hospital than be without it. . . . hospital employees are entitled to a good living wage and I am willing to side with them to get it" (CHC 1937, 91–92). No resolution, however, was passed by the membership at the time regarding what the council's position should be on unionization.

The Federal Move into Provincial Jurisdiction

The economic depression changed Canadian society in ways that were unexpected and unforeseen as the country drew closer to war by the late 1930s. The health care landscape in Canada had started to change prior to, and continued to do so, during World War II. Various prepaid plans for the provision of health, hospital and medical services had been or were being developed across Canada to provide relief for hospitals, physicians and Canadians in general. Blue Cross Plans had been adopted in Manitoba in 1939, Ontario in 1941, Quebec in 1942, British Columbia and the Maritimes in 1943 and Alberta in 1948. These plans were often operated by the provincial hospital associations as was the case in Ontario.[1]

Alongside these plans, medical associations were developing voluntary insurance schemes to cover the cost of medical care. One of the earliest plans was set up in Toronto by Associated Medical Services in 1937. These plans continued to grow across the country well into the late 1940s.

Commissions set up in Quebec, Alberta and British Columbia in the early 1930s had all recommended government-sponsored health insurance plans. In fact, Alberta had passed legislation for such a plan in 1935, as had British Columbia in 1937, but it was never enacted. (Saskatchewan had established cooperatives to pay doctors and to finance and pay hospitals before the 1920s.) In 1933, the Dominion Council of Health also approved the introduction of a national health program.

Pressure continued to mount on the federal government to provide funding assistance to the provinces, to set up universal health insurance for Canadians and to help relieve the burden on provincial and municipal governments, which were increasingly unable to pay hospitals for their services. The difficulty for the federal government was that it too was incurring a deficit due to its large unemployment payments to the provinces. But it had no jurisdiction to determine how its money was being spent or how the program was being administered.

In 1937, Prime Minister Mackenzie King appointed the Royal Commission on Dominion-Provincial Relations, more commonly known as the Rowell-Sirois Commission, to investigate the fiscal relationship between the two levels of government. Specifically, the commission was asked to look at 1) the different economic systems in the country, 2) the constitutional issues involving both levels of government and 3) the various financial agreements binding both the federal and provincial governments. In December 1937, the Canadian Hospital Council submitted its brief to the commission providing the hospital point of view on behalf of its members. (Both the brief and report to the assembly were fully endorsed by the membership at the 1939 biennial meeting.)

The Rowell-Sirois Commission submitted its report to the prime minister in 1940, making four recommendations that, even today, continue to impact the relationship between the provinces and the federal government. The recommendations would establish federal spending power over the provinces in areas traditionally allocated to the provinces by the constitution. Namely, the commission suggested that the provinces 1) should relinquish jurisdiction over areas such as unemployment and old age security—programs that the federal government had already taken over—but maintain other social programs; 2) consolidate their debt and transfer it to the federal government; 3) grant the federal government the exclusive right to levy direct taxes; and 4) permit the federal government to set up an equalization program so that the provinces could stabilize their financial base and place all provinces on an equal footing.

But the outbreak of World War II created different priorities for the federal government. While the Department of Pensions and National Health did set up the Advisory Committee on Health Insurance under Dr. J. J. Heagerty in 1942, this was purely a departmental activity. The federal government did not act on the Rowell-Sirois recommendations during the war. However, it did use its power under the War Measures Act of 1942, to consolidate its authority further. And in the Fiscal Agreement between the Dominion and the Provinces Act of 1942, the federal government formalized its 1941 request to the provinces in which it asked them to cede to it the personal and corporate income tax fields.

The Rowell-Sirois Commission recommendations and the takeover of major tax powers by the federal government to conduct the war effort inevitably changed Canadian society both economically and socially. These changes would also impact the Canadian Hospital Council and its relationship with the federal government. In 1945, the federal government convened the Dominion-Provincial Conference to look at the commission and other recommendations for reforms. The federal government proposed a redistribution of revenues through equalization payments to the provinces and the establishment of a welfare state, including health insurance. But both Ontario and Quebec rejected these proposals outright.

The Council through the War, 1939 to 1945

As the 1930s drew to a close, the country, the federal government and Canada's hospitals were becoming more preoccupied by the ever-increasing possibility of war in Europe, a war that would inevitably impact all areas of Canadian society. In fact, the Fifth Biennial Convention of the council, held in Toronto between 22 and 23 September 1939, was affected by the lack of representation from the federal government. Representatives were already caught up with preparations for war and could not attend the meeting.

The council had advised the federal government that it was prepared to work with it in delivering care for the defence forces. Yet, at the same time, hospitals would be expected to care for the civilian population. The federal Department of Pensions and National Health had contracts with hospitals for the treatment of ex-servicemen. The Department of Defence was recruiting or conscripting nurses, physicians and several other health professionals into the armed forces to care for troops in the field of combat or on their return from service overseas, thus depleting the number of professional staff available to deliver hospital services.

Dr. George Stephens, president of the council at the time, reported to the membership that the council had sent a telegram to the prime minister pledging the full support of Canada's hospitals to the war effort. This action was further confirmed in a resolution by the members at the 1939 meeting. The membership was also advised that the hospitals of Canada were poorly prepared for a coastal or gas attack, or for the casualties resulting from air raids. The pending war also prompted the American Hospital Association to pass a resolution decreasing Canadian hospital membership fees by twenty-five percent to spare hospitals the financial hardship that would fall on them with the outbreak of war. (At the time, Canadian hospitals held individual membership in the AHA.)

The outbreak of World War II eased the economic burden for Canada's hospitals for a short time. The economy was recovering under preparations for war, which provided work for the millions who had been unemployed throughout the 1930s. Men and women were needed in the forces both for combat and also for the tremendous war effort that would be required to support Canada's troops and allies overseas.

As the war progressed and the federal government designated more and more of the country's resources and manufacturing toward the war effort, hospitals were forced to pay more for food, fuel, clothing, linens and blankets, and much more for drugs, surgical supplies and equipment, most of which were intended for overseas shipment. Canada's hospitals were also expected to provide care for the civilian population and the dependents of servicemen, as well as work with local authorities, particularly in the Maritime region, to prepare for invasion and massive casualties. The executive of the Canadian Hospital Council also encouraged hospitals to expand their training programs for technicians, physiotherapists, medical anesthetists and others who might be needed for wartime work (CHC 1941, 17). The council had managed to secure an exemption for hospitals from paying unemployment insurance premiums, which further relieved some of the financial burden for hospitals.

The three armed forces—the navy, army and air service—were among the delegates noted at the Montreal meeting of 10 to 11 September 1941. Dr. Stephens, still president, reported to the members that the council had secured an agreement with the federal government regarding the building of defence hospitals; the Department of National Defence would try to build annexes or wings on community hospitals, wherever possible, and not stand-alone facilities. These annexes would then be turned over to the local hospital under the terms negotiated at the time of construction. This was an important agreement because community hospitals were already competing for personnel, supplies and drugs; they hardly needed defence hospitals in their backyards.

The agenda of the Seventh Biennial Meeting of the council shows clearly its preoccupation with the war effort. In fact, there was an increasingly large delegation from various federal departments at this meeting: representatives were on hand from the Dominion Bureau of Statistics, the Department of National Defence, the

National Selective Service and the Department of Munitions and Supplies. Dr. J. J. Heagerty, chairman of the Advisory Committee on Health Insurance from the Department of Pensions and National Health, also attended the meeting and spoke to the delegates about the proposal for federal health insurance legislation.

By 1943, the hospitals were reporting severe staff shortages and, in the roundtable, each provincial association commented on the impact of the wartime recruitment drive noting ". . . that the personnel situation [was] acute and that hospitals . . . [had] had to accept less competent employees" (CHC 1943, 28). The director of the National Selective Service explained that everything possible was being done to protect hospital personnel. Hospitals were encouraged to hire personnel officers to work with service staff and to employ more part-time workers. The director also assured the delegates that women would not fall under compulsory service, thus, further cutting into the hospital staff pool. Over twenty resolutions were approved, most of them having to do with shortages of personnel and canned foods, rationing quotas, and hospitalization of servicemen's dependents.

The council presented its brief to the House of Commons Special Committee on Social Security that year. In any government hospital insurance system, the council would support voluntary hospitals, reasonably complete benefits, provision for indigents and services delivered by the provinces but coordinated at the federal level. Because of the war, there was little action resulting from this special committee review at the time. But the recommendations of this committee would have consequences in the future.

Although a tragedy in terms of the disruption and death it caused worldwide, World War II provided the impetus for medical breakthroughs such as new and improved surgical and rehabilitation techniques, the development of new drugs such as sulfa and penicillin and the refinement of mobile and massive blood transfusion services and anesthetic techniques. All of these provided benefits to Canada's hospitals, which were now the place of choice for Canadians to receive their health care services. In fact, the demands on hospitals increased throughout the war. Canada's hospitals would need considerable financial support at the end of the war, if they were to continue to meet Canadians' expectations for access to better health services. Canadians had paid the price when called on to do so to support the war effort; now they would expect their government to ensure that their lives improved for the better because of their sacrifices (Ostry 2006).

Postwar Construction and Hospital Growth

By the end of the war, the hospitals of Canada were in dire need of upgrading. Hospital construction had lagged way behind the demand for increased care throughout the war and well into the late 1940s. At the 1945 Canadian Hospital Council biennial meeting, delegates approved a motion asking the federal government to consider low-interest loans for construction of hospital facilities.

Hospitals were now focused on reestablishing returning and discharged veterans, particularly former hospital personnel, to their previous positions within hospitals. Because of the lower wages and salaries being paid by hospitals, versus those paid to armed forces personnel, hospitals now needed more money to compete for qualified staff. Inevitably, this money would have to come from increased rates to patients and from provincial and municipal governments which paid for indigent care. Organized labor was also demanding better pay and other benefits such as pensions plans for their members, additional costs that hospitals would have to bear if they were to continue to provide care to Canadians.

Canada's hospitals, and the Canadian Hospital Council, were about to enter the postwar period. A universal hospital insurance plan was already being readied for implementation in Saskatchewan. Fiscal issues between the federal and provincial governments needed to be resolved, if any progress was to be made in creating a better society for Canadians. And tremendous strides in the medical, technical and pharmaceutical fields would further establish hospitals as the centre of the health system in Canada and place even more demands on them to provide care.

Federal versus Provincial Domination of the Health Field

The federal government was not oblivious to the expectations of the Canadian population with the ending of World War II. In fact, the then Liberal government, under William Lyon Mackenzie King, was well aware of the political, social and financial ramifications, if the federal government failed to provide Canadians with a better society than the one they had encountered though the 1930s and the war years.

First, the federal government had to deal with the inevitable return of the economy to postwar conditions. Many feared that a major recession would occur and the federal Liberals were determined to ensure full employment for the country. Under

King, the government was prepared to negotiate with the provinces to implement a social safety net in the form of a welfare state to be based on the plan being implemented in Great Britain.

Second, the Commonwealth Cooperative Federation (CCF) party, led by Tommy Douglas, had been elected in Saskatchewan in 1944 on a platform to introduce hospital insurance. This new threat from the political left, which was deeply committed to providing social benefits to its provincial constituents, would need to be watched on the federal scene. If the incumbent party at the federal level did not move to implement social benefits, the provinces no doubt would. And, in 1946, the CCF government in Saskatchewan passed legislation to set up a provincial universal hospital plan, which came into effect in 1947. Not long after this, British Columbia also introduced a hospital insurance plan. It would only be a matter of time before other provinces followed with their own insurance plans.

Third, by 1945, Prime Minister Mackenzie King was prepared to present his plan (the Green Book proposals) to the provinces, which included the Liberal vision for postwar Canada. The 1941 dominion-provincial conference had failed to gain provincial support for the redistribution of revenues (mostly because of objections by Ontario and Quebec against further federal intrusion into provincial fiscal and social jurisdiction). But, based on the proposals from the Rowell-Sirois Commission, the federal government was prepared to try again to reach an agreement. It convened another Dominion-Provincial Conference in Ottawa in early August 1945.

The federal government had compiled its recommendations in the Green Book proposals from three sources: 1) the Rowell-Sirois Commission, 2) the House of Commons Special Committee on Social Security—to which the council had presented a brief—and 3) the Heagerty Advisory Committee on Health Insurance. The plan contained the federal government's vision for Canada's future. This would include a welfare state, offering universal health insurance, full employment, cost-shared arrangements with the provinces and equalization payments to level the fiscal field for the have not provinces. As Malcolm Taylor described it, this was ". . . the Dominion government's design for a new post-war world for Canada . . ." (1978, 1).

For the Canadian Hospital Council, the most important issue on the table in these federal-provincial discussions was health insurance and how the federal government proposed to protect Canadians in the future against sickness, disability and old age. The council was also concerned about what impact this would have on Canada's hospitals, which were seriously underfunded, understaffed and short of beds. Facilities across the country needed major upgrading, if not outright reconstruction and expansion.

The federal government was prepared to offer assistance to the provinces through 1) grants for planning and organizing their hospital system, 2) health insurance for a wide range of benefits, 3) outright health grants and 4) assistance for hospital construction. The Canadian Medical Association, many other national health associations, several provincial governments and labor unions were all supportive of the federal plan. But, as Malcolm Taylor noted: "Because of its unique combination of constituents which included not only provincial hospital associations but the Catholic Hospital Associations, the provincial departments of health, and the federal Health Department, the Canadian Hospital Council could not give to the health insurance proposal the unanimous (or ringing) endorsement of the Canadian Medical Association" (1978, 29). Nevertheless, when the federal-provincial conference collapsed in 1946, the council advised the federal government that it would assist in any way it could to work out a universal health care plan.

Despite the failure of the Dominion-Provincial Conference, plans for provincewide health insurance programs were still alive. Saskatchewan's Hospital Insurance Plan had come into effect in 1947. With a system of municipal hospital cooperatives and physician payment plans already in place, it was inevitable that Saskatchewan would move forward quickly after the federal-provincial talks failed. Physicians in Saskatchewan were supportive of such a plan, as was the Saskatchewan Hospital Association. Thus, the province became the pioneer for the first universal hospital plan in North America. Several provinces watched as the plan was implemented and many provinces sent representatives to Saskatchewan for a first-hand look at how the plan was progressing.

Although it had failed to implement its Green Book proposals, the federal Liberal government found another way to package its cost-shared matching grants. In 1948, it offered a National Health Grants Program that supported hospital construction, along with financial assistance for health planning and professional training. These grants were readily accepted by the provinces. With the financial incentives provided by the federal government, one of the largest hospital construction booms in the history of Canada's health system was launched in the early 1950s.

Along with the growth in construction, the demand for more and better trained health personnel steadily increased across the country. The National Health Grants also contributed financial support for professional training and, in 1950, the federal government offered postsecondary education grants for nondenominational universities. Several new medical schools were established which resulted in more demands on hospitals. They needed to provide internships, new equipment, laboratories, operating rooms and additional facilities to support both the growing expectations of the postwar population for access to hospital care and for training facilities for physician internships.

Canadians were now expecting some form of prepaid hospital care to be available for them. Being admitted to a hospital for any sudden health crisis in the early 1950s could still result in a serious financial burden for a family. Both British Columbia and Alberta had introduced their own provincial hospital insurance plans in the late 1940s, and even Ontario, which had been hostile toward federal funding, was beginning to change its mind.

Council Changes for the Coming Decade, 1950 to 1952

In 1949, Dr. Harvey Agnew, the long-time executive secretary of the Canadian Hospital Council advised the Executive Committee that he would be retiring from the council to go into partnership in a consulting firm. Murray Ross, who became the council's first assistant secretary, recalled that Dr. Agnew was not only regarded as the council's founder but also its moving spirit and greatest strength. "There was no joy in Mudville" at the news that he would be leaving. As the council was preparing to enter a new decade, the loss of Dr. Agnew with his incredible knowledge of Canada's hospitals, his major network of colleagues in every member association, provincial health department and at the federal level, presented new challenges, as well as opportunities, for positioning it for the future.

Dr. Leonard O. Bradley was hired as the new executive secretary of the council in 1950 and Murray Ross was appointed to the position of assistant secretary effective 1 January 1950. The hiring of an assistant was an acknowledgment by the council members that the growing demands being placed on the council could no longer be handled by one individual. As the council entered the new decade, the Executive Committee charged Dr. Bradley and his assistant with total responsibility for the council's services and operations.

Offices of the Canadian Hospital Council at 280 Bloor Street West, Toronto, 1953.

For the Canadian Hospital Council, the evolution occurring in Canada's health system meant changes for it as well. Several Blue Cross Plans across Canada had applied for membership in 1952. And the issue of membership and ongoing financial support for the council were becoming urgent matters that the membership had to address, if the council was to become self-supporting. With the introduction of universal hospital insurance plans in some provinces, new and more demands were being place on the council's provincial members, many of which were in even less stable position than the national council (*see* chapter 6 for more information).

The issue of better hospital standards came to the forefront of hospital concerns once again with the rapid construction program underway. There was considerable pressure from Canadian hospitals to set up a Canadian accreditation standards program. The current program was still being delivered by the American College of Surgeons. This organization was encountering further rising costs and looking to get out of the program. The council was directed to deal with the need for uniform accounting practices and standards for Canadian hospitals, to find funding to set up a hospital management course for administrators, to acquire more office space for its growing staff and to work with the Canadian Nurses Association to deal with chronic nursing shortages which hospitals were experiencing.

By the early 1950s, the Executive Committee also sensed that the time might be right to propose a name change for the council. The membership might be ready to create a truly national association that could look out for the interests of all Canadian hospitals at the federal level—a notion first introduced by Dr. Harvey Agnew in 1931 and a vision he supported throughout his term as executive secretary.

Summary

The Canadian Hospital Council was established in 1931 during one of the worst economic depressions of the twentieth century. Supported by the generosity of the Sun Life Assurance Company of Canada and directed by dedicated men and women who gave freely and generously of their time to the hospitals of Canada, it barely managed to survive through the difficult thirties. By the end of World War II, the council was expected to support its hospitals and their growing demands. Various provinces—beginning with Saskatchewan in 1947—had set up their own universal insurance plans, and the federal government's cost-shared arrangements were providing for a major hospital expansion in the 1950s, which was inevitably going to impact the council's members and the council itself.

Endnotes

1. The first hospital plan in Alberta was set up in 1933 as the Edmonton Group Hospitalization Plan, which included the four general hospitals in the city.

3

THE CANADIAN HOSPITAL ASSOCIATION, 1953 TO 1977

". . . hospitals are now the most expensive public facility in existence."

(MONTEITH 1960, 37)

By the early 1950s, Canada's hospitals were undergoing one of the most significant expansions in the history of the health system. Gearing up for the expected implementation of a national hospital insurance program and the problems that were developing because of the pace of hospital growth across Canada, the Canadian Hospital Council needed to look to its future and how it would cope in an environment of national hospital insurance, rising costs and Canadians' increasing expectations for access to health care whenever they needed it.

With the resignation of Dr. Leonard Bradley in 1952, the council had a new executive secretary in the person of Dr. Arnold Swanson by 1953. This was a time of major growth for the association as the members had approved the establishment of a distance education program (the HOM program) and the publication of its first hospital directory to meet the demands for more information about Canada's expanding hospital field. CHA had also released the first *Canadian Hospital Accounting Manual* in 1952, a much-needed reference to prepare Canada's hospitals for improved accounting practices.

The Association's New Name and Focus

In May 1953, the membership approved a new name for the organization. It would now be known as the Canadian Hospital Association-Association des Hôpitaux du Canada (CHA-AHC), as well as an expansion of the association's membership. But the main focus of the Twelfth Biennial Meeting was the issue of the accreditation of Canadian hospitals: How would the program work? Who would deliver this program? And, most importantly, how would a Canadian program be paid for?

The other issue was one of governance of the association. The original structure had served the council but was no longer capable of directing a national association. There was no equitable membership at the board table and no sustained financial support from current members to enable CHA to carry out the activities and demands that would inevitably develop from the introduction of national health insurance. Both the governance and financing of CHA would need to be dealt with before the decade was over. (*See* chapters 5 and 6 for details on governance and membership.)

Delegates at the Chateau Laurier in Ottawa for the 12th Biennial Meeting, 18-20 May 1953 Where the Council Was Renamed the Canadian Hospital Association.

But, first, CHA had to tackle accreditation. For more than thirty years, hospitals in North America had been accredited by the American College of Surgeons. This program had been transferred to the new American-based Joint Commission on

Accreditation of Hospitals effective 1 January 1953. The commission, representing several American health organizations and the Canadian Medical Association (CMA), carried on with the voluntary accreditation program, which included Canadian hospitals.

At the same time, the CMA and the hospital council had formed a committee to study accreditation for Canada. This committee, renamed the Canadian Commission on Hospital Accreditation, presented its report at CHA's 1953 biennial meeting. The report recommended that a Canadian program be set up in cooperation with the Joint Commission in the United States. Although the debate was contentious and heated at times, and lasted until well past midnight the first day of the meeting, the delegates did eventually agree to support a Canadian program (Swanson 1953, 37). The membership accepted the compromise proposal that the Canadian Commission would hire an additional surveyor to supplement the American program in Canada. and seek representation on the Joint Commission board. The membership also agreed to accept the additional cost to them of approximately $10,000 annually to be paid to the CHA through their membership fees (Ibid., 60).

This was the beginning of the ongoing debate about accreditation in Canada both at CHA's board table and among the members throughout the 1950s. One of the main obstacles in setting up an all-Canadian accreditation program was the cost. CHA's board had formed a Committee on Accreditation in 1953 which represented the association on the commission.[1] The committee reported at each board meeting and received direction. Various CHA presidents also reported on the progress— or lack thereof—of the accreditation program at each biennial meeting. This issue was never an easy one to resolve. Although CHA had applied for representation on the American Joint Commission, this was denied and Canadian hospitals continued to be represented by the CMA. Nevertheless, in 1957, the membership—twenty-seven delegates out of thirty-five—voted in favor of establishing an all-Canadian program. Henceforth, this program would be organized and carried out by the Canadian Commission on Hospital Accreditation effective 1 January 1959.

Canadian hospitals showed considerable reluctance to undergo this voluntary accreditation process even when Canadian surveyors were hired. By 1957, of the 682 eligible hospitals in Canada, only 292 had been surveyed (Fraser 1957, 40). Reporting to the membership in 1957, President Gilbert Turner warned the delegates that, if the hospitals of Canada did not accept responsibility for undergoing an accreditation process, he believed that the federal government would impose one, especially under a national hospital insurance program which was expected to be implemented by 1959.

By 1961, the cost to CHA and the other organization members was beginning to increase to the point where the Canadian Council on Hospital Accreditation, as it was now called, had approached the federal government for financial assistance. CHA continued to oppose any such assistance to avoid government influence in the accreditation process. (*See* chapter 10 for a detailed description of the launch of the accreditation commission.)

CHA was also undergoing rapid expansion internally. By the late 1950s, its programs and services were growing and its staff was increasing to meet the demands, especially for its education programs. It now employed nineteen full-time and two part-time staff and occupied rental space in downtown Toronto at two locations. In 1954, Dr. Swanson resigned as the executive director of the association and, for the third time in less than four years, the board was searching for a new CEO once again.

In August 1954, Dr. Douglas Piercey took over as executive director. His more pressing duties included to plan and deliver a first joint conference with the Western Canada Institute, in cooperation with the Saskatchewan Hospital Association, for the 1957 biennial meeting. He was also asked to arrange a meeting with the federal minister of health to present the CHA and members' perspective on the federal government's proposed national hospital insurance program. His other key priorities were to ensure the implementation of the medical record librarian educational program; support the work of the board's Committee on Accounting and Statistics, which was revising *CHAM*; and hire sufficient staff to collect and update information on Canada's hospitals for publication in the *Canadian Hospital Directory*. This latter activity was a lengthy and time-consuming project which involved more than eight staff at the time. The postal service was the main vehicle for transmitting large amounts of information across the country between hospitals and the association at the time.

To add to the already growing workload for Dr. Piercey, delegates at the Fifteenth Biennial Meeting approved the CHA Building Committee's recommendation that CHA construct its own building at 25 Imperial Street in Toronto. By 1959, CHA was renting office space at both 57 and 280 Bloor Street West and needed office space to accommodate staff in one location. The Building Committee had concluded that it was cheaper in the long term for CHA to own its own building, and assembly delegates approved the building project with the stipulation that it not exceed $175,000. In May 1959, CHA also acquired the property at 23 Imperial Street.

The National Hospital Insurance Program, 1958

Several provinces already operated some form of provincial hospital insurance in the 1950s. In fact, by 1953, more than 6,000,000 Canadians were voluntarily enrolled in third-party prepayment plans that offered coverage for some, if not all, hospital care (Fraser 1953, 50). Hospital insurance plans, either set up by provincial governments or available from private insurers, were the future for Canada's health system. For Canada's hospitals in the early 1950s, these insurance payments were the major source of their funding.

With the federal government proceeding to set up a national hospital insurance plan, CHA hired Dr. Malcolm Taylor to write its brief titled "Hospital Submission on National Health Service," which outlined the direction its membership would like to see a national hospital insurance plan take. Presenting briefs and representing its members was not easy for CHA. With the association located in Toronto, contact with the federal government, particularly the Department of National Health and Welfare, was infrequent. At the 1954 board meeting, this relationship was discussed, especially the lack of coordination between federal government policies and hospitals in Canada. The board set up a committee "for the purpose of interviewing the Minister of National Health and Welfare at least twice a year" (CHA 1954, n.p.). This committee, chaired by Arthur J. Swanson, was to present CHA's brief on hospital insurance to the federal government as soon as possible.

By early 1955, the board approved the brief and directed the chairman of the committee to meet with the minister of National Health and Welfare, Paul Martin, Sr., to inform him of the brief's contents and to gain his support for CHA's position. A first meeting with the minister had already generated positive results; the minister assured CHA that it was not the federal government's intention to ignore the opinions of the association as the national representative of Canada's hospitals.

In May 1957, the deputy minister of health, Dr. G.D.W. Cameron, spoke to the delegates at CHA's biennial meeting in Saskatoon, highlighting the three general principles of the federal government's proposed health insurance program which would:

1. . . . provide a basic standard of in-patient services available to everyone in all participating provinces and allows the provinces to suggest out-patient services.

2. . . . permit a variety of provincial arrangements in the administration of programs which will meet the special circumstances in each province.

3. . . . not in any way "freeze" hospital services but will permit their development in an orderly and sensible manner to meet the changes in demands upon hospitals (Cameron 1957, 32).

CHA's brief, as described in Malcolm Taylor's 1978 book on the implementation of hospital insurance, supported federal government subsidization of low-income individuals rather than universal hospital insurance. This would enable low-income earners to pay premiums to the voluntary Blue Cross Plans already in place.[2] The brief also made a significant statement about the federal government's focus on hospitals. CHA noted:

(3) Unfortunately, this preoccupation with general hospital facilities has resulted in an almost complete ignoring of the needs for alternative types of care, such as convalescent hospitals, homes for the aged, or visiting-nursing services. Consequently, many general hospital facilities are being called upon to provide care which could adequately be given in much less expensive ways and in less expensive types of institutions (Taylor 1978, 192).

The brief pointed out a similar flaw in the federal government's National Health Grants Program which funded hospital construction. CHA believed that these grants should give consideration to supplementing nursing homes, home care programs and homes for the aged rather than focusing on hospital construction only.

CHA was also critical of the fact that hospital insurance excluded any monies for capital expenditures, capital debt and interest, as well as prior debt, interest and depreciation. Nor did the insurance plan include convalescent and chronic care hospitals. In fact, a resolution was passed at the 1957 biennial meeting requesting the federal government to reconsider its position regarding interest and depreciation because these items were recognized as legitimate expenditures in all business enterprises but not under the hospital insurance program.

By 1958, the federal government was in the final stages of implementing its national hospital insurance plan. The plan would provide considerable benefits both to

Canadians and to hospitals, which would receive guaranteed payments for their services. But these payments would come with a price tag. Hospitals would need to account for the expenditure of money and, in turn, they sought assistance from their member associations to learn how to become accountable and how to report to provincial hospital commissions. CHA was also pressured to enhance its activities and services to its membership.

In July 1958, the Hospital Insurance and Diagnostic Services (HIDS) Act came into effect. Federal Health Minister J. Waldo Monteith was a keynote speaker at CHA's last biennial meeting held in Montreal in May 1959. He addressed the delegates by giving a progress report on how the implementation of the federal government's hospital insurance legislation was proceeding across the provinces. His overview noted that, by mid-1959, there were

> a series of [insurance] schemes developed and administered by the provinces and assisted financially and technically by the Dominion government. Their broad outlines must conform to general principles laid down by the federal Act, but their details are geared to local conditions and practices. This is exactly what has happened (Monteith 1959, 37).

The minister went on to describe how the provinces had set about implementing the hospital plan, the various ways in which the plans were financed, with each plan receiving up to fifty percent funding from the federal government. He pointed out that, although there were differences among the plans for waiting periods (residency requirements), out-of-province benefits and in the scope of services covered by each plan, each province was expected to provide the basic core services of inpatient care.

Health Minister Monteith went on to praise CHA for its contribution to hospital accounting practices that would enable the federal health department to collect information and to monitor how federal monies were being spent. He noted to the delegates that:

> the Canadian Hospital Association deserves much credit, particularly with respect to hospital accounting and standards of care. . . . [W]hen public funds are paid for a service, the public is entitled to an accurate report on how they are used. . . . I do not think it is any exaggeration to say this might well have been impossible had it not been for the pioneer work of this organization. Through its publication of the *Canadian Hospital Accounting Manual* and related activities, it has helped raise the . . . level of hospital accounting in Canada (36).

Throughout the 1940s and 1950s, CHA had partnered with the Dominion Bureau of Statistics (DBS) to develop the manual and a uniform reporting system. With the implementation of the hospital insurance act, the federal health department would deliver reporting schedules in the future to DBS, which had been receiving these directly from the provinces in the past. National Health and Welfare would now process and tabulate information for its own purposes. In reporting to CHA's executive about this change, CHA staff noted that: "Furthermore, the major authority in respect to the information contained in the reporting schedules, the form they will take, et cetera, will be that of the Department rather than the Bureau" (CHA 1958, 6). This was a major power shift in Ottawa and CHA had little influence with the federal health department as it had with DBS over the years.

CHA now found itself isolated from the major federal department that could, and often did, implement legislation affecting Canada's hospitals without any input or consultation from the national organization representing them. CHA was also turned down by the department when it sought representation on the Advisory Committee on Hospital Insurance and Diagnostic Services. However, it was invited to sit on subcommittees on quality care and other technical committees as National Health and Welfare set up its monitoring processes for hospital insurance.

Financially, by 1959, the association had attained some stability. The implementation of an agreed-on member fee structure in 1958 and the continuing assistance of both the Sun Life Assurance Company and the Canadian Blue Cross Plans for secretarial support had allowed the CHA to undertake its growing list of activities without the fear of finanical ruin. With the end of the Kellogg Foundation grants, the education courses were also expected to become self-sufficient by the end of the decade, and the journal and directory continued to contribute surpluses to the association's revenues.

In setting the association's priorities for the next decade, Dr. Piercey had advised the Executive Committee in May 1959 he intended to focus on developing education courses; setting up a public relations program for hospitals, hospital associations and CHA; and completing the building project. In fact, he wrote: "I am not one who believes that the primary function of a national association is representing hospitals and hospital associations at the federal level" (Piercey 1959, 2). Given the monumental impact that national hospital insurance was about to have on Canada's health care system, CHA seemed to be out of step as it moved into its new headquarters in late January 1960 at the beginning of a new decade.

Meeting Demands and Expectations

In order for hospitals to meet Canadians' expectations and growing demands for health care, there had to be sufficient beds available, staffed by knowledgeable and well-trained health personnel in order to deliver quality care. Defining what was meant by quality care and finding ways to assess it, as well as setting standards for hospitals and health personnel, were some of the issues that began to emerge as a result of the implementation of hospital insurance.

To understand how the first round of five-year National Health Grants (1948-1953) had changed Canada's hospital scene, Dr. Agnew wrote in *Canadian Hospital* that, in 1948, Canada had more than 116,000 beds set up in active treatment and special hospitals such as long-stay, convalescent and tuberculosis sanitoria. By 1953, including 13,423 federal beds, there were over 173,800 beds set up in Canada's ever expanding hospitals, and the next round of health grants to support further construction would soon be available. In fact, federal Health Minister Paul Martin reported to CHA's annual assembly in 1953 that the federal government would make more than $42,000,000 available to Canada's hospitals for the second five-year grant. Along with the fifty-fifty cost-sharing grants being given to the provinces for hospital insurance plans, the explosive growth of both hospitals and hospital services should not have been unexpected. But, with growth, comes growing pains.

As hospitals expanded across the country, the demand for more skilled health care professional staff also increased. While nursing shortages had been on the CHA agenda for more than a decade, by the mid-1950s, shortages of other health personnel were being reported in various parts of the country. There were requirements for well-trained and skilled nurses and physicians, for hospital support and technical staff, and for housekeeping and dietary personnel. In turn, hospital administrators needed to be well versed in management theory; know how to negotiate with their boards, ministry staff and labor unions; understand new accounting practices; and be able to prepare their facilities for inspections from ministries, local municipalities and accreditation surveyors.

Nor were the hospitals the only group that needed better trained and knowledgeable personnel. Provincial governments required a large number of public service personnel to work in blossoming departments of health or in hospital service commissions to implement, track and support provincial hospital insurance programs. And CHA's member associations also experienced increasing demands on their organizations as hospital insurance schemes were set up. Until the introduction of hospital insurance, most of CHA's provincial member associations and Catholic conferences had been operated by voluntary staff, with hospitals making financial contributions when and if they chose. But the hospital insurance scheme changed the health care environment across the country; CHA's membership needed to set up permanent organizations, staffed with experienced personnel who could deliver programs and services for their member public hospitals. In turn, the membership looked to CHA to lead the way in implementing programs to assist hospitals.

The demand for highly skilled and professional health personnel impacted hospital operations. Frequently, these new health occupations demanded better salaries and working conditions, and improved pension plans. Health personnel often required licensure and registration or set up regulations without any input from the hospital sector about the impact these might have on the delivery of care at the bedside. In fact, this issue was raised at the 1961 annual assembly meeting by President Stanley Martin, who noted to the delegates: "We find, from time to time, that new regulations are introduced by these groups which directly affect the ability of the hospitals to carry on the traditional patterns of care to the patient" (1961, 37). He suggested that CHA needed a clear-cut policy in dealing with these various health professions and that there needed to be more cooperation and communication to resolve some of these problems.

By the beginning of the 1960s, CHA was already engaged in a debate with the Canadian Nurses Association (CNA) over the setting up of standards and the accreditation of hospital training schools. The CNA believed that nurse training should be done in educational institutions and the CHA supported the hospital training schools, which had been in place for several decades.[3] A clash between the two associations was inevitable. A joint committee was set up in 1959 and discussions continued over the next two years. (*See* chapter 9 for more information about this issue.)

As the country entered the 1960s, health human resource issues were moving to the top of the list of health system problems that would require some resolution. CHA was also receiving more and more requests from national professional organizations to form joint committees in order to solve hospital-physician problems. And the problem of quality care, hospital standards and rising hospital costs added to a growing list of issues facing CHA and its membership in the next decade.

CHA in the 1960s

For CHA, the main issue for its members was helping them learn to deal with government commissions and the large public service sector, which had evolved from the implementation of hospital insurance. Provincial insurance commissions and health ministries approved budgets, provided funding and assessed hospital accounting procedures. Most of CHA's membership had to learn how to deal with these government bureaucracies. CHA developed guidelines for hospital-government relations in 1961 to assist both member associations and their hospital memberships. (*See* chapter 15 for more details.)

Increasingly, the provincial member organizations pushed CHA to review and revise its bylaws in order to open up its board of directors to more equitable representation. Amendments were proposed in 1963 to the annual assembly, which partially resolved members' concerns. But the question of membership on the board, increasing fees and what CHA provided for these continued to be raised by member CEOs. Growing costs for accreditation both for hospitals and for the accreditation council were discussed on an ongoing basis at CHA's board, often with little resolution. In both 1964 and 1965, the membership directed CHA to provide adequate funding for the accreditation council and the CHA board agreed to cover the council's $10,000 deficit in 1964.

The association had continued to increase the scope of its services through various representation activities at the federal level and with key national associations such as CMA, CNA and the Canadian Standards Association. In fact, as more and more national professional and allied health associations came into existence, they often sought membership of some type in the CHA. And just as it seemed to be settling into some stability, Dr. Douglas Piercey was forced to resign his position as executive director due to poor health. For several months throughout 1965 and well into 1966, management of the association fell to the assistant director, until Dr. B.L.P. Brosseau was hired and joined CHA in August 1966.

Dr. Brosseau continued to support CHA's commitment to deliver education programs. Enrolment in these courses soared throughout the late 1960s and early 1970s. Dr. Brosseau, who was fluently bilingual in both English and French, also worked hard to ensure that CHA's publications had French editorial content, as well as trustee material, another area where there was a growing demand for education and information. In May 1966, the membership directed the association to review its goals and its role, and the Aims and Objectives Committee was set up to undertake the review. (*See* chapter 5 for more details about this committee's work.)

By the end of the 1960s, the demand for more and better education programs of all kinds for hospital personnel rose sharply. CHA revised and upgraded its hospital organization and management (HOM) course and the program for medical record librarians. Both the CHA and CNA jointly sponsored the Nursing Unit Administration Program to improve the administrative knowledge of head nurses in managing their units and, in 1965, the association launched the departmental management course. (*See* chapter 12 for more detailed information on CHA's distance education programs.) Education of all types was flourishing across the country. New medical schools had been set up at several universities, nursing schools were being opened in provincial colleges and technical schools were graduating more and better educated allied and occupational health personnel to meet hospital staffing needs.

The Implementation of Medicare, 1968

Physicians' services outside hospitals were not covered under the hospital insurance plan implemented in 1959. These were often expensive for individuals and families and Canadians frequently checked into hospitals where they could receive free medical services. Physicians were covered under private insurance schemes and, by 1955, the CMA had established Trans-Canada Medical Services as a coordinating body for several voluntary insurance plans offered by some of its provincial divisions. Some Blue Cross Plans also offered a combination of both hospital and medical care insurance. Along with CMA's group, there were also several commercial insurance companies offering private medical coverage for individuals and families. But, for the most part, visiting a physician could be a costly event for Canadians.

Then, in 1961, Saskatchewan introduced a government-sponsored medical care insurance program. It would be compulsory, universal and would cover "services of physicians and surgeons in the office, hospital, or home" (Taylor 1978, 285). The patient could pick the physician and the physician would have the right to accept or reject the patient. By the early 1960s, Alberta, British Columbia and Ontario also offered subsidized medical coverage for low-income and high-risk groups in their respective provinces. But their programs, as Dr. Malcolm Taylor described: ". . .

acted in such a way as to leave the majority of the population who could afford voluntary insurance to the private sector while government paid part or all of the cost for 'the poor risks.' " (1978, 341).

It was just a matter of time before the federal government moved to implement a national medical insurance plan for the country, following Saskatchewan's lead. But, before it decided to do so, Prime Minister John Diefenbaker appointed Justice Emmett Hall to chair a Royal Commission on Health Services in 1961. Its mandate was to examine the issue of Canada's future health care needs and what resources would be required to support them. CHA asked for representation on the commission and submitted names to the prime minister, Justice Hall and the minister of health. Although it failed to appoint anyone to the commission, it did prepare and submit a brief.

CHA's submission was made in May 1962 with input from its active members, excluding the CMA, which ". . . took no part in the formation of this brief." Among its sixteen recommendations, the association focused on supporting a voluntary hospital system under local ownership, management and control, as well as the establishment of provincial health planning councils. CHA recommended that mental health, outpatient services and transportation of patients be included in an amended hospital diagnostic services act, and that the federal government support alternative facilities to hospitals in its construction grants program, along with more funding for medical research and for training hospital personnel (CHA 1962, 1–4).

The Hall Commission reported in June 1964. Among its recommendations was the need to implement a program to reimburse fees for physicians' services. Hall supported a program that included the principles of 1) comprehensive coverage, 2) portability across provinces and territories, 3) universality for all eligible residents and 4) public administration. Every province would have to meet these standards in order to receive federal funding. The report also identified the need for more and better trained physicians through the establishment of new medical schools in Canada to meet increasing demand and the creation of a health assistance fund of $500,000,000 to reimburse fifty percent of the capital costs of hospital construction and renovations, as well as equipment acquisition.

The national Medical Care Insurance Act was passed on 16 December 1966 but financial concerns, provincial and physician opposition delayed its enactment until 1 July 1968. Unlike hospital insurance, the federal government did not need a majority of the provinces to agree to the program. On its launch date, only Saskatchewan and British Columbia agreed to the program. However, by 1972, all the provinces and territories had joined the plan.

Among the opposition to this plan was federal Finance Minister Mitchell Sharp, who believed that the federal government could not afford it. He thought that Canada's overheated economy of the 1960s would soon cool down and the costs of providing what came to be known as medicare would soon spiral out of control as hospital costs were now doing. He had projected a deficit budget for 1965–1966 and was forecasting an even larger deficit for 1967.

Rising Costs of Canada's Medicare System

The early 1970s marked the end of hospital expansion, which had begun in the early 1950s. Just as Mitchell Sharp, the Liberal finance minister had warned, the Canadian economy cooled off. In 1973, the price of oil around the world skyrocketed, shaking up national economies everywhere. In Canada, the oil crisis triggered stagflation. And both the federal government and the provincial governments had become increasingly dissatisfied with the cost-shared health programs, albeit for different reasons.

In an effort to bring federal health expenditures under control, the deputy minister of health, Dr. Maurice LeClair, appointed a Task Force on the Costs of Health Services in 1968. The task force identified health care expenditures by both the federal and provincial governments as one of the major factors impacting on Canada's gross domestic product (GDP). The task force reported that federal transfers of payments to provincial governments for their hospital insurance programs amounted to more than three times what they had been in 1950.

Among its many recommendations, the task force focused on standards and quality care. It recommended compulsory accreditation of hospitals, which CHA hesitated to support until a more thorough study of the issue had been undertaken. However, the association was much more receptive to the idea of the "licensing and grading of hospital administrators," and suggested in an editorial that "[p]erhaps this is the time to further consider and encourage the formation of a Hospital Administrators' Council of Canada" (Brosseau 1970, 5).

The administration of Canada's hospitals had become more complex with each passing decade. From untrained, inexperienced superintendents of the 1930s and 1940s, hospital managers were now expected to show leadership skills, develop policy, make extensive decisions about facility expansion and recommend the purchase of highly technical and expensive equipment. Senior management needed negotiation skills in order to deal with their boards, provincial ministries and the powerful unions that represented most of the staff within their institutions. In fact, as hospital issues became more complex, the board came to rely heavily on their CEO to provide them with sound advice about a wide range of issues.

Throughout the 1950s and 1960s, more and more universities had established hospital—and broader health—administration programs.[4] For nongraduates of these courses, CHA had launched its own hospital management program. And, in 1954, both HOM and university graduates had sought CHA's support to set up a Canadian organization for hospital administrators. At the time, CHA supported Canadian membership in the American College of Hospital Administrators. But, with the task force pushing for more standards and certification of administrators, CHA decided to look into setting up the Hospital Administrators Council of Canada, which was officially launched in Edmonton on 2 June 1970, at the Third National Hospital Association Convention. More than nine hundred administrators applied for membership in the council. (*See* chapter 10 for more details.)

Another factor driving up health care costs in the 1970s was the impact of new technologies within the health care sector, particularly in hospitals. New hospital and laboratory equipment, better and faster diagnostic services, and new and more expensive drugs continued to be introduced into health care. One of the fastest growing technologies in the 1970s were computers and computer applications for all kinds of work processes.

In March 1970, CHA held a national symposium in Ottawa on the impact of computer technology on health care. (*See* chapter 13 for details.) As a result of the recommendations of this meeting, CHA applied to the Department of National Health and Welfare for financial assistance to set up a collection agency and abstract service on how and where computer applications in hospitals were being developed. In partnership with the CMA, CHA proposed to oversee this bureau, hire a director and manage its finances. It was hoped that this agency could identify how much money was being spent in hospitals on computers and their applications and, specifically, what computers were doing to enhance health care. With CHA's activities growing, by 1971, it needed both more staff and more office space. The board authorized the association to investigate the cost of expanding the building and approved both the addition of two floors to 25 Imperial Street and an addition of five floors to the building on the east side.

Just as funding and the cost of the health system were monopolizing the attention of the federal and provincial governments, CHA's finances also became a serious matter for its board. By 1972, CHA was operating with major and growing deficits. The board was so concerned with the association's increasing liabilities and lack of assets that it hired a management consultant to review all the association's operations, staffing and finances. One of the consultant's recommendations was that CHA should hire "a competent business administrator" to report to the executive director. However, internal staff conflicts had led to his quick departure by 1973 and the growing deficit was beginning to preoccupy both CHA's board and its membership more and more. Finally, the board asked a member of the Ontario Hospital Association to clean up CHA's finances. By 1974, with more stringent accounting practices in place, the board felt reasonably comfortable that CHA now had its finances under control.

By the mid-1970s, as the federal government continued to struggle with an inflationary economy, rising deficits and increasing costs, Marc Lalonde, the federal minister of health, released his landmark book titled, *A New Perspective on the Health of Canadians*. He proposed that the health care system and its components were only one of many ways in which good health could be maintained and improved. He suggested that individual life-styles, biology and environmental factors also contributed to good health. His philosophy regarding the health care organization was that it could no longer simply focus on treating illness; the hospital needed to implement health promotion and prevention programs to educate and support Canadians in developing healthier lives. This new focus on health promotion created opportunities for CHA to look at how its members could move into this new area of health delivery in 1974.

With Canada looking at other ways to improve Canadians' health—aside from putting more and more money into the system—CHA was asked at the 1974 annual convention "to take a more positive leadership approach relating to an integrated health care system for Canada with hospitals to be regarded as only one component of the system" ("Future" 1974, 15). It was also directed to adopt a new name, broaden its membership, improve communications with its members, and continue delivering its distance education programs and develop new ones as needed.

CHA also celebrated fifty years in the journal publishing business by changing the name of its long-standing journal *Canadian Hospital* to *Dimensions in Health Service*. This change indicated CHA's shift to a broader perspective on more than the hospital facility.

By the late 1970s, CHA had managed to survive the implementation of two national insurance programs, the expansion and then the downsizing of the hospital sector, the growth of major health professions and that of its own membership. It had helped to create the Canadian Council on Hospital Accreditation and the Hospital Administrators Council of Canada, was heavily involved in setting up a hospital information system and managed the Health Computer Information Bureau in Ottawa. As its

Dr. B.L.P. Brosseau (Middle) Supervising the Packing of the Library at the CHA Toronto Offices at 25 Imperial Street, in 1977, for the Move to Ottawa.

Front row: The past presidents who received pins: (l. to r.) Dr. J. Gilbert Turner, Montreal, Que.; Dr. Angus C. McGugan, Edmonton, Alta.; Rev. Georges Verreault, Montreal, Que.; A. J. Swanson, Toronto, Ont.; and R. Fraser Armstrong, Kingston, Ont.

Standing are those who presented the past presidents with their pins: (l. to r.) Judge Nelles V. Buchanan, Edmonton, Alta.; Dr. G. Harvey Agnew, Toronto, Ont.; George Bourke of the Sun Life Assurance Company of Canada, Montreal, Que.; Dr. Lorne C. Gilday, Montreal, Que., and Dr. D. F. W. Porter, Vallée Lourdes, N.B.

CHA 15th Biennial Meeting, Montreal, May 1959

membership shifted, and member needs and demands changed, the organization evolved to accommodate these changes.

Then, in 1977, after eleven years as the CEO, Dr. Brosseau announced that he planned to retire at the end of the year. This presented an opportunity to move CHA out of Toronto to new headquarters in the nation's capital and to hire a new executive director at the same time. With CHA in Ottawa, it would finally be close to the federal government where its presence could help its membership and increase its visibility at a time when it appeared that the federal government was rethinking its financial commitments to Canada's health system.

Summary

Hospitals became acceptable in the twentieth century as places to go for medical treatment. By the 1950s, they were *the place* to go for women to give birth, for all types of treatment and surgical procedures, and also the place where most Canadians died. People could afford to go to a hospital by the 1950s; their income was increasing and many modern, scientific discoveries, as well as drug therapies and diagnostic procedures, were not only relieving pain but allowing people to recover more quickly or just plain recover and live longer lives.

By the end of the 1970s, Canadians regarded their hospitals and the universal medicare insurance program that supported these facilities as sacrosanct, not a privilege for the well-to-do but a right for every member of Canadian society. Despite recessions, wage and price controls, high provincial deficits and even higher national debt, playing around with—or even suggesting that medicare needed adjusting—was not something any political party on the national or provincial scene wanted to do. Yet the cost of Canada's health care system continued to rise despite all efforts to halt its growth.

CHA had supported its membership throughout the launch of the national medicare program through two decades and had dealt with the periodic demands of its membership to serve their needs more effectively. Now it would have to focus on how it could survive in the future in another city, with hospitals needing ever more support to curtail costs, deliver quality care and meet Canadians' demands.

Endnotes

1. The council had been involved in the issue of standards for hospitals throughout its early years. In fact, a Committee on Standards had been set up by the Executive Committee in October 1949.

2. It's important to remember that the provincial Blue Cross Plans were associate members in CHA and, by the end of the decade, the national association for the plans provided financial support to CHA. Neither CHA nor its active membership was likely to favor a national hospital insurance plan that bypassed or excluded these plans.

3. The hospital-based nursing schools had long been a source of free nursing care as young nurse trainees learned their skills at the bedside.

4. These health administration programs were located at the University of Toronto, University of Montreal, University of Ottawa, University of Alberta, University of British Columbia and Dalhousie University.

4

CHA IN THE NATION'S CAPITAL, 1978 TO 2006

". . . if the Association was to continue to function and be a valuable representative of its members, it should be on the national scene, and this could only be accomplished by being in Ottawa."

(FRITH IN CHA 1976f, 2)

This period in the history of the Canadian Healthcare Association (CHA) begins with its move to Ottawa. Although the issue had been on the agenda for several years, CHA finally moved its headquarters to the nation's capital in late 1977. By moving to Ottawa, CHA would be in a position to carry out its mandate of influencing federal policy regarding Canada's health system. It would also put the association in the same city where most of the other major national health associations were located.

The next quarter of a century for the association was filled with the financial ups and downs that reflected the economic times in Canada. Relations with the membership shifted, deteriorated, improved and changed significantly as health system restructuring across the provinces and territories impacted all aspects of the system, including CHA, throughout the 1980s, the 1990s and into the next century.

The Critical Year of 1977

As the national hospital association, CHA's mandate was to represent the interests of its membership—often perceived as the hospitals of Canada—to the federal government and to other national health organizations. To do this, the best and most effective place to be located was in Ottawa, the nation's capital. The association would be in a much better position to lobby and advocate to federal departments such as Health and Welfare Canada, Revenue Canada and Statistics Canada, as well as crown corporations and parliamentary committees that reviewed and recommended legislation affecting Canada's health system.

Most of the major national health associations—the Canadian Medical Association (CMA), the Canadian Nurses Association (CNA) and the Royal College of Physicians and Surgeons—had already moved to Ottawa. Other organizations such as the Canadian Dental Association (CDA) and the Canadian Council on Hospital Accreditation (CCHA) were considering a move, and the Canadian College of Health Service Executives (CCHSE), which rented space in CHA's Toronto building, was enthusiastically committed to the move.

After years of delay and debate, postponement and petitions from staff, the CHA board finally agreed at the March 1977 meeting, that the association was to move all its operations to its new rental location at 410 Laurier Avenue West, just a few blocks south of Parliament Hill in downtown Ottawa. (*See* chapter 5 for more details.) This critical decision changed CHA's focus, its members' expectations and its core business over the coming decades.

At this same meeting, the board endorsed CHA's brief to the health minister on the upcoming Established Programs Financing (EPF) Act. This legislation would also change the relationship of the federal government with the provinces and with Canada's health system. In fact, in a question-and-answer session at the March board meeting, federal Health Minister Marc Lalonde summarized the department's position regarding the new financial arrangements. He advised the board that: "The federal department would be going away from the detailed auditing it had been involved in. It was hoped that there would be more flexibility, but also departmental resources would be relieved and allocated to areas in the line of preventive medicine. . . . It was not intended that less money be spent, just that resources be re-allocated" (CHA 1977c, 18).

The EPF legislation changed the federal payment scheme from fifty-fifty cost-sharing arrangements to block funding through a combination of tax points and cash payments to the provinces. The legislation had no built-in requirements that federal monies had to be applied to provincial health programs. Nor did the federal government intend to track the dollars as they had under the previous hospital insurance act. EPF retained the four principles of medicare but downplayed the federal role in health delivery and left decision-making for the allocation of health funds to the provinces.

Health Minister Lalonde was more interested in shifting the federal health focus to health promotion and improving the health status of Canadians by changing their behavior and improving the other social factors that impacted on health. He and his department officials sought CHA's support on issues such as banning the sale of tobacco and tobacco products in health facilities, which CHA endorsed in 1976 and reconfirmed in 1984. The minister intended to make every effort to implement his health objectives as presented in his 1974 vision outlined in *A New Perspective on the Health of Canadians.*

In the dialogue with Minister Lalonde, board members asked for his support for two major CHA projects, both of which required considerable monetary support from the federal government if they were to continue. One was the Health Computer Information Bureau (HCIB), which had been operational for only a short time, and the other was the hospital information system (HIS). The EPF arrangements would now impact the collection of health statistics. Under the hospital insurance act, Health and Welfare Canada monitored how federal funds were spent on health delivery in the provinces. But the health department would no longer collect this information under EPF. There was an urgent need now for some type of integrated information reporting system that included the Statistics Canada collection system and incorporated CHA's *Canadian Hospital Accounting Manual (CHAM).*

In May 1977, the CHA assembly had approved the formation of a committee to study CHA's role and organizational structure, as well as to investigate a more equitable voting formula at assembly meetings. The coming years would be crucial for the association in terms of its credibility, viability and relevance on the national scene. The ongoing question of CHA's financial stability had plagued the membership and its board over the decades; it would be an even more critical issue as CHA tried to establish its presence in Ottawa. CHA would need the strong support of its membership, its board, dedicated and knowledgable staff and adequate financial resources to move its advocacy and representation activities forward at the federal level.

Before 1977 had ended, the board and CHA staff said good-bye to Dr. Brosseau who had led the association for more than ten years. CHA also left behind almost all of its Toronto-based staff, many of whom had served the association for several years as program directors in education, editors in both the journals and the directory, and as administrative and financial support to management. While the decision to move CHA was extremely disruptive to its operations, the board had approved the move to take place over a six-month period. The new CEO, Jean-Claude Martin, would operate in Ottawa to find new office space and hire new staff. Dr. Brosseau would carry on current activities in Toronto and assist staff in winding down CHA's operations and organizing the move to Ottawa.

Establishing Roots in Ottawa, 1978 to 1980

By 1978, with a full complement of entirely new staff, as only three had made the move from Toronto, CHA unpacked and set up its offices in January. Almost before the packing crates were removed from the floor, the association was thrown into the fray of preparing for a first board meeting in March, an annual conference and annual meeting, reestablishing publishing schedules that had fallen behind, reviewing CHA's bylaws and getting to know who was who in this new organization. Sharing floor space with CHA were the Canadian College of Health Service Executives and the Nursing Unit Administration Program staff.

The CHA board had its first opportunity to meet the new health minister, Monique Bégin, who along with several department officials, addressed the board at its March 1978 meeting. This would be the first of many face-to-face meetings between Health and Welfare Canada officials and CHA during the year and over the next three decades. Although the federal health minister had always been invited to address the annual assembly, the minister's presence at the CHA board table enabled cordial relations to be established. This set the framework for future interactions between the two groups, which would prove to be mutually beneficial in the coming years, as health system issues became more visible on the national scene for both groups.

A first call for action came in September 1979, when the provincial ministers of health requested a review of Canada's health system after their meeting. The major issues were 1) the lack of adequate control at the federal level of the money spent by the provinces, 2) increasing expenditures in the hospital sector and the implementation of user fees for some services, 3) the appearance of excessive extra-billing by physicians and 4) the recurring confrontations between provincial governments and the medical profession over fee payments. Following another federal election, which resulted in a Conservative government, in November 1979, Health Minister David Crombie appointed the Health Services Review '79, under the chair of special commissioner Justice Emmett Hall.

CHA, in cooperation with the Catholic Hospital Association of Canada, the Association of Canadian Teaching Hospitals and the Association of Canadian Paediatric Hospitals, submitted a brief in March 1980 to Justice Hall. The brief represented the collective views of the four organizations and presented seventeen recommendations. Some of these included opposition to direct user fees, the recognition of local autonomous boards of trustees, more provincial funding for teaching hospitals, the need for a better definition of comprehensiveness as it applied to the health care system and, finally, the establishment of a Health Council of Canada.

The Hall Report was released in August 1980. By this time, the country had been through yet another federal election and Justice Hall delivered his recommendations to Monique Bégin, who was once again the federal health minister. The report concluded that there was no evidence of misappropriation of federal funds by the provinces and that there should be no extra-billing by physicians; however, provinces should set reasonable compensation levels for the profession. (*See* chapter 14 for more details on this joint submission.)

DIMENSIONSNEWS

C.H.A. brief to Hall Review

L to R: Ralph Moore, Association of Canadian Teaching Hospitals ; Cam Voelker, Jean-Claude Martin, Fred Lamb, A.G. Ayers, and W. Kilpatrick, Canadian Hospital Association.

CHA — A brief on the Canadian Hospital Association's recommendations to the federal Review of Health Services '79 was presented in March by Fred Lamb, CHA Chairman, to Mr. Justice Hall, Chairman of the review. The brief examines the original intent of the "Health Charter for Canadians". The review will present its findings and recommendations at the end of April.

L to R: Mr. Justice Emmett Hall, Chairman, and Prof. Malcolm Taylor of the Review of Health Services '79.

By 1981, the board was again debating the location of CHA's head office. CHA's rental agreement was up at the end of 1982. This time the issue was whether CHA should continue renting its office space, construct its own building or work with a consortium of national health organizations to finance and build a unique facility to house them. When CHA had sold its property in Toronto in 1977, the money generated from the sale had been put into a special fund designated for the eventual purchase of a permanent location in Ottawa. After an extensive search and failed efforts to persuade others to join CHA in a health building, CHA signed a fifty-year lease with the National Capital Commission (NCC) to renovate a building at 17 York Street in the Byward Market, just east of Parliament Hill.

In March 1983, CHA, along with the Canadian College of Health Service Executives, the Nursing Unit Administration Program, the Energy Task Force and the Canadian Institute of Child Health moved into its newly renovated, but not yet completed, office space. In April 1983, Health Minister Monique Bégin was invited to officially open the building at a ribbon-cutting ceremony and reception.[1]

As she had promised to do on her reelection, in 1984, Health Minister Bégin proposed amendments to the existing health legislation to create one health act for Canada. The Canada Health Act 1984 banned the practice of extra-billing, reinforced the four key principles of universality, comprehensiveness, portability and public administration, and added a fifth principle—accessibility—defined as "reasonable access by insured persons to insured health services unprecluded or unimpeded, either directly or indirectly, by charges or other means" (Crichton et al. 1994, 218). The provinces would be required to uphold these key principles or risk being penalized and losing federal funding.

(Top) Jean-Claude Martin, CHA President, with Federal Health Minister Monique Bégin (middle) with Claire Labrèche, Chair of the Board.
(Bottom) Cutting the Banner and Officially Opening the Building at 17 York Street on 12 April 1983. (Photos courtesy of Eleanor Sawyer)

By the mid-1980s, many of CHA's board-approved projects were in the early stages of starting up with grants obtained from the federal government. By the summer of 1982, CHA had hired a project director for the Management Information System (MIS) Project and additional funding had been approved for 1983 by the Federal/Provincial Advisory Committee on Institutions and Medical Services. CHA was also committed to a greater role in telecommunications and had received financing for its Telidon telecommunications project.

As more technology was introduced into the hospital, CHA focused on the need for information on medical, communication, management and information technologies and their impact on the hospital. Consequently, the association implemented the first phase of the Hospital of the Future Project in 1984. The communication project, under its coordinator, was well underway and the Job Exchange Project finally seemed to be paying for itself. Elma Heidemann had been hired on contract to move CHA's long-term care agenda forward and the association appeared to be moving ahead with some of its major projects.

To support additional staffing for these projects, the board had approved the expansion of CHA's office space at 17 York Street to an adjacent building at 24 Clarence Street. In a leasing arrangement with the Federation of Canadian Municipalities (FCM) in 1984, both organizations undertook to occupy part of the building for their own office needs and to rent unused space to commercial tenants. But, by 1985, with an economic downturn continuing to impact Canada's health system and, thus, CHA's membership, the association's financial position began to deteriorate. CHA was overbudget in some areas and headed for major deficits for the coming year. What had looked like a good investment in leasing another building, in partnership with FCM, was now in danger of becoming a financial albatross for the association. CHA was also struggling with long-term financial commitments to pay off the mortgage at 17 York Street.

Since its foundation in the 1930s, CHA had fought constantly to establish financial stability. By the early 1980s, not much seemed to have changed for the organization. To resolve its recurring financial problems, the board looked at various solutions over the course of the decade by requesting that CHA cut programs and services and downsize staff where possible. This option was chosen in 1984 to reduce the projected deficit. The Job Exchange was shut down and the already limited library service was cut back once again.

The board authorized a review of the organization's performance through the American Hospital Association's State Hospital Association Review and Evaluation (SHARE) Program. CHA management invited a SHARE team of six surveyors, including Sister Lucy Power and Peter Carruthers, two past-chairs, to review CHA's internal operations, conduct interviews with staff and member organizations, and submit their report to the board. Among areas identified for additional action, the SHARE Report recommended a publications audit to determine target audiences and the effectiveness of CHA's various publications. The report also recommended that CHA develop a strategy for the collection, analysis and publication of national health data on such areas as utilization and length of stay, with costs recovered through charges to users.

The surveyors also suggested in their report that an organization such as CHA should expect the level of financial support from its membership to be around fifty percent of its total operating budget in order to provide the services and representation activities identified as important for the association to undertake. In 1983, CHA's membership fees contributed around twenty-three percent to the overall operating budget, with the projects and services of the organization contributing around seventy-seven percent. The SHARE Report suggested that membership support should be increased or the budget reduced accordingly. CHA's financial situation tended to shift with the needs of the membership and the overall financial health of Canada's health system. It continued to do so throughout the 1980s.

Before the end of the year, the Long Range Planning Committee, which had been set up in 1981, had also reported back to the board. Although it made no recommendations to change Bylaw 1 specifically, it did suggest that the preamble be amended and that CHA change its name to the Canadian Association of Health Organizations and publish an annual report. One of its major recommendations was to restructure membership fees in such a way to fund corporate affairs, representation activities, administration, and research and development. The committee also made several recommendations to overhaul CHA's representation function, reinvest in its Education Department, continue to support a strong print communication mandate and move into the electronic communications field. In response to the recommendations on representation, CHA's CEO, Jean-Claude Martin, hired a vice-president of public affairs in 1984 to focus on getting CHA's message out and to increase these activities. (*See* chapter 15 for more details.)

Establishing Links in the Capital

One of the first and most important objectives on CHA's arrival in Ottawa was to establish strong links with the federal department of Health and Welfare Canada. Before 1980, CHA usually submitted an annual written brief to the health minister. But, after 1980, bilateral meetings between the minister and CHA officers were held at least annually and, more frequently, when required. Over the course of the 1980s, CHA met with five different health ministers, each of whom was asked to address the board and, occasionally, the membership at its annual assembly.

At the senior level of Health and Welfare Canada, the deputy minister and CHA's president met almost every month and, more frequently, if necessary. Meetings at both these levels provided access to senior officials in the other health branches of the department as well. CHA met with other federal officials among which were the Chief Electoral Officer of Canada to discuss voting for hospitalized patients. The association also liaised with the Metric Commission of Canada on the introduction of the metric system in the health sector and opened discussions on the transportation and incineration of hazardous waste materials with Transport Canada. CHA also cooperated with Health Canada in setting up standards for medical devices and on developing ways to assist hospitals in implementing health promotion activities. (The details of some of these interactions can be found in chapters 14 and 15.)

By moving to Ottawa, CHA renewed relationships with two of its closest health allies as well, namely, the Canadian Medical Association (CMA) and the Canadian Nurses Association (CNA), which had moved from Toronto and Montreal many years previously. Throughout the 1980s, there were bilateral and joint meetings to discuss common issues and make joint presentations to the federal government on matters of common concern. The three associations also partnered in various research projects or cosponsored joint programs and conferences and, occasionally, ended up on opposite sides of an issue. But, more often than not, the three organizations found common ground to work together. (*See* chapter 9 on key partners for more information on these relationships.)

With the Canadian College of Health Service Executives moving from Toronto at the same time as CHA, and into the same office space in downtown Ottawa, the relationship between the two organizations continued uninterrupted. CHA was able to establish closer links with the Association of Canadian Teaching Hospitals (ACTH), the Canadian Public Health Association (CPHA) and the Catholic Hospital

Association of Canada (CHAC), which was also an active CHA member. These regular meetings allowed for the open exchange of opinions and information, and the resolution of problems and conflicts. (For more information about these interactions, *see* chapters 9 and 10.)

At the international level, CHA was an active member of the International Hospital Federation (IHF) and of the American Hospital Association (AHA). In July 1980, CHA and AHA held a joint annual convention in Montreal, which was attended by over 7,000 participants of which 2,400 were Canadian. (*See* chapter 13 for details.) Although the event was considered a major success, it had required considerable work on the part of all CHA staff to prepare for such a large undertaking. And, along with the Alberta Hospital Association and the British Columbia Hospital Association, CHA cohosted the IHF Study Tour in western Canada in June 1986.

A New Health Care Focus

In 1986, under the leadership of the health minister, Jake Epp, and with the support and participation of numerous national associations, the federal government undertook a major project to review and update information on the subject of health promotion in Canada. At the same time, CHA, with funding from Health and Welfare Canada, conducted surveys and interviews with hospitals to identify their role, involvement and the comprehensiveness of hospital activities in health promotion. CHA presented its preliminary findings to the health minister and, in late November 1986, Mr. Epp released his report titled *Achieving Health for All: A Framework for Health Promotion*. In it, he identified concepts, challenges and strategies for discussion and action in the future, particularly in the implementation of health promotion to improve the health of Canadians.

Among CHA's conclusions in its analysis of health promotion activities in hospitals, the association had identified the lack of funding and staff to implement health promotion (1987a, 24). CHA pointed out that there were no provincial funding incentives or policies in place for the hospital to undertake health promotion. In its brief in January 1988, CHA replied to the health minister's working document by presenting five recommendations to improve collaboration between governments, health authorities and health care facilities for the implementation of the global concept of health promotion across Canada. CHA had been critical of the Epp document in that it had not looked at any role for the health care facility in delivering health promotion to Canadians.

The 1987 stock market difficulties and the recession that followed in the early 1990s created more turbulence for Canada's health system. The impact of increased deficit spending at all levels of government, the accumulation of massive debt and ongoing federal cuts in transfers to the provinces were hitting provincial budgets heavily by the mid-1980s. To reduce their costs, provincial governments increasingly cut their budgets, tightened up controls on hospital costs and began to investigate how provincial reforms could be implemented to ease the burden on provinces for their increasingly costly health systems. Beginning in Alberta in 1988, all the provinces and territories began to cut hospital services. The provinces also looked at ways to develop outpatient services and to shift care to the home and community as less costly ways to relieve the burden of funding expensive hospital care.

Across the health system, reviews, commissions and task forces were springing up in every province. In most cases, they were mandated to review health delivery systems and present suggestions for reform of these costly components of provincial budgets. Newfoundland had set up the Royal Commission on Hospital and Nursing Home Costs, which had reported back in 1984. Throughout 1986 and 1987, Quebec had established an inquiry into its health and social services, plus several other reviews and investigations of various components of its health delivery system. In Ontario, there were review panels between 1984 and 1987 to look at health promotion and to set health goals for the province. By the late 1980s, both Saskatchewan and Alberta had undertaken reviews of their health services either through advisory committees and commissions or both (Angus 1991). From these reviews, provincial governments began major overhauls of their health systems throughout the 1990s. This impacted CHA's provincial and territorial member organizations. CHA's relations with its membership and its own mandate would also change in unforeseen ways as provincial health reforms and restructuring began to impact every level of the health system throughout the country.

In September 1988, with Jean-Claude Martin's term as president winding down, the board authorized a strategic planning exercise for CHA. The preliminary report suggested that CHA's main focus in the future should be advocacy, supported by a strong research and development component. The organization also needed to broaden its base to that of the continuum of care and look at the role of the provincial CEOs as possible advisors to the CHA CEO. There were also three other recommendations from the strategic planning exercise. First, the board agreed to establish the CHA Foundation as a way to fund and support CHA's research function. Second, the board announced that Jean-Claude Martin would become the director of development with responsibility for raising money for the foundation. Third, the implementation of the strategic plan would require an additional special levy from the membership.

Discussion at the board table was lengthy and, at times, quite heated as various members spoke about the current financial situation in their provinces and how they doubted that their provincial member would support this budget item. With a new president about to take over the helm of CHA, and with the members becoming ever more resistant to any fee increases, the association was headed for choppy waters in the last decade of the twentieth century.

The Turbulent 1990s

As the Canadian Hospital Association entered the 1990s, it was becoming increasingly evident that the inflationary years of the late 1980s could not be sustained much longer. Given this conclusion, provincial and territorial governments began to explore new ways to tighten controls on health care organizations at both the management and governance levels in an effort to reduce costs. Consolidation, amalgamation, integration and regionalization became the watchwords of the day as new and different health organizations began to emerge.

Such actions were led by New Brunswick in 1993, which set up eight hospital corporations to take over all the hospitals in the province. This process included the extramural hospital as part of the consolidation. Saskatchewan then followed in 1994, closing a number of hospitals and consolidating many others into thirty district health boards, which incorporated acute and long-term care facilities, as well as home care and community and mental health services. That same year Prince Edward Island went even further in the regionalization concept by including not only hospitals, long-term care facilities, home care, public health, addictions and mental health but also social services and corrections within five new health regions. Regionalization also followed quickly in British Columbia, Alberta, Nova Scotia and was well underway in the mid-1990s in Newfoundland and Labrador.

This type of consolidation and downsizing had a domino effect. By reducing and changing the focus of the membership in CHA's provincial hospital and health care member organizations, their funding was often either curtailed or frozen complete-ly. Several of the provincial associations underwent major downsizing as a result of the provincial regionalization process. Many of CHA's provincial member organiza-tions were either dissolved or reemerged as different types of organizations with a different membership base and uncertain funding. Resistance to increased funding to CHA became a significant agenda item at board meetings and its expansionary programs had to be curtailed.

Effective in January 1990, Carol Clemenhagen began her term as president of CHA. Despite the development of a strategic plan and its approval by the board at the end of 1989, the plan was never implemented. CHA was entering the 1990s on rocky financial ground and there was some unease at the board table among certain members around financial decisions taken by the board in 1989. At her first board meeting as president in March 1990, and with the financial picture somewhat improved for CHA, nevertheless, four provincial member associations refused to endorse the additional $80,000 levy, which had been included in the 1990 operating plan and budget to support the work of setting up the new foundation.

The board reversed its decision to allocate funds to support the foundation and refocused the president's broad-based priorities on more specific goals. She was to stabilize the association's finances, develop a long-term financial plan, articulate and implement a strategic vision for CHA, prepare and set up a corporate affairs plan and implement a communications plan. To assist in implementing these new objectives, Carol Clemenhagen had already reorganized the internal structure of the association and had hired a new vice-president of policy and communications, who would join CHA in May 1990. With the board having approved her internal restructuring, CHA's president could now focus on some pressing advocacy issues.

Among the priorities identified for advocacy, the board had directed CHA staff to set up a task force on national health policy and health objectives, and work to ensure the integration of mental health into Canada's health system. CHA was also to assist in developing environmental guidelines for health care facilities, which it did through a working committee of the board and with considerable collaboration and funding support from Environment Canada. The result was the publication of bilingual guidelines for auditing hospital waste management processes. CHA also lobbied to obtain a rebate or exemption for public hospitals from the Goods and Services Tax (GST).

First elected in 1984 and then again in 1986, the Conservative government under Brian Mulroney was determined to put the federal government's financial house in order through debt reduction. It cut transfers to the provinces, reduced the public service and closed many public agencies such as the Science Council of Canada. Through the Spending Control Act of 1990, the government intended to bring its spending under control by limiting its annual growth to three percent on expenditures. To do this, it implemented major cuts in provincial transfers. This had serious implications for provincial programs partly or wholly funded by federal money, most particularly health delivery. Other social programs such as unemployment insurance and family allowances were also cut (Crichton 1994, 308–309). And to increase its revenue, the Mulroney federal government introduced the GST in 1989 against considerable opposition.

For CHA, one of its biggest battles in early 1990 was to attain a zero rating for non-profit health care facilities from GST payments. Barring this, CHA's second option was to lobby for a one-hundred-percent rebate for facilities. Over months of lobbying, letter-writing and through representations to Revenue Canada, the federal finance minister and senior department staff, CHA was successful in obtaining an eighty-three-percent rebate for health care facilities. To assist health facilities in understanding how the GST applied to them, how it was collected and what was included or exempted, CHA's president worked closely with Ernst & Young to publish the successful title, *The Goods and Services Tax: A Question and Answer Guide for the Health Care Sector*. CHA also lobbied vigorously to delay the implementation of the tax for health facilities until 1991.

The ongoing federal funding cuts in EPF transfers, among other cuts, had become of such concern that seven national health organizations joined together to form The Health Action Lobby, commonly known as HEAL.[2] In March 1991, CHA, along with the other six founding members, met with Health Minister Perrin Beatty to express their concerns about the ongoing cuts and to urge sustainability of Canada's health delivery system. CHA's board endorsed the aims and proposed lobbying activities, as well as its membership in HEAL and CHA worked closely with the other members to lobby the federal government for adequate funding of the health system.

In efforts to ensure that CHA's financial status continued to be relatively stable, in February 1991, the board approved a final offer on the sale of the InfoHealth Project, although CHA retained the use of the trademark and name to promote and sell products until 2004, when it let the trademark lapse. This project had involved much of CHA's staff time and financial resources over the years. But it had failed to produce the expected revenues, so the organization needed to disengage from the project and focus on other priorities. The CHA Foundation was also dissolved and the board directed CHA to sell its interest in the property at 24 Clarence Street, which it did in 1991. In 1992, the board also approved CHA's withdrawal from the Nursing Unit Administration Program because of future potential liabilities and dropping enrolments. As the impact of restructuring and reduced funding to the provincial health delivery systems continued to impact CHA's member organizations, the association froze membership fees in 1992 and closely monitored its own activities and expenses.

By the mid-1990s, many of CHA's member organizations had adopted new missions and roles and had changed their names to reflect this broader mandate. The membership also expected CHA to look at its board structure, deal with its financial vulnerabilities and explore ways in which it could work closely with its membership to develop and implement a member-driven policy agenda. Member organizations urged a name change for the association as well. Finally, after intensive bylaw reviews through the early 1990s, the membership approved the new name—the Canadian Healthcare Association/Association canadienne des soins de santé—at the June 1995 special meeting.

Despite the tremendous financial pressures exerted on CHA in the 1990s, the association completed the National Health Policy Reform Project, the Vision Project, in 1992. The recommendations were approved by the board in March 1993. The intent of the report, titled *An Open Future: A Shared Vision*, was "to be the benchmark for judging health reform in Canada" (CHA 1993b, 4). The document was widely circulated among provincial and territorial member organizations and discussed extensively with their governments. It was also distributed at the federal level to senior officials, including a major presentation to the health minister in the summer of 1993. The project and document received wide media coverage and formed the basis of a more focused advocacy approach to the federal government, backed by a comprehensive communication and public relations plan, one of the most extensive undertaken by CHA at the time. The report became the rallying point for all of CHA's advocacy efforts that year. It also formed the basis for dialogue with politicians, including focusing all federal parties on health issues during the 1993 fall election, resulting in a Liberal government under Jean Chrétien. (*See* chapter 16 for more details about the Vision Report.)

Although it would appear as if the association and its membership were almost entirely focused on their own internal operations throughout the first few years of the 1990s, in fact, there were many issues of national significance for Canada's health system that CHA focused on through representation and lobbying efforts. In the early part of the decade, when the federal focus was on constitutional reform, including enshrining health care principles in the constitution, CHA lobbied vigorously against this action. As first the Meech Lake Accord failed and then the Charlottetown Accord, CHA continued to press the federal government to put money back into the health system through stable and adequate federal cash transfers. This was to become CHA's long-standing and major advocacy position throughout the decade. The association saw some success, when the 1993 federal budget did not include any further cuts in transfers to health care.

For health facilities in Canada, the stresses and strains of delivering care during this period of funding cutbacks, which in turn led to staff layoffs, never seemed to end. Then, health facilities were dealt another blow when it was revealed that Canada's blood system had been infected through the late 1970s and 1980s by HIV and hepatitis C. In 1994, CHA issued a policy statement on the need for a national approach to communicate information on these transfusion-related infections. The association also worked closely with its membership during this time to help the public and the media to understand the risks involved.

But the real issue for CHA through much of the 1990s was the organization's ever-worsening financial position. Much of Carol Clemenhagen's term as president was spent downsizing and consolidating CHA's programs and services. In fact, CHA was so seriously undercapitalized that members of the board's Finance Committee and senior staff met with the auditor to discuss its underfunding in early 1994. CHA had kept membership fees to a minimum through a long-standing commitment made in 1992 as its members worked through the changes occurring in their provinces. But, by late 1995, CHA was entering into a period which can only be termed as survival mode.

CHA's financial problems really came to a head in late 1995 and throughout 1996, as the association struggled to carry out its mandate without its member organizations' ability to commit either to paying their annual fees or even to their ongoing membership in CHA beyond 1996. At any time during this period, if the bank had withdrawn CHA's line of credit, the organization would have been in dire straights and it would have been forced to declare bankruptcy. In fact, many board members came to each board meeting during the two-year period of 1995 through 1997 wondering whether this meeting might be the last one.

In January 1996, Carol Clemenhagen announced her resignation as president of CHA. The sole remaining vice-president, Tim Julien, was appointed acting president in March 1996 to carry the association through what would became one of its most intensive and thorough reviews ever undertaken by the association and its membership. The board also decided to seek partnerships or affiliations with outside organizations and approached several national health organizations to determine their interest in discussing a merger, an amalgamation or some other integration process to share services. Acting President Tim Julien restructured the internal operations under a senior management team. At the direction of the board, he also hired CHA's auditor to conduct an extensive financial analysis of its services to determine the impact of devolving its programs.

Throughout the summer of 1996, CHA undertook a review of its mission and services with input from board members, member organizations' CEOs and chairs, and other external health organizations. Based on this feedback, options would be presented to the board in September. Mr. Julien was also meeting with the acting president of the Canadian College of Health Service Executives to discuss how both organizations could work together more closely. The results of these discussions were also to be presented at the September meeting.

The crucial turning point for CHA's survival into the next century may very well have been the September 1996 board meeting. Just as board members and the member CEOs were about to debate the report titled "Review of Mission and Association Services", the board member from the Ontario Hospital Association announced its intention to withdraw from membership in the federation by the end of the year. Stunned by the ramifications of losing its largest fee-paying member in an organization where several other members could not commit to their annual fees for 1997, the board asked CHA to downsize staff and begin cutting back on services wherever possible. In the late fall, CHA laid off more than one-third of its staff, sold its journal and made preparations to begin selling off or closing down services such as education and publishing.

At the board meeting in December 1996, CHA did not have either an operating plan or a budget for the next year, as the board would not approve the budget that had been prepared, which was based on closing CHA operations. Nor did the association have a CEO. Tim Julien announced that he would be leaving CHA soon after the meeting to take another position. Focused on internal stability throughout most of the year, the board had decided not to recruit a new CEO until a secure financial base had been established for the organization.

By the end of 1997, however, CHA's board and membership could rightly say, "What a difference a year makes!" Under Interim President Joyce Bailey, hired out of retirement by chair Dan de Vlieger in January, CHA had set up a new fee structure, which had been accepted by the membership and approved by the board in June 1997. CHA's internal operations had once again been reorganized to focus on financial stability, and on lobbying and representation activities that would be fully supported by member fees. Ancillary services such as conferences, education and publishing programs would have to generate revenue and be self-supporting or be curtailed. And, in late 1997, the board had hired Sharon Sholzberg-Gray as the incoming president and approved a budget that projected surpluses for the coming year. The next century was beginning to look much brighter for CHA.

During the 1997 turnaround, CHA had been able to win back the confidence and support of its largest member—OHA—with Joyce Bailey, a former OHA employee, at its helm. The Association des hôpitaux du Québec had given notice at the beginning of the year that it would not be able to continue as a member, because it could not pay its dues. But the members in British Columbia and Manitoba recommitted their organizations to membership in CHA during the year. The association had also recaptured its lost influence and respect in advocacy and representation during the latter half of 1997 through its restructured Policy Development Department.

In January 1998, the new president, Sharon Sholzberg-Gray, joined CHA. With her extensive knowledge of the federal political system, her experience of the health system as the former co-executive director of the Canadian Association for Community Care and her innumerable contacts at both the federal bureaucratic and political levels, the return of credibility for CHA on the federal scene was immediately restored. Expectations were high for her to move CHA forward in advocating for improved health care for Canadians and to new heights of credibility and respectability in the national health arena.

And there was much for CHA to do. In late 1997, Finance Minister Paul Martin and Health Minister Allan Rock tabled proposals to amend "the Federal Provincial Fiscal Arrangements Act to increase the floor for cash transfer payments to the provinces under the Canada Health and Social Transfer (CHST) from $11 to $12.5 billion" (CHST 1997). According to the federal government press release, this would bring cash transfers to the level recommended by the National Forum on Health.[3] The CHST had come into effect in April 1996 and replaced federal transfers to the provinces under the Canada Assistance Plan (CAP) and the Established Programs Financing (EPF) Act. As with CAP and EPF, transfers to the provinces and territories would be in the form of cash and tax points.

Renewal Becomes the New Watchword

As the new century drew closer, CHA continued to improve its financial position and to become more relevant as a voice for Canada's health system. The years between 2000 and 2006 were a period of intense focus on a member-driven and board-approved advocacy and policy agenda that included renewal of Canada's health system, as well as the renewal of CHA as an influential organization. The early years of the twenty-first century also brought renewed commitment by CHA's membership to the federation.

It was in the aftermath of the era of federal cutbacks to Canada's health system that CHA really made its major impact. By the early 1990s, federal cash transfers to the provinces and territories for health were on track toward zero. As a result of CHA's advocacy efforts in the late 1990s and early 2000s, this was reversed. While CHA was at the forefront in advocating for sufficient federal funding for health, funding in and of itself was never considered to be the message. CHA always linked funding to the issue of health system renewal. To support its advocacy efforts, the association launched its Policy Brief Series in 1999. One of the documents in the series, *CHA's Framework for a Sustainable Healthcare System in Canada*, was used as a key element in its advocacy work. It outlined the essential issues that needed to be addressed to achieve a sustainable health system to meet Canadians' needs.

CHA focused on influencing the 1999 federal budget which became known as the health budget. While the federal government did allocate $11.5 billion for health care through the CHST over five years, this was still not enough money to sustain the system and to address other issues that were emerging. Additional money was needed for capital investments to improve health information systems and to upgrade diagnostic equipment and health infrastructures such as physical plants.

Funding was also needed to integrate programs across a broad continuum of care and to deal with shrinking health human resources. Disparities were beginning to appear in the health system as some provinces deinsured some core medical services and shifted services to other parts of the system, which did not fall under the Canada Health Act and its insurance coverage.

The year 2001 was a key period for CHA. The association was front and centre in presenting briefs to the Commission on the Future of Health Care in Canada. This commission, under the chair of Roy Romanow, had been established in April 2001 by the Chrétien government "to review medicare, engage Canadians in a national dialogue on its future, and make recommendations to enhance the system's quality and sustainability" (Romanow 2002, xv). CHA presented its brief to the commission in October 2001. CHA also made presentations to the Standing Senate Committee on Social Affairs, Science and Technology, commonly known as the Kirby Committee, named for its chair, Michael Kirby. This committee was set up in 2000 to examine and report on the state of the health system in the country with a two-year mandate that required it to report in 2002.

These major reviews, which frequently overlapped, required considerable work on the part of CHA and its membership to ensure that the voice of Canada's health system was clearly heard and present during consultations being held across the country. CHA produced its advocacy plan through the development of a document entitled *A Responsive, Sustainable, Publicly Funded Health System in Canada: The Art of the Possible*. Commonly known as the Ten Point Plan, it was released in November 2001 and informed key stakeholders in the federal government, in other national health organizations and the media, generating a wide understanding of CHA's position. Advocacy was further supplemented with regular policy and annual financial briefs submitted to parliamentary standing committees and to Finance and Health Canada key officials.

In 2002, with the release of the Kirby and Romanow reports, they provided a blueprint for federal/provincial/territorial meetings of the ministers of health and subsequent meetings of the first ministers. Culminating in the 2003 Health Accord and the federal budget, CHA was a credible and important participant in these events providing rational advice and input into all these processes. Although CHA believed that the 2003 Health Accord was yet another step forward in the journey to achieve adequate and sustainable funding for health care, it did not provide enough money to meet CHA's funding proposals and vision for the health system.

The ultimate success for CHA can be measured in the influence it exerted on both the 2003 and 2004 Health Accords. CHA's influence at the national level reached its zenith when President Sharon Sholzberg-Gray was able to acquire credentials for the Canadian Medical Association, the Canadian Nurses Association, the Canadian Pharmaceutical Association and CHA—better known as the Group of Four (G4)— to be present in the meeting room at the Confederation Building in Ottawa in September 2004, while negotiations were taking place between the first ministers. This historical event enabled CHA to play a significant role as an honest broker and to contribute to a much better agreement than would likely have resulted. The accord included provincial/territorial commitments to pan-Canadian objectives and deadlines for achieving them. As well, there were commitments to broaden the continuum of care and to dedicate funding to address the wait times issue.

In 2004, CHA also released several major briefs, including a joint publication with the CCAF (formerly the Canadian Comprehensive Auditing Foundation). Entitled *Excellence in Canada's Health System*, this key document addressed the members' concerns about governance and accountability in their provincial health systems. These concerns, among others, had emerged regarding the lack of independent community representation on regional health authority and hospital boards. Increasingly, provincial governments were appointing CEOs to manage the provincial organizational health delivery structures with a direct report to the deputy health minister. Questions about who was in charge and who was ultimately accountable for these provincial health systems needed to be addressed.

As the end of 2004 approached, CHA's future for the remainder of the decade seemed to be tracking success. It had reinvented itself as a major voice on the federal health scene with considerable support and input from its members and its board. Although the issue of financial stability never quite disappeared, CHA was enjoying some relief from years of cutbacks, downsizing and an uncertain future. As the board approved plans for the association to prepare for its seventy-fifth anniversary two years hence, they did so with confidence that CHA would be around to celebrate its significant accomplishments.

Summary

The years between 1978 and 2006 had created a different kind of CHA than the organization that had been located in Toronto since its founding in 1931. Out from under the shadow of its largest member in Ontario and permanently relocated in a heritage building in Ottawa, CHA had become one of the most influential voices speaking on behalf of Canada's health system on the federal scene. In fact, the 2006 version of CHA no doubt represented very closely the organization that had been envisioned in 1931 by its early founding members, who believed that it was destined to achieve "great things."

Endnotes

1. Initially, CHA occupied all the space in the building except the second floor. By 2006, CHA occupied the third floor, with some staff working in the mailroom in the basement, and rented two offices on the fourth floor.

2. The founding members were the Canadian Hospital Association, the Canadian Medical Association, the Canadian Nurses Association, the Canadian Long Term Care Association, the Canadian Public Health Association, the Consumers Association of Canada and the Canadian Psychological Association. The lobbying activities of the coalition were aimed at informing the public about the current state of Canada's health system (CHA 1991, 10).

3. The National Forum on Health was set up by Prime Minister Jean Chrétien in October 1994 as an advisory body to the federal government to recommend national policies to improve Canada's health system and the health of Canadians. The two-volume report was delivered in 1997 with much fanfare but with limited federal followup.

Part II

GOVERNANCE, MEMBERS AND LEADERSHIP

This part of the book focuses specifically on three key areas in the association's history—the evolution of both its governance and management structure, how its membership was determined and who those members were and who they are today. It provides a brief look at the leaders—both paid and unpaid—of the organization over its seventy-five-year history. Inevitably, there will be some repetition of events in order to provide a context for how these key areas in CHA's history developed and to showcase CHA's leaders.

Chapter 5 gives a more in-depth look at the governance structure of CHA. It follows the same time frame established in part one, beginning with the hospital council in 1931 and following through the years to CHA's current governance structure of a thirteen-member board of directors. The chapter describes the constitutional changes that occurred over the various stages of the association's history to meet the changing needs of the members. While there may seem to be a never-ending focus on finances, financial stability and the need to find more funding to enable the hospital association to survive, this has been the story of most not-for-profit associations over their history. Finally, the chapter briefly shows how the management of the organization developed over the years.

Chapter 6 describes who CHA's members have been over the course of its history. Although today, the members are the provincial and territorial hospital and health organizations, this was not always the case. In fact, during the 1960s and 1970s, many national health associations sought some form of affiliation with CHA. The chapter outlines the evolution of its membership and the changing relationship of CHA with its members throughout the course of its history. The chapter ends with brief descriptions of CHA's current members.

Chapter 7 presents thumbnail sketches of the volunteers who were elected to CHA's highest office either as president or as chair of the board. Between 1931 and 2006, fifty-two individuals have served CHA as its volunteer leaders. From 1931 to 1959, CHA's membership only met every two years. From 1959 onward, annual general meetings were held and a president was elected each year. In 1980, CHA adopted the corporate structure in which the chair of the board became the highest elected officer and the chief executive officer (CEO) was now called the president.

Chapter 8 presents brief descriptions of the ten men and women who were hired to lead the organization as its CEO. It begins with an overview of Dr. Harvey Agnew, the first manager of the hospital council, although he was the secretary-treasurer and a member of the Executive Committee initially. His position was eventually designated as executive secretary responsible for the day-to-day operations and the position evolved from executive director in 1954 to president in 1980.

5

THE GOVERNANCE, STRUCTURE AND MANAGEMENT OF CHA

"A board which is blessed with sound judgment, which realizes that its primary duties are to establish policies and to leave the details of management to its administrative staff is the greatest asset an [association] can have."

(KEITH 1947, 29)

The early Canadian Hospital Association set a precedent by ensuring that the organization had a written constitution and bylaws which identified the objectives of the organization and clearly defined its membership, where and with whom its authority was vested, and who would be responsible for ongoing operations. These first members, all of whom were either hospital superintendents, trustees or other individuals interested in hospital work, approved a draft constitution and bylaws, and elected a slate of officers at the founding meeting in April 1907. This first organizational meeting also set another precedent in that the members intended to establish a national association whose membership would come from across Canada.

The records from this meeting indicate that the founding members spelled out exactly what the objective of the association would be:

> the meeting together at stated times of those in immediate charge of hospitals, for the interchange of ideas, comparing and contrasting methods of management, the discussion of hospital economics, the inspection of hospitals, suggestions of better plans of operating them, and such other matters as may affect the general interests of the membership (CHA 1907).

Although this early CHA ceased all operations in 1914, it was only a matter of time before the need for a similar organization would emerge again.

By the mid-1920s, improving the delivery of care in hospitals was becoming a major issue in Canada, especially when the American College of Surgeons launched its hospital standards program. These standards were to be adopted by Canadian hospitals as well and many physicians in Canada were opposed to such a move. However, the Canadian Medical Association (CMA) took up the cause of ensuring that hospital standards were in place. The CMA set up the Department of Hospital Service in 1928 to handle matters pertaining to hospitals, among its other objectives.

The administration of this department fell to Dr. Harvey Agnew, who was also hired as the associate secretary of CMA. He, in turn, worked closely with the chairman of the Hospital Advisory Committee; this committee determined the objectives of the department and its program. The work of the department increased substantially in the late 1920s, as hospital superintendents sought the advice and leadership of Dr. Agnew. These same superintendents believed that there was a growing need for a more visible and independent hospital voice at the national level. This led Dr. Agnew and Dr. Fred Routley, secretary of the Ontario Hospital Association, to invite Canadian hospital superintendents to a founding meeting of a national hospital organization.

Governance and Structure of the Council, 1931 to 1952

The 1931 founding members decided at the September meeting that the Canadian Hospital Council would be a federation of the legally constituted provincial hospital associations and the Department of Hospital Service of the CMA.[1] (*See* chapter 6 for more information on the membership and appendix 1 for a list of the founding members.) The organization would take the less formal name of council rather than association to allow for more informal meetings as needed (Agnew 1974).

This founding group directed Dr. Agnew to draft a constitution and bylaws, and the delegates worked through each of the articles, discussing among others, the eight objectives of the council, its membership and delegates, attendance and balloting privileges, the officers, the executive committee, other committees, the business and powers of the council, and the time and place of meetings.

Governance—that is, final authority—was vested in the General Assembly, which was made up of delegates and alternates appointed by the membership. The delegates elected the officers of the council. These officers included a president, immediate past president, first vice-president, secretary-treasurer and other members elected by the delegates.[2] They formed the Executive Committee, which conducted the day-to-day business of the council, and were required to report to the delegates at each biennial meeting. In turn, the president and secretary worked closely to carry out the council's objectives and activities between general assemblies.

The General Assembly chose a broad mandate for the council. It was to collect information pertaining to the hospitals of Canada in order to represent the members' viewpoint to the proper authorities. The General Assembly also set up an adequate administrative structure to achieve the mandate, supported by adequate funding. Each General Assembly met every two years, with the Executive Committee taking decisions on their behalf between biennial meetings. These meetings were entirely informal, with the first two days devoted to discussions of various subjects, which were preselected and sent ahead of time to the named provincial delegates. On the third day, the special business meeting would take place.

The Executive Committee was required to report to the membership through both written and verbal reports at each biennial meeting. Its members had full authority to direct and manage the operations of the hospital council. The executive could conduct council business either by mail, telegraph, telephone or by ballot as spelled out in the bylaws. The executive could negotiate financial transactions, sign cheques, make purchases and appoint members to the nine standing committees, as well as designate specific roles and responsibilities to them. The committee members received and reviewed all standing committee reports as well.[3]

Members of the Executive Committee could decide on new studies or determine other activities for the council to undertake and appoint people to carry out these decisions. The members also had full authority to fill any vacancies that occurred on the committee between assembly meetings. Considerable operational and management responsibility was vested in the council's Executive Committee, much of it in the two elected positions of president and secretary-treasurer.

In 1931, the position of secretary-treasurer was held by Dr. Harvey Agnew, who also continued as the associate secretary of the CMA with full responsibility for its hospital department. Dr. Fred Routley, the secretary of the OHA, was elected as the council's first president and acted as advisor and counsel to Dr. Agnew. Dr. Routley also took on some of the work, particularly cross-country representation at provincial and other national health meetings. Both men were expected to represent the council's viewpoint to the federal government. Both men consulted each other as often as necessary to conduct council business. What one man could not undertake, the other often would in order to ensure the council's work was completed.

From 1931 to 1937, the council had no legal status. It was an autonomous body or ad hoc group headquartered at the CMA in Toronto, partly funded by voluntary donations from its members and partly by Sun Life Assurance Company of Canada through the CMA. On 7 August 1936, the council was granted a Charter and received Letters Patent from the secretary of state of Canada giving it legal status. The Charter created a corporation without share capital. The Letters Patent describe the purpose and objects of the council as follows:

(a) To enable the hospitals in Canada to participate with still greater efficiency in a national program of health conservation;

(b) To co-relate and co-ordinate the activities of the various hospital organizations in Canada;

(c) To represent the hospitals of Canada in those matters of general or of national interest which concern the welfare of the hospitals or the sick public whom they serve;

(d) To undertake the study of various hospital problems, such as organization, administration, finance, construction, medical staff, nursing and nurse education, and the relationship of the hospital and the medical and nursing professions to the public generally;

(e) To co-operate with the governments, federal and provincial and with the municipalities and with any other body or organization in promoting the public health and welfare and in furthering the purposes and objects of the Council herein set forth;

(f) To study hospital legislation in Canada and abroad and to assist the various hospital organizations in Canada in the improvement of hospital legislation;

(g) To undertake whatever proceedings, activity or development would best achieve the objects herein set forth including the publication of books, magazines, pamphlets, and other types of literature, subject to the limitations defined in this Constitution;

(h) To form the nucleus from which, at a later date should such a development be deemed advisable, may be formed a Canadian Hospital Association (CHC 1936).

The founding members of the council were foresighted in suggesting that a Canadian Hospital Association should eventually be formed at some time in the future when the circumstances were right. During the next twenty-one years, the council held eleven biennial meetings of the General Assembly in different cities across Canada under seven different presidents.[4]

At the September 1937 Fourth Biennial Meeting, the General Assembly ratified the new constitution and approved the transfer of all assets to this new legal organization. The council maintained its offices at CMA headquarters in Toronto until it moved into its own head office in 1946. Day-to-day operations continued to be handled by the secretary-treasurer, Dr. Harvey Agnew, in close consultation with the various elected presidents of the day, who held office for two years.

In 1945, at the Eighth Biennial Conference in Hamilton, the future of the hospital council was discussed by the delegates. Dr. Agnew advised the assembly that the Executive Committee was not inclined to recommend setting up a Canadian Hospital Association at this time. However, a significant change occurred that year, when the council was separated from the CMA hospital department. As Dr. Agnew explained, this meant "the assumption of more expense and the likely loss of a considerable source of revenue" (CHC 1945, 55) which the council had received in the past because of its close relationship with the CMA. On a motion from Dr. Routley, the delegate from OHA, "the incoming executive [would] be empowered to study the costs, to inform all of the component associations what the costs are and to get as quickly as possible the reaction of the associations as to what they are prepared to do" (CHC 1945, 56).

Delegates to this General Assembly argued that the membership also needed to rethink its purely voluntary contributions in favor of "a definite and compulsory levy" (Ibid.). In turn, this led to the suggestion that the executive of the council needed to be much more representative of its membership. At the time, all the associations and Catholic conferences that were members of the council had two votes each; however, the OHA had four votes because it represented so many more hospitals and beds.

In a footnote to the minutes of this meeting, the setup of the executive was described as follows: "An Executive Committee of six members is selected by the Council delegates each two years to conduct the business of the Council between the biennial sessions" (Ibid.). The roll call of the membership, recorded for this particular assembly meeting, showed that there were seventeen provincial organizations sending delegates. An executive of six members was hardly representative of this extensive membership.

Canada

By the Honourable FERNAND RINFRET,

Secretary of State of Canada.

To all to whom these presents shall come, or whom the same may in anywise concern,

GREETING:

Whereas, in and by Part II of The Companies Act, 1934, it is, amongst other things, in effect enacted that the Secretary of State of Canada may, by Letters Patent, under his Seal of Office, grant a Charter to any number of persons, not less than three, who having complied with the requirements of the Act, apply therefor, constituting such persons, and others who thereafter become members of the Corporation thereby created, a Body Corporate and Politic without share capital, for the purpose of carrying on in more than one province of Canada, without pecuniary gain to its members, objects of a national, patriotic, religious, philanthropic, charitable, scientific, artistic, social, professional or sporting character, or the like, upon the applicants therefor establishing to the satisfaction of the Secretary of State of Canada, due compliance with the several conditions and terms in and by the said Act set forth and thereby made conditions precedent to the granting of such Charter.

And Whereas, WALTER RICHARD CHENOWETH, of the City of Montreal, in the

Province of Quebec, Superintendent, FREDERICK WILLIAM ROUTLEY

and GEORGE HARVEY AGNEW, both of the City of Toronto, in the

Province of Ontario, Physicians, -----------------------------

have made application for a Charter under the said Act, constituting them, and such others as may become members in the Corporation thereby created, a Body Corporate and Politic, under the name of

CANADIAN HOSPITAL COUNCIL

for the purposes hereinafter mentioned, and have satisfactorily established the sufficiency of all proceedings required by the said Act to be taken, and the truth and sufficiency of all facts required to be established previous to the granting of such Letters Patent, and have filed in the Department of the Secretary of State a duplicate of the Memorandum of Agreement executed by the said applicants in conformity with the provisions of the said Act.

Now know ye, that I, the said FERNAND RINFRET, ------------------------------------
Secretary of State of Canada, under the authority of the hereinbefore in part recited Act, do, by these Letters Patent, constitute the said

WALTER RICHARD CHENOWETH, FREDERICK WILLIAM ROUTLEY and

GEORGE HARVEY AGNEW, --

and all others who may become members in the said Corporation, a Body Corporate and Politic without share capital, by the name of

CANADIAN HOSPITAL COUNCIL

with all the rights and powers given by the said Act and for the following purposes and objects, namely:—

(a)   To enable the hospitals in Canada to participate with still greater efficiency in a national program of health conservation;

(b)   To co-relate and co-ordinate the activities of the various hospital organizations in Canada;

(c)   To represent the hospitals of Canada in those matters of general or of national interest which concern the welfare of the hospitals or the sick public whom they serve;

(d)   To undertake the study of various hospital problems, such as organization, administration, finance, construction, medical staff, nursing and nurse education, and the relationship of the hospital and the medical and nursing professions to the public generally;

(e)   To co-operate with the governments, federal and provincial and with the municipalities and with any other body or organization in promoting public health and welfare and in furthering the purposes and objects of the Council herein set forth;

(f)   To study hospital legislation in Canada and abroad and to assist the various hospital organizations in Canada in the improvement of hospital legislation;

(g)   To undertake whatever proceedings, activity or development would best achieve the objects herein set forth including the publication of books, magazines, pamphlets, and other types of literature, subject to the limitations defined in this Constitution;

(h)   To form the nucleus from which, at a later date should such a development be deemed advisable, may be formed a Canadian Hospital Association.

The operations of the Corporation to be carried on throughout the Dominion of Canada and elsewhere.

The head office of the said corporation will be situate at the City of   Toronto, ------- - *in the Province of* Ontario.

And it is hereby ----- ordained and declared that, if authorized by by-law, duly passed by the directors and sanctioned by at least two-thirds of the votes cast at a special general meeting of the members, duly called for considering the by-law, the directors may from time to time:

    (a) borrow money upon the credit of the corporation;

    (b) limit or increase the amount to be borrowed;

    (c) issue debentures or other securities of the corporation;

    (d) pledge or sell such debentures or other securities for such sums and at such prices as may be deemed expedient;

    (e) mortgage, hypothecate, charge or pledge all or any of the real and personal property, undertaking and rights of the corporation to secure any such debentures or other securities or any money borrowed or any other liability of the corporation.

Nothing in this clause contained shall limit or restrict the borrowing of money by the corporation on bills of exchange or promissory notes made, drawn, accepted or endorsed, by or on behalf of the corporation.

And it is further ordained and declared that the business of the said Corporation shall be carried on without the purposes of gain for its members and that any profits or other accretions to the Corporation shall be used in promoting its objects.

That the said   WALTER RICHARD CHENOWETH, FREDERICK WILLIAM ROUTLEY and GEORGE HARVEY AGNEW, ---- -- ---------------------

are to be the first directors of the said Corporation.

under my hand and Seal of Office, at Ottawa, this seventh ------day of August, ------- 1936.

F. H. _____

Under *Secretary of State.*

In January 1946, the council became a truly independent organization. CMA transferred the annual grant it received from Sun Life Assurance Company to the council and permanently loaned the Blackader Library and Blackader Fund to it. The council also moved into new rental offices in Toronto.

At the 1947 assembly meeting, the constitution was amended to separate the office of secretary and treasurer, with the latter remaining on the executive. However, the position of executive secretary was removed from the executive to become a salaried staff position.[5] The duties of the executive secretary were also changed. Whereas, in the past, the secretary had represented the council at various Canadian and American health organization meetings, this responsibility would now reside with a member of the Executive Committee, which would also be responsible for issues on policy. The members of the General Assembly, as the governing body, retained their mandate over the charter, determining the role and objectives of the council. Management of the council on a day-to-day basis was slowly being consolidated in the position of the executive secretary, held by Dr. Agnew.

To understand the role of the governing body of the council, the General Assembly gave specific directions to the Executive Committee at the May 1949 Tenth Biennial Meeting. These proceedings were extensively recorded in *Transactions* and provide a picture of the assembly meeting held in Quebec City that year. Since the assembly only met every two years, a good part of the meeting was devoted to reports from the officers and the executive secretary.

The president's report highlighted council activities over the past two years and presented the views and opinions of the Executive Committee about the future of the council. This opening address was followed by a series of more specific reports, specifically those of the treasurer. His report included the financial statements and an update on the financial status of the council. At this particular assembly meeting, Dr. A. Lorne C. Gilday, the treasurer, suggested that the delegates needed to increase their financial support to the council by more than just voluntary contributions.[6] The executive secretary's report included a summary of his main activities of the last two years and pointed out key issues, often adding more detail to the highlights presented by the president. The business portion of the meeting also included the editor's report on *The Canadian Hospital* journal; this report was presented by the secretary of the council, who was also the editor, and, occasionally, an additional report from Charles Edwards, the journal's business manager.

Guest speakers were invited to these biennial meetings as well. In 1949, the main speaker was the federal deputy minister of health, Dr. G. D. W. Cameron. He spoke at length about "the grants-in-aid program," that is, the 1948 National Health Grants Program and described activities in the federal health department. At the end of his presentation, there was a long question-and-answer session, with the delegates asking for further details about the various components of the health grants program. There were also numerous other guests representing government authorities, provincial hospital associations and other health organizations.[7] Reports on the activities of these organizations were presented and delegates were invited to ask questions and make comments. These discussions were meticulously recorded and provide detailed information about the health system and main areas of concern at the time.

In keeping with its mandate, the Executive Committee had appointed four members to the Resolutions Committee prior to the 1949 biennial meeting. Based on the items on the agenda, resolutions were suggested either by this committee before the meeting or by voting members during it. These resolutions represented the decisions of the membership, as the ultimate governance authority of the council. They set the direction for the council's activities and its management—shared between the Executive Committee and the executive secretary—for the next two years.

In 1949, twenty-eight resolutions pertaining to the views of the membership on hospital and health issues of the day, and on the management of the council, were duly proposed, discussed and approved. Two of these resolutions highlight some of the members' concerns at the time and provide direction to management for the next two years. These included:

12. Broader Construction Grants

THEREFORE BE IT RESOLVED that the Canadian Hospital Council request the Minister of National Health and Welfare to extend the scope of hospital construction grants to cover part of the cost of construction of nurses' residences and other essential and supporting services, and furthermore be it resolved that construction grants apply to all new construction regardless of net gain where it can be shown that an existing structure is obsolete for efficient patient care.

20. Pension Plan

THEREFORE BE IT RESOLVED that the Canadian Hospital Council urge its member hospitals to make a study of the report of its Committee on Pension Plans and to implement an adequate pension plan as soon as possible (CHC 1949b, 122–126).

The most important task of a governing body is the election of its officers. The members of the Nominating Committee, having done their work of recruiting qualified and available candidates, presented their recommendations to the 1949 General Assembly. This assembly elected seven officers to the Executive Committee, plus the outgoing president as an ex officio member. On completing its work, the assembly adjourned to await the call to meet again in 1951.

One of the Executive Committee's most important duties was to hire the secretary for the council. Until 1949, this had not been a problem as Dr. Agnew had occupied the position continuously since the council's formation. But, in 1949, Dr. Agnew advised the Executive Committee that he intended to resign effective 1 August 1950. The Executive Committee hired Dr. Leonard O. Bradley, the front-runner, to replace him in 1952. The committee also created an assistant secretary position to help with the increasing workload. Murray W. Ross, the future executive director of the Alberta Hospital Association, became the first person to hold this position and joined the council in early 1950.

In 1951, the General Assembly approved some minor amendments to the constitution on the recommendation of both the Constitution and Executive Committees. The General Assembly was to continue as the governing body of the council with no change in the number of delegates and alternates as provided for in the 1936 constitution. But the executive body of the assembly would now be known as the board of directors and consisted "of the officers of the Council and not more than six others, all elected by the Assembly" ("C.H.C." 1951, 44). With these changes in place, the organization was being positioned for further reorganization in the new decade.

Governance and Structure of the Association, 1953 to 1977

In May 1952, the board of directors approved a resolution recommending a name change for the council, which was to be presented to the 1953 general assembly meeting. The board members also endorsed the need for a strong national organization. In the present organization, the council was responsible to the provincial associations and Catholic conferences, with voting power vested in their hands to determine policy at the national level. The board wanted to develop and maintain even stronger provincial organizations if possible.

At the Twelfth Biennial Meeting of the council in May 1953, "Bylaw No. 14, enacted by the Executive Committee was unanimously sanctioned" (CHC 1953a) and the name change became official. From then on, the parliament of the hospital field would be known as the Canadian Hospital Association/Association des Hôpitaux du Canada. This name change ensured that other organizations would understand the national nature of the organization and Supplementary Letters Patent were issued by the secretary of state on 9 October 1953.

At this same assembly meeting, the Executive Committee recommended an additional change to Bylaw No. 15, which repealed the original thirteen bylaws of 1936 and confirmed the new general bylaws (clauses 1 to 44) governing the association. The bylaws were approved by the secretary of state in January 1954. This new constitution and bylaws provided for a board of directors, which had not been the case in the original constitution of 1936. This was clearly a major change in the governance structure of the organization.

The constitution named the president, first vice-president, second vice-president and treasurer as the officers of the association. All of them were to be elected by the active members, along with eight other directors, who would comprise CHA's board. This governing body would, in turn, appoint the executive secretary of CHA. Under the section on officers of the association, their roles and duties were clearly defined and the executive secretary was described under clause 24 as the chief executive officer. For the first time, this position was given the full responsibility for the management of the association's business under the board's direction.

But governance and control of the association remained with the active members, as described in clause 10 of the constitution. The meetings of the members would be called "the assembly" and the members were defined under "Conditions of Membership" as active and associate members. The active members could be any organization such as an association, a council, a conference of a national, provincial or regional nature that represented hospitals or similar allied institutions. The membership could also comprise national, voluntary organizations that were interested in the operation of hospitals; this left CHA membership open to a fairly broad number of organizations (Ibid.).

While the name change and the new constitution and bylaws did not appear to be particularly contentious issues, the future of the association, particularly its composition and funding, was a matter of considerable concern at the 1953 assembly meeting. In his address to the assembly, Dr. Owen Trainor, president at the time, noted that the board of the association was not properly representative of its membership and the council had no financial autonomy. In his eloquent address to the delegates, he stated:

> While the constitutional set-up of the Council has served reasonably well in the past, it is becoming more and more inadequate to allow it to fulfill the purposes of a national association. In the first place, it is not properly representative, particularly with regard to the composition of the Board of Directors. . . . Secondly, the Council has no financial autonomy. It is dependent solely on the whim, or, . . . the good will of its constituent associations. . . in the form of purely *ex gratia* contributions which may be given, altered, or withheld entirely at the will of the donors. . . . Can you conceive of an organization so constituted continuing to function efficiently? (1953, 34, 116).

He went on to say that it was time to reexamine the basic principles of the association on which it had been founded. If the hospitals of the country needed a national association to represent their interests, then they needed to pay for it. Dr. Trainor then proposed that each provincial association should become a division of the national association, that each hospital should hold membership in both associations and that the annual CHA budget should be allocated equally across all the hospitals of Canada on a bed basis or some other arrangement.

In order to deal with the ongoing question of how to finance CHA, a motion to amend Bylaw No. 16, as enacted by the board of directors, was passed unanimously by the members at the 27 May 1957 assembly in Saskatoon. The bylaw read: "The annual financial contribution of any member towards the cost of maintaining Association services and activities shall be determined by the Board of Directors, based on such formulae as may be approved from time to time by the Assembly. Payment of membership fees so established shall be a condition of membership" (Fraser 1957, 41). The formula for calculating membership fees of active members would be based on "the number of beds in public general hospitals holding membership in the association" (Ibid.). This formula was also approved as part of the bylaw. The new fees became effective 1 January 1958. Twenty-six years after its formation, the association finally had a stable financial base on which to build its programs and activities. But the issue of member fees and how to determine them continued to be raised throughout the coming decades.

The 1957 assembly also struck a Committee on Constitution that was to report at the next biennial meeting on any necessary draft amendments. While the members of the assembly were still considered the ultimate authority of the association, their authority was slowly shifting to the board of directors, which had been legally constituted in 1953. But the board still remained unrepresentative of the membership. This was the next area where constitutional changes were required.

At the December 1959 meeting, the board approved recommendations from the Executive Committee, which had been asked to study the bylaws. The board agreed to maintain the ratio of votes in the assembly for both provincial hospital associations and Catholic conferences. It also recommended the appointment of a Nominating Committee consisting of four members, including the president and the immediate past-president as chairman. The Nominating Committee would consult each member association for the names of board members and was to ensure that the board had reasonable geographical representation, as well as continuity. The 1960 General Assembly approved the recommendations with no requirement to amend the bylaws, as the board had full authority to recommend rules and regulations for the active members' approval. That same year, CHA moved out of its rental space and into its own permanent headquarters at 25 Imperial Street in Toronto.

During the presidency of Arthur Westbury (1963–1965), a new bylaw was adopted which eliminated the positions of first and second vice-presidents and created the position of president-elect. The bylaw also provided for the annual election of officers and directors. Under the amendments adopted and passed by the board of directors on 26 March 1964, in future, the board was to consist of the president, president-elect, immediate past president and treasurer, all of whom would be ex officio members. The assembly would elect thirteen other board members from the active membership at the assembly meeting, as well as three directors-at-large. The General Assembly would now be held annually and could be called at any time by the board of directors. This major shift in governance authority from the assembly to the board was spelled out in article 22, which stated: "Except when the Assembly is in session, the Board of Directors shall have full authority to act on behalf of the Association" (CHA 1964b, 4). However, these amendments were not approved by the members at the time.

In 1966, the Aims and Objectives Committee, under the chairmanship of Chaiker Abbis of New Brunswick, was appointed by the board to reappraise the association's objectives and find new methods to attain them. All the provincial hospital associations, interested organizations and individuals in the health field were invited to submit briefs concerning the CHA's organizational structure, its current role, its relationships with government and allied organizations, its services and leadership, and its coordinating function. Public hearings were held in Toronto, Winnipeg, Saskatoon, Vancouver, Moncton and Montreal and forty-five briefs were submitted to the committee.

Consensus from the feedback that the committee received indicated that CHA's organizational structure and current role were acceptable. However, the association's relationships with the various levels of government and with allied organizations were considered to be inadequate. Its information services were not good enough and, although it was meeting an educational need, CHA would have to adjust to the changing educational requirements in the health system. CHA also needed to be involved in research, offer consultative services on request and should study and inform the members about the latest developments and trends in the provision and organization of health services in the country.

The committee responded to these concerns by recommending that the annual assembly meeting be changed to a convention and that educational programs be expanded, specifically departmental programs. Other recommendations included developing a public relations program; publishing a regular news bulletin to be distributed directly to hospitals; and reshaping, expanding and adding a trustee section to the journal. The committee also recommended that CHA undertake to collect and interpret statistical data in the health field, strengthen its relations with the federal government and assist in the continued development of the Canadian Association of Hospital Auxiliaries. All the committee's recommendations were unanimously accepted by the membership in 1968. The board was directed to "speedily implement" them and to use the association's reserves to do so as soon as possible.

In addition to the recommendations of the Aims and Objectives Committee, the May 1968 annual general meeting—as it was now called—approved the 1964 proposed amendments to the bylaws. Three directors-at-large were added to the board and the executive was expanded to include two additional members.

By the late 1960s, CHA's finances were becoming a troubling issue for the board once again. In 1968, the board approved terms of reference for the Finance Committee, which was to review CHA's finances quarterly, supervise all accounting procedures and prepare a budget. The rapidly expanding association also needed more office space, so the board set up the Building Committee in 1967. This committee recommended that the association construct an additional two floors on its headquarters at 25 Imperial Street. The committee also supported adding five more floors to an adjacent property that CHA owned at 21 Imperial Street. The committee suggested that $100,000 from the CHA reserve fund be earmarked for this construction; in 1971, CHA completed the work.

In 1972, the board became fully aware of exactly how bad CHA's financial situation actually was. In fact, the association's finances were in such a mess, and the financial statements were so unreliable, that, in spite of concerted efforts by the Finance Committee to correct the situation, very little had been done. As a result, the association's financial officer resigned. A firm of management consultants was engaged to look at CHA's internal operations and functions, and prepare recommendations and a report. And to add further to the problems, the Association des hôpitaux du Québec had requested that its fees be reduced by fifty percent. The board hired a business manager as recommended by the consultants to straighten up the association's finances. Unfortunately, this arrangement proved to be unworkable internally and OHA staff were seconded to CHA to put its finances back on track.

Between 1965 and 1971, CHA was reorganized and restructured internally several times to cut costs and stabilize finances. But the governance structure of CHA remained fairly stable until 1972. As a result of an assembly resolution in May, CHA was directed to reexamine its role, structure and title "to recognize the changing pattern of the provision of health care in Canada." The Study Committee on the Role of the Association and Sources of Finance was appointed by the board of directors later that year. In 1973, this committee, in turn, suggested that an ad hoc committee be set up to look at the member fee structure.

One of the main results of the study committee's deliberations was agreement in principle that the current per bed membership fee was both unrealistic and inequitable. The committee members also agreed that the association should remain in Toronto for the time being. CHA's location was becoming an issue in terms of its ability to represent members' interests at the federal level. According to the committee chairman's report to the board, dated 29 March 1973, there was a general expression of satisfaction with the current activities being carried out by CHA, particularly in the areas of representation and education. However, the report recommended ". . . that any new programs or any changes at this time should be self-supporting. Further increases in membership fees, except for an annual cost of living, should not be considered for a period of some three years" (CHA 1973a).

This document was revised before being presented to the assembly in May to include a paragraph about a possible change in both CHA's membership and its name. But, more importantly, an extremely strong and lengthy section on the association's finances was added. Specifically, the document noted the depletion of CHA's cash reserves and a series of deficits or near deficits over the past several years. It advised that "[t]he capability of the Association to take on

Dr. B.L.P. Brosseau, Executive Director, Assists Past President L.R. Adshead in Removing the Presidential Medal at CHA's 27th Assembly Meeting in Edmonton, 3-5 June 1970. (The Medal Is a Gold Medallion Donated in 1970 by Dr. G. Harvey Agnew.)

new responsibilities or more importantly, to react spontaneously to any emergency situation . . . has all but been eliminated . . . " (Ibid.). The report concluded by noting that "there are winds of change currently within the health field which may have a very definite bearing on future activities of the Association" (Ibid.). It was recommended that the committee's mandate be carried over for another year.

In September 1973, a two-day meeting of the CHA board was held in Toronto with the elected officers and chief executive officers of the provincial member associations in attendance. Six discussion groups—one on its future and others on conventions, the annual meeting, education, publications and finance—looked at CHA's operations. In reading the verbatim report of the discussions that took place at the meeting, several very interesting concepts surfaced a number of times. For instance, there were suggestions that the association's objective should be restated in order to orient it toward the health system rather than hospitals. The first serious recommendation that the association should change its name to reflect a broader orientation was also suggested. That is, the association should be renamed the Canadian Association of Health Organizations.

In June 1974, the document titled "The Developing Role of the Canadian Hospital Association within the Changing Pattern of the Provision of Health Care in Canada" was presented to the annual assembly. In essence, it recommended that CHA should take a more positive leadership approach relative to an integrated health care system for Canada. The report also suggested that, since change in the health care system rested primarily at the provincial level, with the agreement of the provincial hospital associations, CHA should channel its participation and influence more heavily toward provincial patterns of developing an integrated health care system.

Other recommendations proposed that institutional membership in CHA should not be direct but rather through the provincial associations and Catholic conferences, that allied national health organizations should be offered affiliation with CHA and that a suitable new name for the association should be adopted once a broadened role and membership structure were implemented. This document also recommended that there should be better communications between CHA and its members and that voting at annual and board meetings should be based on one vote for each $5,000 of dues assessed to each member. While this recommendation was defeated, the concept of changing the voting structure to more accurately reflect the financial participation of the members was raised once again.

In 1974, CHA's board was made up of one director for each province, except Ontario and Quebec, which had two each, one representative from the Catholic hospital conferences and three directors-at-large. In 1975, the board proposed an amendment to the bylaw at the assembly, which basically disenfranchised the provincial Catholic conferences and replaced them with the Catholic Hospital Association of Canada. After a heated discussion, the amendment was approved. Then, the membership approved a resolution that the board study CHA's organizational structure once again to come up with an equitable voting formula.

With more and more authority now residing with the CHA board, the question of the assembly needed to be examined. President George Sherwood noted in his report to the delegates in 1976 that

> . . . this body known as the 'Assembly' is according to the bylaws, the legislative level of authority of the Association, and yet it comes into existence once a year, for the purpose of this annual meeting and then, for all intents and purposes, is dissolved to become non-existent, with its members having no further responsibility nor involvement in the association's affairs, until by happenstance they may be re-appointed to serve again the following year (CHA 1976d, 2).

As a result of his comments, the Executive Committee recommended that a Standing Committee on By-Laws and Regulations be set up to address the matter of CHA governance. The board agreed and the committee was set up in November 1976. Judge Chaiker Abbis, who had chaired the 1966 Aims and Objectives Committee, was once again invited to chair this committee.

After a number of years of waivering and reconsideration, CHA's board finally decided that the association would move to Ottawa in 1977. But this decision was not an easy one. Moving CHA's headquarters from Toronto to Ottawa was both difficult and disruptive for the organization internally. It had also divided the active members and the members of the board for years. In fact, the issue was debated several times over the years, according to President George Sherwood, before a final decision was eventually taken

As a national hospital association, CHA's main mandate was to represent the interests of its membership to the federal government and to other national health organizations. Therefore, its natural location should be Ottawa, the capital of Canada. By the mid-1970s, most of the major national health organizations such as the Canadian Medical Association, the Canadian Nurses Association, the Royal College of Physicians and Surgeons of Canada, the Canadian Public Health Association and others had already relocated to Ottawa.

One of the major obstacles to the anticipated move was the reaction of CHA staff each time the issue was raised. On many occasions, they had indicated their opposition to a move in petitions signed by a large majority of staff. The board of directors postponed a decision on the move because they were concerned about the impact that a loss of so many skilled and knowledgeable staff might have on the continuing operations of CHA. When Dr. Brosseau announced his intention to retire in 1977—and as opposition by staff continued—the board of directors reconsidered their previous decisions about moving to Ottawa. Then, in March 1977, the board accepted the recommendations of the Committee on Headquarters Relocation, chaired by William Kilpatrick, the incoming president of the board, that CHA was to relocate to Ottawa in September 1977.

While the Education and Publications Departments would not move immediately, all of CHA's operations would eventually be headquartered in Ottawa. By September, CHA had rented new offices in downtown Ottawa under a five-year lease. The board had also decided that CHA was to eventually build its own permanent offices in the city. Of the forty-one staff at CHA in Toronto in 1977, only three were in a position to move to Ottawa. Although very disruptive for a time, the relocation allowed CHA to hire new staff and to refocus its operations and activities on the federal government, where its membership was asking for more representation of its views.

Governance and Structure in Ottawa, 1978 to 2006

With CHA now located in Ottawa, the organization was positioned to increase its representation activities on the national scene. Occupying rental offices on Laurier Avenue, the CHA was only a few blocks from Parliament Hill and mere minutes away from National Health and Welfare and Statistics Canada, two federal departments where the association's presence could be most influential on behalf of its members.

The issue of a name change for CHA came up once again in 1980, when the Manitoba Health Organizations, Inc., proposed a resolution that its name reflect more adequately the condition of its constituent members, some of which had changed their name to encompass their long-term care members. But the resolution was roundly defeated. Although the time did not yet appear right for a name change, the members of the CHA board were well aware of the situation with regard to long-term care provincially. Both Manitoba and British Columbia had opened up their membership to include long-term care facilities. The board set up a new standing committee on long-term care to examine the needs of these facilities and prepare a plan of action. In addition, a trustee committee composed of all trustee representatives on the board was formed to deal with governance issues.

In November 1976, the board approved the terms of reference of the Committee on By-Laws and Regulations to ". . . review the structure of the Association and recommend whatever changes should be made to provide better representation, more involvement of the membership, and better continuity of reporting to the membership" (CHA 1976a). The standing committee met on several occasions over the next three years to draft various changes to the bylaw. Finally, in July 1981, the members determined that its main focus would be to create a true CHA federation.

The committee recommended that CHA adopt the corporate structure for its organization. This resulted in changes to the board structure as well. The officers of the board would now include a chairman (formerly the president), a chairman-elect, an immediate past-chairman—all of whom had to be members of the board. Two other officers—the president (formerly the executive director) and a secretary—were also officers but not members of the board. However, the president would be an ex officio member of the board. Rotating two-year terms were implemented for directors.

The board would now comprise one representative from each active member in Saskatchewan, Manitoba, New Brunswick, Nova Scotia, Prince Edward Island, Newfoundland and the Northwest Territories. Alberta and British Columbia would each have two representatives, Ontario would have five and there would be four from Quebec. The board was now made up of twenty directors. The amendment also provided for regional representation, that is, a representative from the Atlantic provinces, Quebec, Ontario and the Western provinces. The bylaw also deleted any power for the assembly and gave the board the responsibility to meet once a year as the annual general meeting of the association.

The committee recommended other changes to CHA's membership, all of which were approved by the board and adopted under Bylaw No. 1 at a Special Assembly Meeting called on 15 December 1981. The new bylaw in effect dropped the American Hospital Association, the Canadian Medical Association and the Catholic Hospital Association of Canada (CHAC) from CHA's active membership. The association was finally a true federation of its provincial/territorial members.

There were mixed feelings about dropping the CHAC from active membership. Many delegates thought that it should be retained as a full member of the CHA. However, there were even stronger feelings that CHA should become a true federation. An amendment to add at least one representative from the Catholic Hospital Association was defeated. After a fifty-year involvement in the affairs of CHA, the CHAC would no longer sit at the board table or vote in the assembly.

It is interesting to read the preamble to the bylaw as it proposed a major change in the orientation of the association:

> This Association shall be known as the Canadian Hospital Association-Association des hôpitaux du Canada and is a federation of active members.
>
> The mission and purpose of the Canadian Hospital Association are reflected in the following general objectives:
>
> (a) to assist the membership in the promotion of a humane, efficient and integrated health care delivery services system of the highest possible standard

and towards that end, sponsor or co-operate in such activities or programs as would assist in achieving this;

(b) to represent the opinion of the membership to those who could be influenced by the knowledge of that opinion (CHA 1981b, 1).

With CHA now located in Ottawa, the organization was in a much better position to fulfill this new mandate. The association was also actively searching for a new location for its offices as the five-year lease at Laurier Avenue would expire at the end of 1982. The board had placed some limitations on where the organization should be located. There had been discussions about constructing a health head-quarters building that would include several major health organizations in Ottawa. When these discussions collapsed, CHA entered into negotiations with the National Capital Commission (NCC) to renovate an old heritage building located at 17 York Street in the Byward Market. Signing a fifty-year lease with the NCC, the association undertook major renovations in 1982 and moved into its permanent headquarters in March 1983. In April, the building was officially opened in a ribbon-cutting ceremony presided over by federal Health Minister Monique Bégin. CHA is still located at 17 York Street today only a few minutes walk from the Parliament Buildings.[8]

In 1983, the Long Range Planning Committee delivered its report to the board at the November meeting. The committee had been set up in 1981, under the chair of Sister Mary Lucy Power, to review and evaluate CHA's original objectives and goals and to assess their current relevance. The committee also looked at the association's activities, programs and services to determine if they fulfilled the stated objectives (CHA 1983b, 5).

The committee's report reminded the board of CHA's traditional and long-held support for a voluntary health system and the importance of the trustee in that system. The committee members wrote:

> The role of the Trustee has never been as important. This has been recognized by the Association and its programs have been adjusted accordingly. However, the committee feels that the Association must intensify its efforts aimed at the protection and strengthening of this valid and time-proven system. To this end, the committee strongly believes that the Association must take a leadership role and it must be credible and visible (Ibid., 1).

The report proposed thirty-three recommendations pertaining to a wide range of areas from corporate affairs such as the bylaws, membership representation and the annual general meeting. Many of these dealt with the association's services and programs, and lack of financing to improve them. The committee's proposals for CHA's future supported its current programs and projects and encouraged the development of many more to meet the changing needs of the health system. As for the governance structure, the committee made no changes. Nor did they recommend any changes in the membership. They did suggest that CHA publish an annual report and structure membership fees "to completely fund corporate affairs, representation activities, administration and research and development" (Ibid., 8).

While the relationship between the CHA board and its CEO was defined under the bylaw, there were no rules regarding relationships between the CHA CEO and the CEOs of its member organizations. The secretaries, as they were called in the 1960s, began to meet informally across the country to exchange information and coordinate joint activities. In September 1985, the provincial CEOs identified a need to clarify the relationship more formally. In March 1986, the CEOs approved the establishment of the Chief Executive Officers Advisory Committee (CEOAC). It provided a forum where the CEOs could exchange information; discuss common concerns; and advise the CHA board, committees and the president, their own provincial boards and others as appropriate. It would provide advice based on majority consensus, meet twice a year, as well as request special meetings.

Under the chairmanship of Peter Carruthers (1986–1987), the board held an all-day retreat on 16 March 1987 to review and discuss the association's mission, objectives and priorities, as well as to plan its future activities. William Kilpatrick, a past chairman, was asked to facilitate and chair the meeting. The board rewrote the mission statement for CHA, a mission statement that was retained by the association until 1995, when it was changed again. The 1987 mission statement read:

> The mission of the Canadian Hospital Association is to promote a humane, effective, efficient, and integrated health system of the highest quality,
> - through leadership at the national and international levels,
> - through advocacy/representation.

From the new mission, the board also identified new objectives for the association:

> To pursue its mission, the Canadian Hospital Association has these objectives:
> a) to represent its member associations on national and international health related issues;

102

b) to assist in communications and access to information on health related matters;

c) to facilitate the exchange of ideas and information through national conferences on relevant and timely topics;

d) to offer educational programs in support of the mission of the Association;

e) to stimulate, facilitate and undertake research related to health care;

f) to collaborate with other organizations in activities consistent with the mission.

Essentially, the 1987 retreat focused the organization's activities on broad-based health issues through wide-ranging activities, programs and services. CHA retained its older services of distance education and publishing and continued investing in the future through the MIS Project and the Institute for the Hospital of the Future. These projects required more staff and additional office space to accommodate them. In 1986, CHA acquired the building at 24 Clarence Street, renovated it and moved project staff into these offices. By the end of the decade, however, CHA's expansion had resulted in serious deficits. This situation created concerns among the membership yet again about the association's financial stability, and the direction and focus of the organization.

In September 1988, the board set up the Strategic Planning Committee to review CHA's internal operations and management, and to prepare a plan for its future. The committee collected information through questionnaires, interviews with board members, representatives of provincial member organizations and national health organizations, as well as from CHA staff. Two special board meetings were held and a preliminary report was presented at the March 1989 board meeting for discussion. In June, the board approved the final report that established an effective organizational vision for the future of CHA. The board believed that CHA should become the voice for its provincial and territorial hospital and health associations at the national and international levels.

Massive changes were taking place in Canada's health delivery system, many of which had begun in the late 1980s and continued through the early 1990s. Provincial health systems were being restructured, downsized and regionalized to reflect a more integrated continuum of care. The impact on CHA's membership often left active members in limbo as they waited to learn what role—if any—they would play in these newly regionalized governance structures being set up in many provinces. The exception was Ontario, although it was not immune to the changes occurring in other parts of the country.

Often, provincial members could not even commit to paying their annual fees for the next year because they were so uncertain of their future. This made it extremely difficult for the association to plan ahead because of the uncertainty about future funding. With CHA experiencing serious financial problems as well, the organization restructured internally in 1988, 1990 and, again, in 1993, in efforts to rollback services, combine programs and cut expenses. Still, the financial future for CHA remained unstable.

In 1993, the board set up the Corporate Innovation Committee to review CHA's mission, bylaws, board composition and the membership fee structure. The recommendations of the committee were approved at the November 1994 board meeting and ratified by the membership at the March 1995 annual general meeting. The committee had recommended a name change for the association to that of Canadian Healthcare Association/Association canadienne des soins de santé. This name change reflected the changing nature of CHA's membership much better. Many of its members now represented the continuum of care.

CHA would remain a federation of the provincial and territorial hospital and health associations, which represented regional and individual governing bodies and the management of health facilities and agencies. In addition to these active members, the association would include associate, personal and life members, and a new category of corporate members.

Board composition was reduced from twenty to eleven individuals, who represented CHA's active members in the federation. Other changes included shifting the annual general meeting from March to June to be held in conjunction with the joint annual conference. Board meetings were reduced to three a year from the previous four, and the Executive Committee would meet at least three times a year.

Among the other changes that were approved in 1995, there was a new mission statement which read: "The mission of the association is to improve health services delivery in Canada through policy development, advocacy, leadership and association services." The committee also recommended that the population-based fee formula for active members be maintained. But the board did suggest that CHA reduce the fee to the members by ten percent for 1996.

These changes were intended to focus CHA on the reality of Canada's health delivery system structure and the broader composition of its active membership. The

Figure 1: Canadian Healthcare Association's Chain of Office, 1995

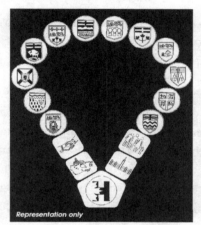

A New Chain of Office for the CHA Board Chair

CHA is very proud of the new ceremonial chain of office which was presented to the association's new chair, Gaston Levac, president of the Thunder Bay Regional Hospital, at the joint national conference. The new chain of office, which replaces an outdated medallion, is more reflective of the structure of the CHA federation.

The chain of office is made up of a number of small medallions, each depicting an element of significance to the Canadian Healthcare Association:

The round medallions are decorated with heraldic shields, representing the provinces and territories of Canada.

Four square medals represent various aspects of the mission of the Canadian Healthcare Association:

The **Houses of Parliament**, signifying CHA's role in the shaping of policy;

Hands in fellowship, symbolizing both service to members, and the coalitions and partnerships in the healthcare domain of which CHA is an integral part;

The **generations**, illustrating CHA's vision and goal of an integrated continuum of healthcare services centred on consumer needs; and

A **map of Canada**, depicting CHA's role in representing the regions of Canada.

The final central piece, a pentagonal medal, depicts the logo of the Canadian Healthcare Association.

Representation only

grassroots of the federation now encompassed regional health authorities, health facilities and agencies across a broad continuum of care, including home care and support services, tertiary care and teaching facilities, long-term care, community care, cancer treatment centres and public and mental health. In some jurisdictions, alcohol treatment centres and correctional facilities were also included in the provincial membership.

To focus CHA's advocacy and representation activities, the Chief Executive Officers Advisory Committee was set up as a permanent committee under the bylaw change of 1995. The CEO Advisory Committee (usually called the CEO Forum) included the president of CHA and the CEOs of the active members. The chair of the committee would rotate annually with the rotation of the board chair. The CEO Forum chair would report to the board either through the CHA president or directly to the board. It was mandated to consider matters referred to it by the board or the Executive Committee and to make recommendations. It could also make recommendations based on issues arising from its meetings.

To ensure more equity at the board table in filling the position of chairman, the membership was divided into regions across Canada as follows:

(1) Region I consisting of the provinces of Newfoundland, Prince Edward Island, Nova Scotia and New Brunswick;

(2) Region II consisting of the Province of Quebec;

(3) Region III consisting of the Province of Ontario;

(4) Region IV consisting of the provinces of Manitoba, Saskatchewan, the Northwest Territories, (with Nunavut added in 2000); and

(5) Region V consisting of the provinces of Alberta, British Columbia (and the Yukon added in 1999).

As the association entered 1996, it did so in both a precarious financial position and without a president at the helm. The incumbent president had resigned in January and the board appointed an acting president to lead the organization temporarily. In an effort to shore up its dwindling revenue base, CHA launched its corporate partner's program in March 1996. Corporate partners, as provided for in the amended bylaw, could pay an annual fee of $2,000 and, in turn, receive discounts on CHA products and services.

In March 1996, CHA's board held a one-day retreat to review the association's mission and services again and to look at how to improve board effectiveness. An outside facilitator was hired to conduct the retreat and introduced the board to the principles of the Policy Governance Model™. The summary report provided to the board concluded that CHA's mission focused more on who the organization was and what it would do but was vague as to the results it expected to achieve. The board needed to establish a clear picture of why CHA existed and what results it was expected to accomplish for its membership. CHA should then focus on this purpose, divesting itself of all other roles.

Because of its financial instability, the board looked at options for CHA's future and suggested at this same meeting that discussions be held with other health organizations to determine possible options for amalgamation. The chair of the board, Gaston Levac (1995–1996), had already contacted several national health organization chairs and a roundtable was scheduled for March 1996 to determine interest among these groups. The discussions were wide open to all options, including a full merger, shared services or integrated programs. The chair was asked to report back to the June board meeting on the results of the roundtable.

At the joint meeting of the chairs and CEOs of the member associations in June 1996, it was apparent that there was intense dissatisfaction among the membership about CHA's role, focus and current services. Several CEOs suggested that CHA divest itself of all but its representation, advocacy and policy development activities. Some members indicated they would support the ancillary services, if they were self-supporting and if they did not take CHA's focus away from its main purpose. As a result of the discussions, the board members directed CHA's acting president and senior staff to conduct a review of the mission and services of the association for presentation to the board in September.

At this board meeting, the acting president presented the report "Review of Mission and Association Services." The conclusions in the report were based on input from the active member CEOs through several consultative processes over the summer. Other input was provided by senior management and a management consulting firm, which had reviewed CHA's operations earlier in the year at the board's request.

The September board meeting of 1996 was in many ways a turning point for the organization. The board did take several decisions that would result in CHA divesting itself of most of its ancillary services such as publishing, distance education programs and conferences within the next year. In efforts to further stabilize the organization financially, CHA cut one-third of its workforce that fall at the board's request. But the major blow to the organization's stability—possibly even its future existence—came when the board representative from the Ontario Hospital Association advised that it would be terminating its membership in the federation by the end of the year. Without its largest member at the table, CHA's credibility and viability as a national health organization was seriously threatened. Nor had the board filled the position of president as the association was about to enter a new year.

In 1997, the board chair, Dan de Vlieger (1996–1997), hired an interim president to clean up both CHA's ongoing financial instability and win back its largest member in Ontario. She had barely settled into her office, when the Quebec Hospital Association, CHA's second largest member, gave its notice that it would not be able to pay its fees after 1997. Well into the late summer of 1997, board members focused on CHA's survival and little else. The board did hire a new president, who joined CHA on 1 January 1998.

CHA's board remained fully committed to ensuring CHA's survival during what can only be described as one of the most perilous periods in its history. Because of the board's exercise of its authority and its ultimate responsible for CHA's survival, the organization came through the crisis stronger, more focused and better situated to deal with the many problems facing Canada's health system. The time of crisis for many of the association's active members also seemed to peak during this period, so that several problems seemed to be resolved at the same time.

In March 1999, under the chair of Jean Graham, CHA's board undertook a review of its governance processes. The objectives of the session were to clarify the roles, responsibilities and relationships among CHA's board, chair, CEO and staff. The focus was on the vision, strategy and policy; the CEO selection/appraisal process; member relations; human resources management; image and communications; and the budget.

By the end of the morning session, which had been guided through an outside facilitator, the board reached a consensus that, overall, it operated well as a committee of the whole. The members agreed this was the preferred model and that all major discussion should take place at the board level and not in committees. Only the Executive Committee was considered to be necessary and appropriate terms of reference needed to be prepared by CHA's president for board approval. The other area identified for work was the need for CEO objectives and an evaluation process. Both documents were prepared and approved by the board before the year was over. The board also approved the board orientation manual that had been written by the board chair. CHA's governance processes were well in place by the time the organization entered its next decade.

In 2001, CHA's Executive Committee recommended to the board that it approve the proposed amendment to the bylaw regarding associate membership in the organization. This amendment, in particular, was intended to accommodate the possibility of other provincial health organizations, which represented various parts of the continuum of care, who might request a relationship with CHA in the future. They could join the association but would not have a seat on the board. Nor would they be accommodated as participant-observers. This amendment was approved by the board.

CHA entered the twenty-first century with a clear mandate about its purpose and where its resources should be directed. Board meetings in the years from 1999 to 2006 rarely dealt with financial matters or CHA's stability. The board's agenda was clearly focused in these years on setting policy priorities, approving CHA's position on major health issues and directing its CEO on lobbying and representation efforts. The federation's members entered a more stable period as well, although from time to time, provincial health restructuring meant changes at the board table. CHA's bylaw was able to accommodate these member changes. The active membership was able to commit to paying adequate fees to support the association's policy and advocacy agenda. For the most part, the years up to 2006 were a reasonably successful time for the organization and boded well for its future.

Management of the Association, 1931 to 2006

Council Administration, 1931 to 1952

As noted earlier in the chapter, the management of the Canadian Hospital Council was relegated to the Executive Committee. However, most of the day-to-day work was carried out by Dr. Harvey Agnew as the council's voluntary secretary-treasurer. He also continued as the associate secretary of the Canadian Medical Association (CMA), with full responsibility for the Department of Hospital Service, which provided most of the secretarial, clerical and financial support for the council. In 1945, the council became a fully autonomous organization and moved into its own rental space to accommodate its growing staff.

In 1947, under a constitutional amendment, the executive secretary of the council became a paid position. This was a clear recognition by the Executive Committee, supported by the membership, that the workload was becoming too much for one person—and a volunteer at that—to carry out. It is also important to remember that, when the council acquired the journal (*The Canadian Hospital*) in 1936, Dr. Agnew also assumed editorial duties in addition to his other extensive administrative responsibilities.

When Dr. Agnew announced his retirement in 1949, the Executive Committee reassessed the executive secretary position and made two recommendations regarding council management in future: 1) the new executive secretary would continue to be a physician and 2) an assistant secretary would be hired to help carry out some of the administrative work. His duties would be determined by Dr. Leonard Bradley, who was hired to manage the council. As the membership continued to approve more and more activities, the need for both strong leadership and administrative or management experience became vital for the senior management person. The council also hired more staff between 1950 and 1952, and Murray Ross joined the council in 1950 as the first assistant secretary of the council.[9]

Association Management, 1953 to 1977

On Dr. Bradley's departure in 1952, the CHA board of directors once again hired a physician with strong managerial capabilities to lead the council. With the issue of accreditation moving to the forefront, the board wanted a man who was capable of understanding this important area and one who also had ties to the University of Toronto's health administration department. Dr. Arnold Swanson met this criteria and was hired in 1952.

In his first report to the General Assembly in 1953, he noted that the council's programs and services had expanded considerably and that the staff now totaled twenty-one from a high of fifteen in 1951. With the launch of the Hospital Organization and Management (HOM) course in 1951, increasing demands on the library service to support the students and work underway on the *Canadian Hospital Accounting Manual*, the council needed more and more staff to carry out these activities. During Dr. Swanson's brief time as executive secretary, the council was renamed the Canadian Hospital Association. With his resignation in 1954, the board had another opportunity to review how this position would be staffed.

In 1954, the CHA board continued its policy of choosing "a medical man," changed the senior management position title to executive director and hired Dr. Douglas Piercey. He was the hospital administrator at the Ottawa Civic Hospital at the time, and brought both medical knowledge and hospital administration experience to the council. He was also very familiar with the association, having served on its board for three years as the Ontario Hospital Association (OHA) representative. The board authorized that a second assistant director be hired in 1955 to provide additional administrative support and approved extensive personnel policies for CHA staff that included enrolment in OHA's Blue Cross Plan and a pension plan operated by Sun Life Assurance Company.

During Dr. Piercey's term, CHA grew significantly to the point where it acquired its own office building in Toronto, with all staff moving into their new headquarters in early 1960. Up until then, CHA staff were split between two rental locations. During Dr. Piercey's tenure from 1954 to 1966, several distance education programs were developed and expanded and considerable work was done to improve hospital accounting practices through revised editions of *CHAM*. He also believed in the need for national unity among all the Canadian hospitals and hospital associations regardless of their denomination or ownership and was highly visible at provincial association meetings.

When Dr. B.L.P. Brosseau became the executive director of CHA in mid-1966, the association had more than forty employees and an operating budget of around $472,000, with membership fees assessed at $145,000 and the remainder of funds coming from advertising in the journal and directory, sales of subscriptions and fees for education courses. Many staff were involved in delivering education programs and publishing a journal and the directory. Staff also supported four annual board meetings and nine standing committees, arranged an annual convention and annual business meeting, as well as monthly Executive Committee meetings.

Dr. Brosseau also worked very hard to establish amicable relations with the federal health department and succeeded in persuading them to support several major national conferences, special national symposia and seminars during his term. CHA's headquarters were expanded to include additional space for the growing staff, as well as to accommodate the newly established hospital administrators association. As more and more new professional associations appeared on the scene, much of his time was spent establishing relations with them. He also wrote the editorial for twelve issues of the CHA journal in both official languages as part of his duties. Daily internal operations of the association were increasingly handled by the associate and assistant directors, a business manager or both.

In mid-1975, at the recommendation of the Executive Committee, the board decided to hire an associate executive director, preferably bilingual, who could be trained to take over Dr. Brosseau's duties on his retirement at the end of 1977. But there were few qualified bilingual candidates who applied for the position and the search was eventually put on hold as the association began to prepare for its move to Ottawa in 1978.

Managing CHA in the Capital, 1978 to 2006

When Jean-Claude Martin was hired in mid-1977, he was the first nonphysician to become executive director of CHA. However, he did bring considerable hospital administration experience to the position. His first major task was to find rental accommodation for CHA in downtown Ottawa. He also had to hire all but three staff for the association, including a new management team as only one director had been able to move to Ottawa. The association had to be rebuilt from the ground up.

During his twelve years in the position as chief executive officer, the association adopted the corporate structure which became effective in 1982. Under this organizational structure, the CEO became the president of the association. Because the position included significant representation and advocacy activities, CHA's management structure included a senior vice-president responsible for dealing with many day-to-day operations, particularly the administrative and financial side of the association.

It was during the period between 1980 and 1989 that CHA moved into the computer age by adapting many of its administrative, financial and communications functions using computer and other communications technologies. These changes made the association both more efficient and more effective and, at the same time, were intended to provide additional revenues. In 1983, CHA moved into its permanent headquarters in the Byward Market.

The association also expanded rapidly during these years as more and more projects were approved for implementation by the board and funded by the various federal granting agencies. With more staff, the association needed more space. As with its members, CHA was also subject to downturns in the economy, inflation, debt reduction by government and cutbacks to the health system. In both 1984 and 1988, association staff were laid off to reduce deficits and cut costs. Some services such as the library were eliminated entirely.

By 1990, the association was again under new management. President Carol Clemenhagen was the first person to be selected from within CHA as its CEO. She spent much of her term on ensuring financial stability by reorganizing and restructuring the association's internal operations. Although she was able to maintain a full complement of CHA staff during her term, she did so often without the ability to take on new activities and under very tight financial circumstances. She was directed by the board to sell InfoHealth and the leasing arrangement at 24 Clarence Street to ensure a balanced budget. In some cases, she was forced to shut down projects such as the CHA Foundation because of lack of funding. The onus throughout her term was on cost-cutting and tight financial management to ensure CHA's survival.

On his appointment as acting president, Tim Julien's role in 1996 was to continue with more of the same financial controls. He set up a management team, cut his position as vice-president and worked mostly to find solutions to refocus CHA for the future. Along with board-mandated responsibilities to review the association's services and finances, he oversaw a major downsizing of CHA in late September 1996, when almost one-third of its staff was laid off. He was also directed by the board to begin the process of selling off most of CHA's programs and services.

In 1997, the focus for Interim President Joyce Bailey was to stabilize CHA both financially and by regaining the members' commitment to the federation. She worked closely with senior management and a board task force to review and propose a new member fee structure. She also strengthened CHA's policy development and external communications functions, so that they could respond to members' expectations and the board's policy and advocacy focus for the future.

By the time that President Sharon Sholzberg-Gray arrived in 1998, the organization was more stable and pulling out of a major slump after almost two years of review, downsizing and rebuilding. Although neither a physician nor a hospital administrator, Ms Sholzberg-Gray brought extensive association management and policy development experience to the position of president. While finances have not dominated either the board agenda or her presidency, the association is never truly free and clear from reviewing and watching its financial position. The onus has been on advocacy, representation and policy development, with ancillary services such as education, conferences and publishing expected to contribute revenues or at least be self-supporting. Today's CHA is a smaller organization of just twenty people, the majority of whom either work on policy and advocacy or in communications and corporate services to support the work of the board and CHA's members.

George Findlay Stephens Memorial Award

When Dr. George Findlay Stephens died in 1947, the Canadian Hospital Council 's Executive Committee recommended that an award be established in his memory. The General Assembly approved setting up the George Findlay Stephens Memorial Award in 1949. The award would be given for distinguished service in the hospital field and for contributions to its advancement. Although Dr. Agnew submitted a proposal for a medal to be given to the winner, the Executive Committee, which made the selection, decided that it would present a wrist watch.

The first award was presented to Dr. Alfred K. Haywood, who was one of the founders of the Montreal Hospital Council and the first chairman of the committee that directed the work of the CMA Department of Hospital Service. He also worked very hard to establish the Canadian Hospital Council and served on its executive for several years.

Over the years, many distinguished leaders in Canada's health care system have been selected to receive this honor, including many who have served as presidents and chairs of CHA's highest elected office. Only once in its history has the award been presented to a non-Canadian. In 1982, Andrew K. Pattullo of the W.K. Kellogg Foundation was presented with the award in recognition of his commitment to improve health care in Canada through considerable grant support for many Canadian health care projects.

The only time the award was given to two people at the same time occurred in 1981, when it was impossible to choose between the two candidates that year—Justice Emmett Hall and Dr. Gustave Gingras—both of whom had made significant contributions to Canada's health system. On occasion, the award has not been presented at all to prevent the selection process from either turning into a popularity contest or becoming too political.

In June 1991, on the recommendation of the Policy and Planning Committee, CHA's board agreed to change the name of the award to the CHA Award of Excellence for Service and Leadership. The procedures for selection and the conditions for nomination were also changed and adopted by the board. Most of the winners were either health system trustees or administrators, many of whom served on CHA's board during their careers. (*See* appendix 2 for a list of the recipients of this award.)

CHA Award of Excellence Winner Jean-Claude Martin, past president, with CHA Chair Alex Taylor, Saskatchewan, on 10 June 2006 in Victoria. (Photo courtesy of Eleanor Sawyer)

Summary

CHA began as ad hoc group of hospital administrators in 1931, directed by an assembly that met only every two years, and managed by an Executive Committee of volunteers. Member input was limited both by distance and by time. By 1953, the membership had set up a board, albeit one that was often more involved in administrative matters than in governance at times. By 2006, CHA was directed by a strong governing board, representative of its active membership, supported by adequate funding, and focused on clearly defined goals and objectives. Clear lines of authority between governance and management, which was vested in a president, enabled the association to carry out its goals and objectives.

CHA has managed to change both its governance and organizational structure as and how it was needed to meet its members' expectations and needs over the course of its history. These changes were neither easy nor accomplished quickly. They were often driven by changes within the health system or by outright demands from the membership. Whatever factors drove these changes, CHA has been able to meet the challenge and come out more focused and stronger over the course of its history.

Endnotes

1. To review this period (1931–1952), two sources of information were available. First, the CMA Department of Hospital Service produced the *Annual Activities Report* to the Sun Life Assurance Company of Canada (for its financial support) which included a section on council activities. These reports were prepared by Dr. Agnew who was the secretary of both the council and the CMA hospital department.

Second, after 1935, the council, as a legal entity, started to publish a report of its biennial meetings in a document titled *Transactions*. These documents cover the years 1937 to 1953, the second period of the council's existence during nine biennial conventions—as they were called at the time. These were held in the following cities: Ottawa 1937, Toronto 1939, Montreal 1941, Ottawa 1943, Hamilton 1945, Winnipeg 1947, Quebec City 1949, Ottawa 1951 and Ottawa 1953. Interestingly, in the four times the meetings were held in Ottawa, they took place at the Chateau Laurier. *Transactions* was discontinued in 1953.

2. The council also invited the Right Honorable R.B. Bennett, the prime minister of Canada, and the Honorable Murray MacLaren, minister of the Department of Pensions and National Health, to become the honorary president and vice-president respectively.

3. The nine standing committees of the council in 1931 were accounting, constitution, construction and equipment, legislation and resolutions, administration, finance, public relations, medical relations and research.

4. The presidents and a brief description of their term of office may be found in chapter 7.

5. By 1950, this senior management position was known as managing or executive director.

6. Although Dr. Lorne Gilday was never president of CHA, he held the position of treasurer from 1945 to 1957 and served on the board of directors for 12 years. He also chaired the CHA Committee on Accreditation.

7. The 1949 general assembly was also attended by the Canadian Council of Blue Cross Plans; representatives from all the provincial hospital associations and conferences; the Canadian Medical Association; and the federal government, with representatives from the health department, defence and veterans affairs. The provincial health departments, the provincial government insurance plans, the Canadian Red Cross, the American Hospital Association and the American College of Hospital Administrators were also at the meeting.

8. In 1982, CHA also adopted a more modern and stylish corporate logo—the blue international hospital symbol combined with a maple leaf.

9. In 1951, Mr. Ross's position title became associate director and associate editor.

6

CHA's RELATIONS WITH ITS MEMBERSHIP

"We must have a strong national body giving utmost service to its membership. We must have strong and autonomous regional and provincial associations. . . . Within them all there must be [a] degree of unity and cooperation. . . ."

(TURNER 1957, 35)

When Dr. Harvey Agnew, the associate secretary of the CMA—with responsibility for the Department of Hospital Service—sent his initial letters of invitation to hospital superintendents across Canada, he was setting in place the first steps in the formation of the early Canadian Hospital Council. The main issues that these early delegates were asked to address, specifically, were the need for, the purpose and objectives of such a council and the crucial issue of who would make up its membership.

In his letter of December 1930 to the provincial hospital associations, Dr. Agnew suggested that they could become members of a new council, appointing one or two delegates to represent their interests at an annual meeting. This meeting would be held to discuss hospital issues that were of national or provincial interest and concern. In his second letter of April 1931, he provided further details and suggested that the council could act as a link between the various provincial organizations and hospitals in Canada on matters of national importance.

In reviewing the minutes and the literature of these early days, it is interesting to note that Dr. Agnew and other founding members established the following fundamental concepts and principles on which they were planning to build this new organization:

1) They recognized very early that the size of the country created difficulties for hospitals to maintain contact with each other and, thus, to be able to respond adequately to their regional differences.

2) They acknowledged that hospitals in each province had set up or were in the process of creating a provincial hospital association.

3) They understood that the provision of hospital services was governed by provincial legislation.

4) They knew that the federal government had limited and well-defined responsibilities in providing health care services.

These first delegates were not prepared to set up an association, as it would have to compete with the American Hospital Association in which many Canadian hospitals were already members. (*See* chapter 5 for details on the council's governance and organizational structure.)

The initial membership of the council, whose mandate would be to represent the interests of hospitals on matters affecting their operations, was ". . . open to provincial or regional hospital associations and to the CMA through the Department of Hospital Service" (Agnew 1974, 68). The federal Department of Pensions and National Health and the provincial departments of health were also eligible for membership. But their representatives were nonvoting members.

By appointing representatives to the national hospital council, the provincial (and regional) associations and Catholic conferences would set the agenda for the council. Even as early as 1931, the Canadian Hospital Council was being viewed as a federation of provincial and regional associations.

Setting the Foundation for the Membership, 1931 to 1952

The founding meeting of the council took place at the Royal York Hotel in Toronto on 28 and 29 September 1931. Twenty-two official participants attended, representing eleven provincial hospital and other health associations, plus representatives from the federal and provincial governments, hospitals and other national health organizations.

The charter members of the Canadian Hospital Council were: the Hospital Association of Nova Scotia and Prince Edward Island, the Maritime Conference of the Catholic Hospital Association, the New Brunswick Hospital Association, the

Montreal Hospital Council, the Ontario Hospital Association, the Ontario Conference of the Catholic Hospital Association, the Manitoba Hospital Association, the Saskatchewan Hospital Association, the Alberta Hospital Association, the British Columbia Hospitals Association and the Department of Hospital Service, Canadian Medical Association.

Having dealt with the three most important subjects on the first day, namely, who should be a member, how the new organization would be financed and what role the CMA Department of Hospital Service would play in the future, the delegates, based on the discussions that day, mandated a small group under the direction of Dr. Agnew to redraft the constitution where necessary. On 29 September 1931, a duly formed general assembly officially sanctioned the constitution of the Canadian Hospital Council.

Many hospital superintendents still had reservations about the council and how it could speak on behalf of local hospitals. Their fear was that the big issues would supercede the very real local and provincial hospital issues that needed to be dealt with at this time (Agnew 1974). They were prepared to support their provincial organizations but would be watchful of this newly formed national council. Nevertheless, the delegates agreed to meet again in two years at a two-day session.

In 1936, the council requested incorporation and applied for letters patent. To enable the council to do this, it was necessary to adopt a revised constitution which provided eight objectives and detailed membership privileges. (*See* chapter 11 for the reasons behind the council's incorporation.) The incorporation document officially appointed the three applicants—Walter Richard Chenoweth of Montreal, Dr. Frederick William Routley and Dr. George Harvey Agnew both from Toronto—as the founding members of the Canadian Hospital Council. The incorporated council was officially adopted by the membership at the Fourth Biennial Convention in Ottawa on 8 September 1937.

Membership in the council remained essentially the same throughout the 1930s. In 1939, the Committee on Constitution and By-Laws reported to the convention, recommending some further amendments. One such amendment involved the membership. In future, members would be entitled to send two official delegates, or two or more alternates, to sessions of the council rather than both delegates and alternates as had been the case in the past. Another amendment provided for "participating member associations only" to ratify bylaws, resolutions or other business conducted by the Executive Committee. Up to this time, both delegates and alternates were entitled to take part in the ratification process. No further changes were recommended that would impact on the council's ability to eventually reorganize into a national hospital association similar to the American association. This type of organization had always been envisioned by the founding members.

A complete list of delegates to each general assembly was published in *Transactions*,[1] the official record of the proceedings of the biennial conventions from 1935 to 1953. The names of participants and the organization they represented were listed in two distinct sections, namely, those who were empowered to vote—the provincial hospital association delegates or their alternates, plus the CMA Department of Hospital Service—and the nonvoting guests, that is, the federal and provincial government representatives and other distinguished guests.

In the meantime, hospital insurance plans such as Blue Cross were increasingly being set up across Canada during the late 1930s and early 1940s. Some plans such as Ontario Blue Cross were operated by the Ontario Hospital Association, the council member. But, in other provinces, some plans were independent entities and, as such, they applied for membership in the council.

At the Eighth Biennial Convention held in Hamilton in September 1945, the Executive Committee proposed a motion to change the constitution to provide for associate membership for these hospital care plans (CHC 1945, 47). But the membership agreed that only national organizations would be considered for associate membership in the future. Nevertheless, the 1945 assembly delegates did admit the Catholic Hospital Conferences of British Columbia, Alberta and Saskatchewan and the Prairie Provinces Conference as full members. And, in 1949, the Executive Committee delegated Dr. Agnew to issue an unofficial invitation to the hospitals of Newfoundland to join the council either through the Maritime Conference, an association, or as a separate entity.

Throughout the late 1940s and early 1950s, the Executive Committee constantly reviewed the council's finances. For the most part, the council had been funded by an annual contribution from the Sun Life Assurance Company of Canada since 1931 and voluntary donations from the members. When the council and the CMA officially separated in 1945, Sun Life, which had been contributing to the CMA hospital service department, transferred this grant to the council. It notified the council that its grant would be reduced annually and urged it to become self-sustaining.

The financial focus shifted to the journal to increase its profit margins and to the membership to increase their financial donations. The financial statements from the 1940s show voluntary annual contributions ranging from $100 to $3,500 from the various provincial members.[2] In 1950, several provincial associations requested that the council "recommend a formula to be used as a measure by which each Association may judge . . . the relative equity of its contribution to the . . . Council" (CHC 1950, 270). The council needed a sound financial base in order to carry out its agenda. Financing the national hospital organization remained an ongoing concern for both its board and its membership in the coming decades. (*See* chapter 5 for more information on funding CHA.)

A New Association Membership Is Born, 1953 to 1977

At its 1953 General Assembly, the Canadian Hospital Council voted to change its name to the Canadian Hospital Association/Association des hôpitaux du Canada (CHA/AHC). At this same assembly, the original Charter of 1936 was amended and the association applied for supplementary letters patent. The assembly also passed a resolution asking the board to appoint a committee to consider recommendations for "each provincial association [to] become a division of the national association entitled, by constitutional provision, to specified representation on the assembly and on the executive board of the national association" (Fraser 1953, 64). This same assembly also approved active membership for the Comité des Hôpitaux du Québec and associate membership for the Canadian Council of Blue Cross Plans and the National Council of Women's Hospital Auxiliaries.

In January 1959, the Association des Hôpitaux du Québec (AHQ)—formed in 1958 from the membership of the Montreal Hospital Council, which represented all English hospitals and most non-Catholic hospitals—became an active member in the CHA. The Comité des Hôpitaux de la Province de Québec (CHPQ) had replaced the Montreal Council as a member in the national organization in 1948. This now meant that Quebec hospitals were represented by two separate organizations in the province, many of which held membership in both the CHPQ and AHQ. Immediately on its membership, AHQ pushed for the same number of voting delegates as the OHA had.

The Executive Committee reviewed two issues regarding membership in December 1959 and recommended to the board, which reported to the 1960 assembly, that

1) AHQ not receive equal voting strength with OHA and 2) the present ratio of votes in the assembly be maintained. At the time, hospital association members had nineteen votes and the provincial Catholic conference members had sixteen votes in the assembly. In some provinces, a Catholic hospital had dual representation in both its provincial organizations and, therefore, in CHA. As for the issue of two Quebec members in CHA, this was finally resolved in 1968, when the Catholic hospital association in Quebec merged with AHQ to become the Association des Hôpitaux de la Province du Québec (AHPQ) and it became CHA's only member in the province.

Both the CHA president and executive director tried to attend as many member annual meetings as possible throughout the year. But the travel time and expense, as well as the days in which the CEO was absent from CHA, became the subject of considerable discussion at both Executive Committee and board meetings throughout 1959 and 1960. CHA needed to be visible and to participate in member activities but the question was: How could CHA interact more effectively with its members?

Dr. Piercey, CHA's executive director from 1954 to 1966, was particularly concerned about his attendance at member annual meetings. He raised the issue several times in his written reports to the Executive Committee, seeking their advice. He wanted "to strengthen the lines of communication between member associations themselves and the national office (Piercey 1959, 5). CHA had been sending out a monthly newsletter since June 1959 to board members, association secretaries (member CEOs today) and others in order to keep the active membership informed. At his suggestion, the board approved a meeting of association secretaries to be held at the time of the assembly meeting. The first meeting of the provincial hospital secretaries and CHA's executive director, sponsored by CHA, was held on 23 May 1961 at association headquarters. This became an ongoing meeting at CHA assemblies.

The question of dual membership became an issue at the board table again in 1960, when the New Brunswick Hospital Association requested membership in CHA. At the time, the Maritime Hospital Association represented hospitals from New Brunswick, Nova Scotia and Prince Edward Island. But, with the implementation of the national hospital insurance plan, every province was beginning to recognize a need for its own provincial hospital association and, thus, membership in CHA. By the mid-1960s, all the provinces in the Maritime region, as well as Newfoundland and the Northwest Territories, had applied for and were members in CHA.

In May 1965, the general assembly repealed CHA's original bylaws and confirmed new ones. These spelled out under bylaw four who the active membership of the association was. They were to be "(a) Organizations generally known as Associations or conferences of a national or provincial character, representing hospitals or other institutions providing in-patient care. (b) The Canadian Medical Association" (CHA 1969a, 2). The new bylaws also allowed for personal membership in the association and granted all past presidents of CHA life memberships.

One of the thorniest issues raised during President Charles Barton's term (1965–1966) centred around the American Hospital Association's offer of a form of blanket membership in AHA for all Canadian hospitals. While a close relationship had always existed between Canadian hospitals and the AHA (*see* chapters 1 and 9 for a look at the early connections), a lively debate ensued at the 1966 assembly around the AHA's offer; the proposal was finally shelved for further consideration. After negotiations, an institutional associate membership in the AHA was approved in 1967 by the CHA General Assembly. Two years later, CHA negotiated a considerable decreased membership fee and offered the American organization active membership in CHA. This offer was accepted and AHA representatives regularly attended CHA meetings.

With the passage of the national hospital insurance legislation in 1958 and the medical insurance legislation in 1968, the hospital sector in Canada exploded. The demand for health services increased, the need for health professionals to deliver these services rose and so did the operating expenses of Canada's hospitals. Although CHA had established a permanent and growing role for itself, there were still some active members who had not done so; they were operated by voluntary staff through voluntary donations from the hospitals in their province.[3] For provincial association and Catholic conference members with permanent staff, the number of employees and their operating expenses showed marked increases between 1967 and 1972. The active provincial members were also making more demands on CHA to represent them to the federal government.

As hospitals continued to expand their activities at a rapid pace, the number of allied and occupational health professionals increased significantly throughout the 1960s and 1970s. These groups frequently formed their own organizations to license and set standards for professionals. Many of these associations asked for membership in CHA, along with the provincial hospital commissions, which operated the hospital insurance plan in their province. Among these new associate members were the P.E.I. Hospital Services Commission. The Canadian Council of Blue Cross Plans withdrew from associate membership in 1962 and the four provincial Blue Cross Plans applied in its place and, in 1967, the Canadian Physiotherapy Association applied for associate membership.

The number of requests from these newly emerging professional organizations for membership in CHA required it to spell out the conditions and privileges of both associate and personal membership. In 1970, CHA determined what these would be. These categories would be entitled to attend the annual assembly meeting as a nonvoting member, to receive a copy of the annual report, a subscription to *Canadian Hospital* and a certificate of membership.

In 1972, the general assembly appointed Judge Edward Hughes, CHA's president, to review the association and make recommendations on its future. His report, presented to the 1974 general assembly, made the following specific recommendations regarding the membership.

- Since change in the health care system rests primarily at the provincial level, CHA should, with the agreement of the provincial hospital associations, channel its participation and influence more heavily towards provincial patterns of developing an integrated health system.

- The institutional membership in CHA should not be direct but rather through the provincial associations and conferences.

- Allied national health organizations should be offered meaningful affiliation with CHA.

- A suitable new name for the association should be adopted once the broadened role and membership structure were well on their way towards implementation.

- There should be better communications between CHA and its members.

The 1974 report also recommended some changes to the voting system and the allocation of votes, based on provincial members' financial contribution versus their population. Although the proposition was defeated, the concept of changing the voting structure to reflect more accurately members' financial contributions to the association had now been raised.

As amended at CHA's Annual General Meeting in June 1975, and approved by the federal Department of Consumer and Corporate Affairs in August, bylaw one clearly identified who would comprise CHA's membership in the future. Under article two of the bylaw, the membership was now defined as ". . . available to organizations and individuals interested in the objects of the Association . . ." and divided into active, associate, personal, life and honorary membership (CHA 1975a, 1). Under section three, along with provincial hospital associations and the Catholic Hospital Association of Canada (CHAC), CHA's active members now included the Canadian Medical Association and the American Hospital Association (Ibid.).[4] But despite these changes to the bylaw, not every active member had representation on the board of directors. Although a CHA member, the Northwest Territories Hospital Association had never had a member appointed to the board. In early 1976, this association asked for a seat at the board table (CHA 1976b, 14), which it eventually received in 1979.

N.W.T. presents sealskin wall hanging to C.H.A.

Ottawa — Fred Lamb, Chairman of the Board of the Canadian Hospital Association is shown receiving a presentation of a sealskin wall hanging from the Northwest Territories Hospital Association for the Canadian Hospital Association boardroom. The occasion was in recognition of the N.W.T.H.A. being granted a seat on the Board of Directors of the Canadian Hospital Association for the first time.

Making the presentation is Reverend Ken Gaetz, Past President of the Northwest Territories Hospital Association and Mr. Len Adrian, incoming President. Looking on is Dr. John Phin who attended the Conference on behalf of the Canadian College of Health Service Executives. *November 1979 in Ottawa*

Left to right: Dr. John Phin, Fred Lamb, Reverend Ken Gaetz and Len Adrian.

This same assembly also affirmed membership for the provincial Catholic hospital conferences to become associate members. For many years, they had been active members of the association and were now replaced by the CHAC, their national association. But it was a difficult and acrimonious decision for the membership. Personal and life memberships were also reaffirmed under the bylaw.

As CHA prepared to move its national headquarters from Toronto to Ottawa in 1977, it was still not a true federation. But it was much closer to the type of national organization that the founding members had envisioned in 1931. However, there were still inequities in membership on the CHA board of directors that needed to be addressed.

The Changing Membership, 1977 to 2004

Early in 1977, the Committee on By-Laws and Regulations met in Toronto to discuss redrafting CHA's bylaws. Chaired by Judge Chaiker Abbis, the committee was charged with looking at the bylaws and especially the association's membership. The minutes of the meeting note that ". . . there was considerable discussion on whether CHA should broaden out into a health-care association and whether some provision should be made to accommodate such organizations as the recently formed nursing home association[s]" (CHA 1977a, 2). CHA's members in British Columbia, Alberta, Saskatchewan, Manitoba, Quebec and Nova Scotia had already opened up their membership to nursing homes. Given that the new federal-provincial fiscal arrangements would include level two care offered in nursing homes, so that these institutions would now be funded under the same umbrella as hospitals, the issue of a broadened membership for CHA needed to be dealt with.

Throughout 1978 and 1979, the members expressed concerns about a number of issues regarding their relationship with CHA. The main issue seemed to be a lack of communication between CHA and its members about its activities. Other concerns raised by various provincial members were their uncertainty about what they received from CHA for their annual fees, the need for more executive directors at the board table (versus all trustees) and a need for member fees to cover representation activities only rather than other for-profit or administrative support functions of the association.

In 1979, the general assembly appointed the Special Committee on Role and Communications, chaired by Sister Mary Lucy Power. One of the key recommendations from the committee's 1980 report was that the Catholic Health Association of Canada, the American Hospital Association and the Canadian Medical Association be dropped as active members and offered associate membership instead. In this way, the Canadian Hospital Association would become, in fact, a true hospital/health federation of the provincial/territorial member associations.

The proposed recommendations had a stormy ride at the 1981 general assembly, which approved setting up a special Ad Hoc Committee to Revise Bylaw 1. A special meeting of the general assembly was held in December 1981 to approve the revised bylaw. The committee had introduced a new category of membership— affiliate—for CHA. In describing this to the board, affiliate members would include "national corporate organizations, such as the Catholic Health Association of

Canada, while associate members [would] include national professional organizations, such as the CCHSE [Canadian College of Health Service Executives] and the CMA [Canadian Medical Association]" (CHA 1981b, 6).

On the approval of By-Law 1, CHA's only eligible active members were now the eleven provincial/territorial associations, defined as "organization[s] representing hospitals and other related health institutions providing patient care in a Province or in the Northwest Territories." The members named under the bylaw at this special meeting were: British Columbia Health Association (BCHA), Alberta Hospital Association (AHA), Saskatchewan Health-Care Association (SHA), Manitoba Health Organizations, Inc. (MHO), Ontario Hospital Association (OHA), Association des Hôpitaux du Québec (AHQ), New Brunswick Hospital Association (NBHA), Hospital Association of Prince Edward Island (HAPEI), Nova Scotia Association of Health Organizations (NSAHO), Newfoundland Hospital Association (NHA) and Northwest Territories Hospital Association (NTHA).

CHA's bylaws remained essentially unchanged for the remainder of the decade, although the 1983 State Hospital Association Review and Evaluation (SHARE)—a service organization of the AHA—report did recommend that CHA look at ways to meet with its members to discuss mutual roles and relationships with each other (*see* chapter 5). By 1985–1986, priority-setting exercises had been set up, so that active members could provide input into CHA's national agenda, recommend health policies and set its priorities.

The question of CHA's relationship with its member associations continued to be an ongoing issue as members asked what they received from the association for the fees they paid. Bilateral meetings between officers of the CHA and its provincial and territorial member associations were held regularly throughout the early 1980s. These meetings allowed frank and open discussions and often resulted in solutions to problems.

At the executive level, while meetings between the CHA and the provincial member CEOs were sporadic in the 1970s, they became much more frequent and more formal in the 1980s. There were set agendas and minutes were recorded.

At the end of 1985, in order to give more power and credibility to their deliberations, the CEOs decided to appoint a task force of three members. The task force would formally clarify the relationship between the provincial association CEOs and the CHA chairman, the members of the board, the CEO and other related matters. The report, which was submitted and approved at the CEOs meeting in March 1986, proposed the creation of the Chief Executive Officers Advisory Committee (CEOAC) with the following mandate:

1. to provide a forum for the exchange of views on common concerns among and between provincial/territorial and national hospital association CEOs;

2. to serve in an advisory capacity to such persons or groups as the CHA chairman, the board of directors, the board committees and CEO; the provincial/territorial presidents, boards of directors and CEOs; and other authorities deemed appropriate by CEOAC;

3. to provide advice by a consensus of the majority of provincial CEOs without committing individual associations to a course of action;

4. to act as the appropriate vehicle for vetting hospital/health association concerns across Canada, since the CEOs and their respective boards of directors will ultimately be charged with the execution of policy decisions.

By the end of the 1980s and well into the early 1990s, the Canadian health delivery system underwent tremendous change. Huge provincial deficits and massive cuts in the 1993 federal budget for social programs—most particularly health delivery— had resulted in major provincial reviews of their health systems. These commissions and task force reports generally recommended downsizing the system and closing hospitals. They also supported the integration and amalgamation of services across the continuum of care, and setting up regional health authorities to govern these new health delivery organizations and to set health priorities.

In 1993, another ad hoc committee was created to review CHA's board structure, its name and its financial viability. The Corporate Innovation Committee, as it was called, submitted its report in 1994. The committee made no changes to the active membership established in 1981 and recommended that "the existing population-based fee formula for active members be maintained" (CHA 1994b, 11). The most significant change, effective in June 1995, was a corporate name change to the Canadian Healthcare Association to reflect the changes within CHA's provincial member organizations.

Throughout the early 1990s, almost every provincial and territorial member organization across Canada had changed its name, its structure and its mission and objectives. Many of them faced uncertainty about their futures in the new provincial health structures. In some cases, provincial members advised CHA that they did not know if they would survive and could not commit to paying their fees. By late 1995, an increasingly cranky membership was pressuring CHA to reevaluate where it was going and the types of activities it was engaged in. The members wanted to ensure that they were receiving value for the fees they paid. With the resignation in January 1996 of Carol Clemenhagen, CHA's president, the board was provided with an opportunity to review all CHA activities and reposition the organization, while they conducted a search for a new president. (*See* chapters 5 and 8 for more details.)

At the urging of CHA's active membership, internal and external reviews were conducted throughout 1996 beginning at the March board meeting. Just as the final review document and its recommendations for CHA's future were being discussed at the September 1996 board meeting, the Ontario Hospital Association, CHA's largest member, gave notice that it intended to leave CHA at the end of the year. Because the process for a member to leave had not been properly executed under the bylaw, CHA had a brief opportunity in 1997 to persuade OHA to change its mind. However, the impact of possibly losing OHA as an active member may well have been a catalyst in focusing the membership and CHA's board on the urgency of stabilizing the organization as quickly as possible in 1997.

Then, as 1997 began, CHA received notice from the Association des hôpitaux du Québec, its second largest member, that it would not be able to continue as a member of the federation after 1997. It could not commit to paying annual membership fees beyond that year.

Fortunately, before the year was over, CHA was able to persuade OHA to reconsider its decision and it remains an active member today. Although there had been considerable uncertainty about the future of both British Columbia and Manitoba as ongoing active members, they did recommit to the organization by the end of the year. AHQ has not yet returned to active status in the CHA federation; however, it has signed strategic alliance agreements with CHA since 2000. Additional bylaw changes have provided for the admission of representatives to the CHA federation from both the Yukon Territory in 1999 and Nunavut in 2000. Both territories' representatives have a seat on CHA's board.

CHA's Membership

Many of CHA's original members have disappeared and records of their activities have been lost over the years including those for the Montreal Hospital Council, the Comité des Hôpitaux du Québec and all of the provincial conferences of the Catholic Health Association across the country. Several other organizations have ceased to be CHA members but continue to be viable organizations. These include the Canadian Medical Association (CMA), the American Hospital Association (AHA) and the Catholic Health Association of Canada (CHAC), as well as the Blue Cross Plans, which were associate members of CHA for many years.

Today, the following active members sit at CHA's board table and set the policy agenda for the organization through consultation processes and ongoing dialogue.

British Columbia

The oldest permanent hospital association in Canada was set up in British Columbia in 1917 as the British Columbia Hospitals Association, an idea developed by Dr. Malcolm MacEachern, then superintendent of the Vancouver General Hospital and later a staunch supporter and founder of standards for North American hospitals. The first convention of this early association was held in June 1918 and most members were either hospital superintendents or trustees. There was no permanent paid staff and all work of the association was carried out by the elected officers, usually the secretary, on a voluntary basis.

One of the main reasons for establishing a hospital association in British Columbia was to assist hospitals in dealing with their deficits. Even then the cost of hospital services was greater than available revenues, which came directly from well-to-do patients and private insurance schemes. The BCHA urged the government to pay for certain essential hospital services through a combination of per capita, property and municipal taxes, an issue it raised in 1921 and again in 1923.

In 1935, with the support of BCHA, the provincial government introduced a health insurance act. Although the legislation was passed, it was never proclaimed mostly because of the lack of support from the provincial medical association. The BCHA conducted much of its business through regional conferences and was forced to cancel many of these during World War II. As with the other provincial associations, it urged the Canadian Hospital Council to lobby the federal government for relief from critical shortages such as food and gas and to pay for the hospital costs incurred by soldiers' dependents, major issues for the provincial associations at the time.

With a return to prosperity at the end of the war, British Columbia became the second province in Canada to introduce hospital insurance in 1947 (Saskatchewan having done so in 1946). In 1948, Percy Ward became the BCHA's first executive secretary and remained with the association for the next ten years, during which much of the foundation of the modern association was laid.

As the association developed, committees were created to deal with medical and administrative issues. Regional conferences were reestablished to ensure that all hospitals, no matter how remote, had a reasonable opportunity to be represented. BCHA promoted hospital efficiency, mutual support and further development of hospitals. One of its key objectives during these years of the early 1950s was to find a consistent source of revenue both for the hospitals in the province and for the association.

Although it had professional staff, most of the association's work was still being carried out by volunteers, including trustees. Between the establishment of national hospital insurance in 1958 and medicare in 1968, the main issues for BCHA included funding deficits, the rising cost of health care, long wait lists for surgery, nursing shortages and concerns that government was increasingly interfering with governing boards and physician autonomy.

The labor movement was also gaining considerable strength between the late 1950s and the early 1970s, when hospitals expanded rapidly within the province. As a result, the BCHA entered into the area of labor negotiations with health care workers. In fact, in 1963, Duncan Bradford was hired as executive director in large part because of his experience in labor relations. However, this area became so demanding and complex, it threatened to overwhelm all other association activities. In 1975, the association severed its labor negotiation arm to form the Health Labour Relations Association of British Columbia, an autonomous organization.

In 1975, the association changed its name to the British Columbia Health Association, thus opening the door to other health organization memberships. During the 1980s, the association expanded its programs, created satellite operations and organizations such as B.C. InfoHealth Ltd. and B.C. Health Services Ltd. It also expanded its advocacy and representation role.

In 1990, BCHA responded to the B.C. Royal Commission on Health Care and Costs by proposing a restructuring of the provincial system into a seamless continuum of care with more regional and community responsibilities. In 1994, the Royal Commission recommended that regional health boards and community health societies be set up. On 1 April 1997, authority for health delivery was transferred to eleven regional boards and thirty-four community health councils. Each of these became members of the newly formed Health Association of British Columbia (HABC). The purpose of HABC was to assist in improving the quality and delivery of health services for residents in the province through leadership, advocacy to the provincial government and support services.

Among the other changes that occurred in health care delivery in British Columbia was the creation of the Health Employers Association of BC (HEABC). It was formed under the Public Sector Employers' Act in order to create a single organization to coordinate the human resource and labor relations interests of health care employers in the province. Established from the amalgamation of two associations and the labor relations division of the BC Association of Private Care, HEABC was formally set up on 1 December 1993.

HEABC continues to serve a diverse group of over 315 publicly funded health care employers. It undertakes contract negotiations, research and strategic planning for health reform, provides coordination, consultation and communications in all major human resource areas. HEABC also focuses on physician, nurse, pharmacist and allied health worker recruitment as the needs of the provincial health system evolve. Today, HEABC is the designated member organization at the CHA board table. It appoints a representative to the CHA board and pays annual dues.

The British Columbia Hospitals Association was present at the founding of the Canadian Hospital Council in 1931 and is listed as a charter member. Although the provincial association sent delegates to every general assembly and annual meeting over the course of CHA's history, it was not until 1977–1978, with the election of Gordon Firth as president, that the association held the highest elected position at CHA. In 1989–1990, Dr. Thelma Sharp Cook, a strong advocate of the voluntary trustee in the health system, was elected chair. Then, Robert Smith, a hospital chief executive officer, was elected for the 1993–1994 term, and Lorraine Grant was elected in 2002–2003. She was reelected for a second term in 2003–2004 during unusual circumstances which precluded the chair-elect from taking office at the time.

Alberta

Two hospital superintendents, one from Edmonton and one from Calgary, asked the provincial minister of health to call a meeting of all trustees, superintendents, nurses, medical staff and others connected or working in hospitals in order to establish a provincial association. The inaugural meeting of the Alberta Hospital Association (AHA) was held on 21 September 1919. Its purpose was to serve as a means of intercommunication, cooperation and mutual support; to standardize hospital work and nurse training, as well as to secure more government grants for the care of the chronically ill, those with TB and the aged, among other goals. Dr. James C. Fyshe was elected as the association's first secretary and was one of two superintendents urging the establishment of this association.

In 1920, a second hospital association was formed comprising hospitals set up under the Municipal Hospitals Act. The Alberta Municipal Hospital Association created a competitive environment for government funding, split the voice of hospitals and gave government the means to play one association against the other. A number of hospitals held membership in both organizations.

Separately and together, both associations acted as advocates on behalf of their members to government. Throughout the late 1920s and most of the 1930s, the main issue confronting both associations was the lack of additional funding from the provincial government to support the hospitals, which had seen increased wages and costs of supplies, as well as demands from the public for better services. The difficulty in presenting arguments to the government was that all hospitals handled accounting in their own way. Recognizing that comparable figures on hospital costs would be beneficial, the AHA set up a committee to study the prospects for developing uniform accounting standards.

In 1936, the two associations agreed to hold their conventions conjointly, the first of many. Then, in 1943, the members accepted a proposal to amalgamate both associations under the name of the Associated Hospitals of Alberta (AHA) with goals similar to those initially set up for the first AHA. The new association entered a period of prosperity at the end of World War II, with an oil strike in Leduc in 1948, adding more revenues to the provincial coffers.

The association was incorporated in 1948 to allow for the establishment and operation of the Alberta Blue Cross Plan. This plan traced its development to the 1933 plan of the Edmonton Hospitals Group that entitled people to purchase a subscription to insured hospitalization.

Prompted by high public demand for more and better hospital services, the provincial government was playing an increased role in health care in the 1950s. The association also advocated to the government that payment for hospital care was a provincial government responsibility—not a local or municipal one. The association worked closely with the CHA in 1953 to hold educational institutes in Alberta to introduce the application of the *Canadian Hospital Accounting Manual* to hospitals. (*See* chapter 16 for more information about *CHAM.*) By 1956, the government was developing a provincial hospital plan with input from the AHA and, in 1958, the federal government introduced national hospital insurance, which was introduced in Alberta in 1959.

With the demands on the association growing, paid staff had become a necessity. In July 1959, an office was opened and Murray Ross was hired as the executive secretary, a position he held for twenty years.[5] The office was responsible for establishing a consulting and education service, arranging for collective bargaining and employee relations, and setting up a group insurance and pension plan. The executive secretary was also to coordinate communications between members and with other agencies such as government.

Murray W. Ross, Executive Secretary of the Lamont Public Hospital in Lamont, Alberta, 1937. He Joined the Hospital Council Staff in 1950 as the First Assistant Director. He Left CHA in 1960 to Become the Executive Director of the Alberta Hospital Association.

In 1966, the association had reverted to its earlier name of Alberta Hospital Association (Agnew 1974, 80). By the end of the 1960s, hospital costs were soaring and the provincial government had put limits on financial allocations with the resulting inevitable hospital deficits. AHA responded by meeting frequently with government officials and submitting many briefs on the need for more funding. Throughout the 1960s, the association had grown to include nursing homes as associate members in 1964 and, then, active members in 1966. The role of the association board shifted during this time toward policy development and less administrative oversight. Bylaws were also amended to accommodate the changed membership.

AHA launched its newsletter *HospitAlta* in 1962 as a communications tool with its members and undertook labor negotiations in 1964 on their behalf. The association also encouraged its members to undertake accreditation, set up a group insurance plan, planned and delivered education services, and held an annual conference.

The 1970s and 1980s were both a boom time and a disruptive time in terms of labor relations for Alberta hospitals. From 1973 to 1983, the health budget in the province grew from $295 million to $2.2 billion, with salary increases growing as rapidly. There were also three nurses' strikes during this period—in 1977, 1980 and 1982. The provincial government introduced legislation in 1982 taking away the right to strike. Initially, the AHA opposed the bill, then did an about face in a presentation to a standing committee, citing a significant shift in its membership's viewpoint. AHA's credibility suffered a serious setback as a result, since the membership had been opposed to this legislation barely months before.

Labor unrest and ongoing financial cutbacks continued to plague the hospitals in Alberta well into the early 1990s. Then, in 1994, the government divided the province into seventeen regions and replaced 1,200 voluntary trustees with 252 appointed regional health board members. The regional health boards were given the mandate to manage all health services within their regions, including acute care, public health and continuing care. AHA, in response to provincial changes, sent a discussion paper to its membership in 1994, which looked at possible roles and structure for the association in this new regionalized environment.

To recognize the nature of its new membership, which was no longer the hospital in the province, the association changed its name to the Alberta Healthcare Association (AHA). It also sent out an information package to each regional health authority on the services that the newly named association would offer to its membership. The association was downsized with many of its services such as education being eliminated.

With sweeping changes in the health system continuing, the AHA reinvented itself again in 1995. The Provincial Health Authorities of Alberta (PHAA), which was owned and governed by Alberta's health authorities, organized its services on a fee-for-service basis and offered these in three core areas: secretarial support, human resources management and insurance services. PHAA was often involved in reviewing health legislation and served as a link between the authorities and external agencies, as well as coordinating representation on government committees.

Beginning in 2003, PHAA held policy forums with its members to reexamine its role and responsibilities and its health policy priorities. Governance options were proposed and widely discussed. This resulted in further restructuring and the creation of the Health Boards of Alberta (2005), which is the governance voice of the health authorities, and its service arm, HBA Services.

Throughout the course of its history, the Alberta association has been a strong voice in supporting a national health association to represent provincial interests to the federal government. The Alberta Hospital Association was a charter member of the council in 1931 and, over the years, has held the highest elected office in the CHA seven times. In fact, when the council changed its name, it did so under the guidance of Dr. A.C. McGugan, who was president at the time and a strong supporter of the change. Alberta continues today to sit at the CHA board table as a committed and supportive member, which it has been for seventy-five years.

Saskatchewan

The Saskatchewan Hospital Association (SHA) was formed on 18 October 1918, with its first annual meeting taking place in Regina on 8 October 1919, with sixteen hospitals represented. With no records available, it is unclear who the first elected officers were but it seems that the crucial issues for the members were the need for a centralized purchasing system, hospital standards and nurse training. It appears that the association, run on a volunteer basis, held annual meetings each year up to 1931, when the meeting was reduced to a single day due to the depressed state of hospital finances.

The issue of universal hospital insurance was mentioned at the initial meeting in 1918 and again at three more meetings in the mid-1930s. In 1935, the members asked the association to establish a committee to consider possible plans for provincial health insurance and to examine the effect on the province's hospitals.

In 1946, Saskatchewan became the first province in Canada to introduce a universal hospital insurance plan and became the role model for other provinces and the federal government leading up to the introduction of a national plan in 1958. For the most part, throughout the years, association services consisted mainly of the annual meeting, which was planned and delivered by the volunteer association officers. The association was incorporated and hired its first full-time executive director in 1953.

In 1962, with the introduction of medicare legislation, the Saskatchewan physicians withdrew their services and the province became "a battlefield for the whole

North American continent in the struggle of the big medical organizations against socialized medicine" as the *Regina Leader-Post* wrote on 9 July 1962. SHA played a key, but understated role, in the resolution of this crisis. It held meetings with the College of Physicians and Surgeons, the provincial government and several other associations in the province. Although the crisis was not settled until a negotiator from Great Britain was hired, SHA did intervene again to assist its membership in resolving further problems with the physicians.

In 1972, SHA undertook provincewide bargaining on behalf of its members. It introduced a materials management program in 1978 and continued to manage the provincial health care pension plan, which it had launched in 1962. The association also set up group disability income and life insurance plans for its members.

In 1976, the organization changed its name to the Saskatchewan Health-Care Association, a change that expressed the association's desire to provide leadership to the broader health care community in the province. Special care homes were the first nonacute facilities to become members of the newly name association. In 1977, the board expanded the association's mandate to include representation and to promote the development of a more effective, efficient and integrated system of health care delivery.

From 1978 to 1991, the SHA membership expanded rapidly. Members included hospitals, special care homes, home care boards, ambulance boards, housing authorities and other associations. This membership encompassed the association's vision of a continuum of care, represented by one umbrella association to speak on its behalf.

In 1993, after several years of negotiation, SHA merged with two other associations in the province to become the Saskatchewan Association of Health Organizations (SAHO), one of the few associations in the country to build a comprehensive and cohesive membership out of separate health-related organizations. The province also became the first one in Canada to adopt regionalized and integrated health delivery structures under the province's thirty-three boards. In 1997, SAHO made a significant contribution to the Dorsey Commission, which reorganized labor relations in the province to support the regionalized system. The association also set up the first aboriginal action plan to help fill the labor force and prepare aboriginal people for health care careers.

Today, SAHO provides provincewide payroll services for 36,000 employees, human resource services and employee benefit plans, which save Saskatchewan's health system considerable dollars. The association delivers educational events and an annual conference and trade show and advocates on behalf of its membership. In 2003, it launched the journal *HealthMatters*, and is committed to providing opportunities for members to communicate with each other through other means.

Saskatchewan's member association was a founding charter member of the Canadian Hospital Council in 1931 and continued to send its delegates to each general assembly over the years. However, Saskatchewan did not hold the presidency of the association until 1965, when Charles Barton was first elected to this position. It held the presidency in 1972–1974 under Justice E.N. Hughes and in 1981–1982 with the election of A.G. (Bert) Ayers to the chair. In 1996–1997, during one of CHA's most difficult transition periods, Dan de Vlieger, the Saskatchewan representative in the chair, hired an acting president in a telephone interview to manage the association over this critical year. This proved in the long term to be one of the wiser decisions ever made by a CHA board chair. The chair was occupied again in 2005–2006 by Alex Taylor, who was instrumental in urging an amalgamation between CHA and the Canadian Association for Community Care.

Manitoba

In 1921, a group of hospital superintendents and trustees in Manitoba realized the need for an association to deal with matters of common interest and concern, and to speak collectively on these mutual issues. As Dr. Agnew points out, the "strong man in the hospital field in Manitoba during the 1920s and the 1930s was Dr. George F. Stephens" (1974, 83). He was the superintendent of the Winnipeg General Hospital and helped to organize many of the early meetings of the Manitoba Hospital Association (MHA), a truly voluntary association, which had no staff, no office and, like most of the other provincial associations in these early days, no money.

Dr. Stephens attended the founding meeting of the Canadian Hospital Council in 1931 and continued to represent Manitoba at these meetings over the years. He also persuaded the community leaders in Winnipeg to sponsor the first provincewide Blue Cross Plan in Canada.

During the 1930s and 1940s, despite the lack of paid staff, the association was directed for many years by the voluntary work of E. Gagnon of St. Boniface as secretary and Walter Bell of Souris as treasurer. In 1950, as the workload for volunteers increased substantially, the association hired its first full-time paid executive director. In 1954, with the support of a grant from the Kellogg Foundation, the MHA set up an accounting program for small and rural hospitals. Throughout the late 1950s, the association was caught up in the issues arising from the establishment of the provincial hospital insurance plan. During the years from 1950 to 1965, the provincial association was known as the Associated Hospitals of Manitoba.

During the 1960s, the association and its services rapidly expanded as its hospital members placed increasingly more demands on its staff. In 1965, it introduced a computerized management information system and supported accreditation by setting up a program to help hospitals attain this.

Herman (Herm) A. Crewson, who was the executive director of the association for twenty-five years, was a major driving force in implementing computer systems in Manitoba. He played a significant role in CHA activities as well. He was elected to the CHA board in 1971 and served until 1974. In 1976, he served on the Committee on Research and Statistics, urging CHA to remain involved in developing an integrated hospital information system. Manitoba had developed fairly sophisticated productivity and utilization indicators by 1977, which were the backbone of hospital financial analysis and evaluation in Manitoba. Mr. Crewson was especially concerned that a national system be implemented for comparative purposes. He was also a strong supporter of a research department at CHA to provide consulting services to the provincial members, many of which could not afford to do this kind of work themselves.

In 1973, the organization's board and membership structure were changed to accommodate all types of health facilities and program. But hospitals and nursing homes remained the backbone of Manitoba's membership. The new structure also included a new name: Manitoba Health Organizations (MHO), Incorporated, making the organization one of the first provincial associations to move toward the integration of health services across the province. By 1976, the scope and volume of services to its members had grown considerably, especially the accounting and computer services program. In fact, the province was among the leaders in the country in implementing new accounting technology, due mostly to the forward thinking of its executive director, Herm Crewson.

The MHO was also a major contributor to ensuring that CHA's accounting manual was revised. Herm Crewson again played a major role in 1978 through 1979 as chair of the *CHAM* Revisions Committee. He was also CHA's representative in 1979 on the Canadian Institute of Chartered Accountants, which was studying accounting standards for nonprofit organizations.

By the late 1980s, similar to all the provinces in Canada, Manitoba was becoming deeply concerned about the spiralling costs of its health delivery system. Other issues that concerned MHO included the recruitment and retention of physicians in its northern and rural communities, improved coordination of mental health services, maintaining and improving its home care program and reorienting services from facilities into the community.

Similar to many other associations, MHO had to deal with labor negotiations and disruptions in the delivery of health services due to strikes. In 1990, the province's registered nurses went on strike for thirty-one days, the longest strike in Canadian nursing history at the time. By 1991, the province was focusing on health care reform by exploring ways to integrate service delivery and reduce costs in the system. MHO underwent a strategic planning exercise in order to revise its mission and to set a new direction for the organization. In 1992, it played a major role in creating the Northern/Rural Health Advisory Council, which recommended that the province move toward a regional governance model for health service delivery.

By 1993, MHO had reached a crossroad. It was under pressure by its membership, which was now being restructured into regional health authorities. Its members wanted innovation, efficiency and effectiveness in terms of service delivery. That same year, "the MHO board had approved in principle the division of [it] into two organizations, one focused on advocacy and the other on services" (CHA 1993a, 8).

By 1995, the province was well underway to setting up regional health authorities, with full responsibility for the direction, operation, coordination and delivery of health services across the continuum of care. On 1 April 1997, the Regional Health Authorities Act came into effect setting up regional health authority boards across the province. Since the role of the MHO had been to advocate on behalf of the hospitals and nursing homes, as well as other health organizations in the province, what its role might be under the regionalized governance structure in the province was uncertain at this point. It also meant that Manitoba's ongoing membership in CHA was uncertain.

MHO set up a transition task force in 1997 to determine whether the members wanted a provincial association and, if so, would MHO continue or be dissolved.

The task force had indicated that it would recommend representation at the national level in some form and MHO's executive director advised the CHA board of its continuing membership. Because the MHO was an incorporated entity, dissolving its operations was more complicated than in other provinces. Manitoba continued to pay its membership fees well into 1998 despite the uncertainty of its status.

In 1998, MHO was dissolved and the Regional Health Authorities of Manitoba Inc., a nonprofit corporation, was established under the Manitoba Corporations Act. Its membership is made up of the eleven regional health authorities and governed by a board, whose members are appointed by the health authorities. The corporation provides support services to its members, nurse and specialist physician recruitment and is the labor relations secretariat. In 1998, the corporation was approved for membership in the CHA to represent Manitoba.

The Manitoba Hospital Association was one of the founding members of the Canadian Hospital Council in 1931. The province can also celebrate the significant contribution that Dr. George Findlay Stephens made not only to the council in 1931 but as the council's wartime president, which he was from 1939 to 1945. His contribution to the council during the war years helped to ensure that it survived. He also assisted in setting up the first Blue Cross Plan in Canada in 1939 in Manitoba. It was in his honor that the George Findlay Stephens Memorial Award was set up by the hospital council in 1949 to recognize an outstanding leader in the health field. In 1985–1986, Ted Bartman was elected as chair of the Canadian Hospital Association and Edward Bergen was elected to the office in 2000–2001.

Ontario

On 18 February 1902, a group of socially prominent citizens, politicians and physicians gathered at the Queen's Hotel in Toronto to launch the Ontario Hospital Association (OHA). Listed among its goals were increased government aid for hospitals and more cooperation between hospitals in working toward common objectives. The group met again on 6 April 1904 and then this early association disappeared. It would be twenty more years before it reappeared—this time permanently.

On 23 December 1923, a group of concerned hospital workers assembled at the Toronto Academy of Medicine to lay the foundation to set up the Ontario Hospital Association (OHA). One of the leading voices at this assembly was Dr. Fred W. Routley, the Ontario director of the Canadian Red Cross, who was elected as its first secretary-treasurer. The first official act of the association was to prepare a pamphlet to inform hospitals about its activities. The initial meeting, according to the records, was held in Dr. Routley's office.

The first OHA annual general meeting and convention was held in October 1924, with 106 registered participants. The main issue of discussion was the exorbitant cost of hospitalization. Other subjects included cooperative purchasing, record keeping and whether laundry should be done within or outside the hospital. OHA established the Hospital Standardization Committee in 1924 to look at hospital standards, as well as a legislative committee, and continued to deliver an annual convention. By 1929, this convention included commercial exhibits with twenty-one companies participating.

As with the other provincial hospital associations, the depression of the 1930s had a critical impact on hospitals and, in turn, OHA. Dr. Routley continued to conduct OHA business from his Red Cross offices until 1929, when OHA set up its headquarters on Sherbourne Street in Toronto. However, this was shortlived and the office moved back to Red Cross headquarters in 1933, mostly due to the financial restrictions of the depression. Dr. Routley used considerable ingenuity to keep the association and its activities alive through the financially hard times of the 1930s.

In October 1941, to help offset some of the financial shortfalls, OHA introduced the Blue Cross Plan to Ontario. As this plan continued to expand throughout the 1940s, OHA needed more office space to conduct its activities and, at the end of 1945, it purchased its first permanent headquarters on St. Clair Avenue West. The association set up educational programs for its members, entered the areas of public relations and labor relations and played an active role in the political arena on behalf of its members.

At the OHA's 1947 convention, delegates discussed setting up both theoretical and practical institutes as part of an education program that would contribute to the training of hospital personnel. The first institute was held in April 1948 in London with 112 hospital administrators in attendance. This initial educational forum laid the groundwork for one of the association's main activities—to provide educational opportunities for provincial hospital personnel. In 1949, the OHA celebrated its silver jubilee with more than 1,500 delegates in attendance at its convention.

In 1962, the OHA submitted its brief to the Hall Commission and, in 1964, undertook a thorough study of the 914-page report and its implications for the hospitals of Ontario. The Hospital Medical Record Institute was inaugurated in 1963 as a joint venture of the OHA, the Ontario Medical Association and the Ontario Association of Medical Record Librarians. OHA contributed $100,000 toward its first-year operational costs. The association also supported the accreditation of its member hospitals and encouraged hospitals to undertake the process. OHA invited the licensed nursing homes in Ontario to submit applications for membership in the association for the first time in 1964. This was a first step in bring nursing homes into a closer liaison with public hospitals in the province.

In 1972, OHA moved into its new headquarters building in Don Mills, Ontario. By now, both the Ontario Blue Cross Plan and OHA activities had expanded rapidly, particularly, with the addition of labor relations in 1976. Widespread unionization of hospital workers across Ontario's health system and, eventually, the emergence of provincewide bargaining created an urgent need for one strong voice on behalf of the hospitals in arbitration proceedings. Throughout the 1970s, OHA's relationship with the provincial government remained difficult. Although OHA pressed the government to be consulted on matters affecting Ontario hospitals, nevertheless, the government continued to act arbitrarily in setting its policy. The primary dispute between the two groups was funding.

By early 1980, most members indicated that the two main issues where OHA needed to improve were obtaining increased funding from the government and effectively representing their interests to the government. Hospitals were undergoing expansion, mainly, through private-sector and individual donations; technology was exploding across the health delivery system from scanners to nuclear magnetic resonance machines to improved cancer treatments with practically little or no improvement to hospital capital budgets.

OHA set up four major committees in the 1980s to provide future direction for association activities including a trustee committee, government relations and communications committee, research and development committee and a priorities and planning committee. In 1984, OHA adopted a corporate model, with the elected officer of the association becoming the chair of the board and the president becoming the CEO. By the end of the 1980s, the organization was being positioned for change from a service association for its members to an advocacy organization on their behalf.

In 1990, OHA established Investment Management Limited (IML) as a wholly owned subsidiary to handle investment counseling and portfolio management. This service was quickly expanded to hospitals and their foundations, other health care organizations and individuals. When the governance of the Hospitals of Ontario Pension Plan (HOOPP) changed, IML was reengineered into two arms: one to serve HOOPP exclusively and the other to serve OHA and its members.

In 1991, OHA was restructured to make it more responsive to its members' needs. The association would be committed to leadership, advocacy, representation and service in future. Resources were allocated to advocate to government about consent to treatment, labor relations' reform and other issues identified by its membership for action. The education service component continued to deliver comprehensive programs for trustees, hospital staff and the annual convention and exhibition grew to become the largest health care trade show in North America.

In 1997, OHA announced plans to create a balanced scorecard for Ontario hospitals, the first project of its kind in Canada. The project provided a framework of indicators to measure changes in hospital performance and to understand the various trends in utilization and outcomes. OHA released its first hospital-specific report in 1999.

As the new century opened, the CEOs and board chairs of OHA's membership were asked to respond to a satisfaction survey and needs analysis to rate the quality and relevance of OHA's services. Overall, the response was positive that OHA was doing the things the members wanted and that it was heading in the right direction for the future. Most hospital members continued to identify funding and staffing as the main issues of concern for them. Usually, these issues were focused on shortfalls in operating and capital funding, and retention and recruitment of physicians and other staff. In 2004, the OHA celebrated eighty years of service to its membership.

OHA remains the largest member in the CHA federation, and as such, has made some significant contributions to the ongoing survival of the organization over the years. First, along with Dr. Harvey Agnew, Dr. Fred Routley, the first elected president of the Canadian Hospital Council, virtually ran the council in its early years. He was also present at the founding meeting of the council as a representative of the OHA. Over the years, the OHA has been a major proponent of the need for a national voice for hospitals at the federal level and has had eleven representatives elected to CHA's highest office over its seventy-five years. During the critical transition period of 1997, it was a former vice-president from OHA who was hired to be the interim president and whose leadership helped to ensure CHA survived and moved forward into the future.

Quebec

Records indicate that there was a hospital association in the province of Quebec as early as 1907; nothing is known about it however. The Montreal Hospital Council was established in 1926 as an organization of the Montreal hospitals, and according to Dr. Harvey Agnew, other hospitals outside Montreal joined as associate members. Council sessions were bilingual and the council coordinated internal regulations, charges and practices for Montreal hospitals. For many years, it remained the only hospital organization in the province.

Then, in June 1932, the Quebec Conference of the Catholic Hospital Association was set up to represent the interests of the large number of Catholic hospitals in the province. According to Dr. Agnew, "this group was originally known as the Conference of Quebec Hospitals, but a differentiation was necessary when a second conference based in Quebec City was formed in 1935" (1974, 91). These several organizations appear to have existed side by side over the years, representing the various interests of their member hospitals across the province.

In 1947, a Jesuit priest named Father Hector Bertrand set up the Comité des Hôpitaux de la Province de Québec. In consultation with the Canadian Hospital Council, this organization replaced the Montreal Council as CHC's member in 1948. At first, it was a joint committee of the two conferences located in Montreal and Quebec City representing the needs and interests of the Catholic hospitals of these two groups. Then, it expanded to represent almost all Catholic hospitals in Quebec, all Catholic hospitals in New Brunswick and some in Ontario. Its major activity focused on organizing the annual convention, with an exhibition that eventually grew to become the largest of its kind in Canada during the 1950s.

The committee focused on delivering educational programs for French hospital personnel, organizing workshops and ensuring the availability of French materials. In 1955, Father Bertrand launched the journal *L'Hôpital d'aujord'hui*, a French-language journal, and encouraged French hospitals to become accredited. In 1963, Father Bertrand left the committee and, by the early 1960s, the committee's activities, including publishing the journal, were transferred to the Association des Administrateurs d'Hôpitaux de la Province de Québec.

In 1958, the four provincial groups in Quebec, which represented the hospitals of the province, were amalgamated on 7 March as the Association des hôpitaux du Québec (AHQ). Its membership comprised the Montreal hospitals, all English-speaking hospitals in the province, and most of the non-Catholic religious hospitals. However, the Montreal Hospital Council, the Comité des Hôpitaux du Québec, the Quebec Conference of the Catholic Hospital Association and the Montreal Conference of the Catholic Hospital Association would maintain their autonomy in matters pertaining to their respective interests. But the AHQ would deal with those issues that affected all hospitals in the province. At the time, these were the shortage of hospitals and hospital beds, and the high cost of hospital care.

The association's first convention was held in March 1959 with 66 hospitals represented and more than 1,800 in attendance. The key issue at this meeting was the fact that the province had not yet enrolled in the national hospital insurance plan. The first executive director of this association was Dr. Gerald LaSalle. In 1958, the association asked for membership in CHA and became an active member in January 1959. There were now two CHA member organizations in Quebec: AHQ and the Comité des Hôpitaux du Québec.

Many changes were occurring in Quebec during the 1960s. By 1962, the Catholic hospitals had merged to form one organization called the Association des hôpitaux catholiques du Québec (AHCQ). Then, in 1966, the Montreal Hospital Council ceased to exist after forty years of service to its Montreal-based hospitals. Finally, AHQ and the Catholic association merged in 1968 to form the Association des Hôpitaux de la Province du Québec; it became the official Quebec member in CHA.

Throughout the 1960s, AHPQ lobbied strongly on behalf of its members to the provincial ministry of health on matters such as the unionization of hospital staff and the many labor strikes that occurred in Quebec during these years, which consumed much of the association's time and staff resources. The association was also involved in trying to obtain more funding for its member hospitals, delivering services as required by the membership and ensuring their members had a voice in the provincial capital.

The association changed its name again in 1980 to the shorter version of Association des hôpitaux du Québec (AHQ), a name it retained into the early part of the twenty-first century. In 1998, as regionalization was increasingly being implemented throughout the country, Quebec was also going through its own changes.

The issue for the Quebec member has always been an assurance that services delivered by any organization in which it is a member are delivered in the working language of the majority of its members. That is, services must be in the French language and, frequently, Quebec has questioned what it got for its membership dues from the national organization. (Most CHA services were delivered in English, although CHA made every effort to ensure that corporate services were bilingual and all board documents were translated into French, as well as all key policy and position papers during the early years of the 1990s.)

In January 1997, AHQ notified CHA that it would not be able to pay its member dues and would be pulling out of the federation at the end of the year. In 2000, it signed a strategic alliance with CHA and pays an annual fee to sit as a participant-observer. It does not have any input into policy development or a vote on the board.

In 2003, the Quebec government created new health and social services agencies, which set up local networks. These local networks were the end result of the merger of local community health centres (CLSCs), residential and long-term care centres, as well as general and special hospitals. As a result of the restructuring of the health delivery system in Quebec, AHQ closed its operations in 2005 and a new organization, l'Association Québécoise d'établissements de santé et de services sociaux (l'AQESSS), has been set up in the province.

Three representatives from the Montreal Hospital Council, the only hospital association in Quebec at the time, were among the founding members of the Canadian Hospital Council in 1931. Over the years, the province has sent many able representatives to CHA's annual meetings. In fact, the second president of the council from 1935 to 1937 was Walter Chenoweth from Montreal and his is one of the signatures on the CHA charter of 1936. Between 1937 and 1945, Father Georges Verreault and Dr. George F. Stephens were elected presidents of the council. Between 1955 and 1992, Quebec held the highest elected office at CHA another seven times.

New Brunswick

The first meeting of the New Brunswick Hospital Association was held in 1929, although hospital superintendents at the time had originally agreed to join with Nova Scotia and Prince Edward Island to form a hospital association for all three provinces. The original goals of this first association were to serve as a means of intercommunication for the hospitals of New Brunswick; to improve hospital standards; and to consider, discuss and initiate legislative measures affecting hospitals.

In 1942, the association, along with the Nova Scotia and Prince Edward Island organization, joined together to create the Maritime Hospital Association, and there was a New Brunswick sector of the Maritime Hospital Service Association (Blue Cross) between 1946 and 1956. In the late 1940s, the NBHA, working with the provincial health department, developed standardized accounting practices for the province's hospitals.

With the introduction of the national hospital insurance plan in 1958, the New Brunswick Hospital Association was reborn. An Act to Incorporate the New Brunswick Hospital Association was passed in 1961 and Judge Chaiker Abbis, a charter member of the association, also served as its first board chair.

The association hired its first full-time executive director in 1959 and created a secretarial position shortly thereafter. As the association became more involved in developing education programs and in labor relations for its member hospitals, new staff were hired throughout the 1970s. In 1985, a group purchasing coordinator and an assistant executive director were hired to carry the additional workload.

In 1992, the health minister created regionalized hospital governance structures across New Brunswick and the association's membership dropped from sixty-one hospitals to nine regional hospital corporations. The government also centralized labor relations and the hospital corporations took over the group purchasing function and education services, so that only a splinter hospital association remained by the mid-1990s.

In 1995, the association was renamed the New Brunswick Healthcare Association. Its focus changed from providing services to its members to research and policy development, issues management, and advocacy and representation to the provincial government on behalf of its membership.

In 2002, the hospital corporations were dissolved in favor of setting up regional health authorities with the intent of integrating other health services such as mental and public health under one umbrella. The regional health authority chief executive officers (CEOs) are hired by the deputy minister of health and report to this position. In the shifting health structure in New Brunswick, the provincial association now concentrates its efforts on providing the regional health authorities with a vehicle to improve health care through health policy development.

The New Brunswick Hospital Association was among the charter members at the founding of the Canadian Hospital Council in 1931 and has been a strong and committed supporter over the years; it has held the highest elected office on four separate occasions. In 1957–1959, Dr. D.F.W. Porter was elected president of CHA. In 1961, Judge Chaiker Abbis was appointed to the CHA board and elected president between 1966 and 1968. In 1978–1979, William A. Kilpatrick, chair of the board, was most influential in persuading board members that CHA needed to relocate its headquarters in Ottawa and, in 1992–1993, Michel C. Leger was elected chair of the board from the province.

Nova Scotia

The first annual meeting of the Hospital Association of Nova Scotia and Prince Edward Island was held in New Glasgow on 21 August 1929 and formally adopted a constitution.[6] This early joint association was to develop intercommunications and cooperation between the hospitals of the two provinces, to improve standards of hospital care and to stimulate hospital development. The delegates also decided to approach the NBHA with the concept of amalgamating the two associations to form a single organization.

By 1942, the hospitals of the three provinces agreed to set up the Maritime Hospital Association, which held its first annual meeting in Kentville, Nova Scotia, on 29-30 June 1943. This organization continued into the mid-1970s, even as each province established its own separate and independent association.

In 1960, the Nova Scotia Hospital Association was incorporated under a special act. It was to fulfill two roles: 1) to serve as an information clearinghouse for members and to facilitate a common voice in representing their interests to government (advocacy) and 2) to administer a pension plan and other group life benefits for hospital employees. It held its first annual meeting—independent of the Maritime association—in 1964 and established a permanent office in Halifax in 1965.

The association set up the Hospitals of Nova Scotia Pension Plan in 1961, which is one of the largest plans in Atlantic Canada today. A group life insurance plan was implemented in 1967. In 1971, the association established a third primary role, the provision of labor relations services. Collective bargaining has remained a backbone of the association's human resources service, supporting a total of 127 collective agreements today.

In 1974, the association's board recognized the need to broaden its membership base to represent the health system and changed its name accordingly to the Nova Scotia Association of Health Organizations (NSAHO). This change opened up the association to organizations spanning the entire continuum of care and changed the future and direction of the association.

In 1978, NSAHO established a group purchasing service, funded almost entirely from member fees. In 1979, the association set up an education service for its members which it continues to deliver today through customized services targeted to the specific needs of its members. Throughout these years, the association maintained its fundamental role of advocacy on behalf of its members, supported by research and policy development.

On 1 April 1997, regional health boards assumed responsibility for the delivery of certain primary care services in Nova Scotia, specifically drug dependency and public health. With the transfer of governance from hospital boards to regional health boards, eight large multi-site organizations replaced the hospitals which had traditionally made up NSAHO's largest membership. The association and the acute care sector established a service review process to identify current and future needs for shared provincial programs and to assess the relevance and effectiveness of the association in meeting these needs. The review determined that NSAHO had a role to play within the reformed health system.

Again, in 1999, following a comprehensive review of the province's regionalized health system, the government announced the transfer for governance of the regional health boards to the provincial health department. On 1 January 2001, the Health Authorities Act came into effect; it replaced the four regional boards with nine district health authorities to bring decision-making closer to the community. To accommodate the shift, the association amended its bylaws again.

In its long history, Nova Scotia was a charter member (with Prince Edward Island) of CHA and two individuals from the province are listed among the founding delegates. Over CHA's seventy-five-year history, representatives from Nova Scotia have held the highest elected office three times. In 1974–1975, Dr. L.P. Chiasson became president of the association; 1988–1989, Margaret (Peggy) Davison was elected as chair. In 2006, this position was held by Garnet Burns.

Prince Edward Island

In the late 1920s, the hospitals in Prince Edward Island joined with those of Nova Scotia to form their own association. With the assistance of Dr. Harvey Agnew of the CMA Department of Hospital Service, they set up the Hospital Association of

Nova Scotia and Prince Edward Island in 1929. (New Brunswick decided at the last minute to form their own separate organization, although they had originally indicated their interest in joining with the other two provinces.) The Catholic hospitals already belonged to the Maritime Conference of the Catholic Hospital Association, so there was a representative group already in existence at the time.

In 1942, the Maritime Hospital Association (MHA) was formed, which included both the New Brunswick Hospital Association and the association for Nova Scotia and Prince Edward Island. This association, in turn, set up the Maritime Hospital Service Association, which was essentially the Blue Cross organization in the province. For the next ten years, the province's hospitals participated in conferences, annual meetings and joint education initiatives. Trustees served on the association board and hospital administrators were very active on MHA committees. But travel costs and time, including ferry schedules, were often limiting factors for the province's hospitals and most activities centred around two meetings per year.

By the 1950s, all the public general and special hospitals in all three provinces were members of this successful association. Then, in 1958, with the passage of the Hospital Insurance and Diagnostic Services (HIDS) Act, and with each province implementing its own hospital insurance program, the Maritime Hospital Association broke up and was dissolved by 1962. Briefly, Prince Edward Island and New Brunswick formed a joint association as a federated member of CHA. This association lasted until 1960 and carried on activities similar to the MHA

On 16 March 1961, an Act to Incorporate the Hospital Association of Prince Edward Island was proclaimed by the Lieutenant Governor in Council. The objectives of this organization included liaison with the provincial government and the Hospital Services Commission. The association administered the pension plan and group life, sickness and accident insurance, as well as other welfare plans for hospital employees. Another key objective was to develop and provide education programs for hospital board members and staff either independently or in association with other organizations. The act of incorporation established nine comprehensive and detailed objectives for the association but made no provision for funding to hire staff or set up headquarters to carry out these objectives.

For the first few years, the major emphasis was on the administration of the insurance and pension plans, with work carried out primarily by staff in hospitals. With limited funding, a part-time executive director was hired and casual secretarial services were set up. However, there was no permanent headquarters and the office was based in the Prince Edward Island Hospital. The association made formal application to the CHA to become a member in 1962, when the Maritime Hospital Association formally withdrew its membership effective at the end of that year. Prince Edward Island paid its first membership fees in January 1963 and its membership was ratified at the annual assembly meeting in May. Maintaining contact with CHA was considered paramount and many hospital trustees served on its board over the next twenty years.

After Neil MacLean retired, Edward Porter took over the part-time role of secretary (today's CEO) and hospital staff participation began to grow. During the 1960s and 1970s, the single biggest event of the year was the annual meeting, which was usually held in a rural location in May or June and featured a lobster dinner. The member base in the association increased, when membership was extended to include not only the acute care hospitals but also the provincial government psychiatric and rehabilitation facilities. Hospital auxiliaries could become affiliate members as well. Between 1961 and 1980, board and staff education became major association services and generated some increase in revenues and staff resources.

In 1980, the association was having considerable difficulty continuing to function. Representatives from CHA, headed by the chair Sister Lucy Power, met with the association president Dr. Gustave Gingras. The CHA delegates were asked to approach the provincial health minister to seek his support for a role study of the association. The minister agreed to fund the study and indicated that he favored a strong, independent hospital association for Prince Edward Island.

Following the association role study, additional funding was made available to the province's hospitals to support the association. By the early 1980s, the association had a full-time executive director, its own separate office space and had set up full-time support services.

In the fall of 1984, Robert Hamilton succeeded Edward Porter as executive director, who retired due to ill health. During Mr. Hamilton's tenure, the association focused on group purchasing services after the first committee meeting was held in October 1984. In 1990, the association created a labor relations specialist role, a position held by Frank Gillan until May 1994, when he became executive director.

In August 1991, Carol Gabanna began her first term as executive director, a position she held until May 1994. In April 1995, the provincial government decided to create a separate crown corporation, called Human Resource Management Services Inc., to take over all provincial health, education and general government negotiations and related labor issues. The association's labor relations were officially transferred to the corporation in May 1995. At the same time, Carol Cabana was rehired as the executive director and remained in the position until March 1999.

Between 1975 and 1995, the hospital association was intimately involved in hospital labor negotiations through the Health Negotiating Agency, a government organization with board and administration representatives appointed by the association, Treasury Board and the Hospital and Health Services Commission. During this same period, the association's board evolved from trustee members only to include hospital administrators. In 1994, the association's primary role of administering pension and insurance plans was transferred to a joint union-management committee, coordinated by the Department of Health and Social Services.

When regional health authorities were set up in 1993-1994, the hospital association was dissolved and its original Act of Incorporation rescinded. It was replaced immediately by the Health Association of PEI, created under the Companies Act, in which the health regions became independent shareholders of the corporation. The five health authorities held varying numbers of shares, depending on their size, which were used to vote on key issues.

In 1993, the reconfigured association undertook the primary role of educating its members about the Policy Governance™ model, which had been mandated by the Health and Community Services Agency responsible for regionalization. Executive Director Carol Gabanna became an expert on this form of board governance and worked diligently with the regional boards to establish this approach. She eventually coauthored a book on the subject.

By 1995, the association's advocacy role had been significantly reduced and it functioned primarily as a service organization for the health regions. The association focused on providing group purchasing services, board education and coordinating meetings of the board, CEOs and regional committees. With the loss of advocacy and little authority to develop policy, the regional trustees resigned their positions in June 1996 and were replaced by regional CEOs on the association's board.

Throughout the late 1990s, the association struggled to define its role in the restructured provincial health system and, with the departure of Carol Cabana as executive director in 1998, the regional CEOs assumed the responsibility for ensuring the continuation of the association. From 1999 to 2002, they acted as part-time volunteer executive directors in order to provide administration and supervision, and maintain membership in CHA.

In September 2002, Kenneth Ezeard became the part-time contract executive director on his retirement as CEO of the West Prince Health Region in June. (He continues in this role today.) The association became responsible for risk management and patient safety and hired a part-time lawyer under a joint contract between the association, the Department of Health and Social Services and Provincial Treasury. By April 2005, the association once again faced a reevaluation of its role and membership when the government decided to eliminate the health regions effective January 2006.

Prince Edward Island was a founding member of the Canadian Hospital Council in 1931 (along with Nova Scotia) and has maintained significant ties with the national association over the course of its history. Although one of the smallest members of the CHA federation, Prince Edward Island has nevertheless made big contributions to CHA. In 1984-1985, Dr. Gustave Gingras was elected as chair and was instrumental in reviewing CHA's bylaws and writing new ones to meet the changing needs of the membership. (*See* chapter 7.) The association holds the distinction today of having appointed or elected one of the longest serving board members in CHA's recent history. Kenneth Ezeard has served on CHA's board on different committees since 1991 and, in 2001–2002, he was elected as chair. (*See also* chapter 7 and list of contributors for more details.) Despite the many changes that have occurred over the years, the Health Association of PEI has always valued its role as part of CHA and looks forward to continuing in the federation for the next seventy-five years.

Newfoundland and Labrador

Prior to 1962, a few of the larger general hospitals in Newfoundland were members of the Martime Hospital Association. There had never been a hospital association in the province as most of them were either under the authority of government or the Grenfell Association. However, in response to a growing need for representation, education programs and other services, the Newfoundland Hospital Association was established in 1962.

To understand the circumstances prior to its creation, it is necessary to look briefly at what had happened beforehand in the country. In 1958, universal hospital insurance had been introduced but was being implemented somewhat differently in each province. By 1961, the hospitals in New Brunswick, Nova Scotia and Prince Edward Island wanted their own individual provincial hospital associations, which would represent their interests to their provincial health departments. Although all the hospitals maintained membership in the Maritime Hospital Association, which had three representative members in CHA, the three provinces had set up their own hospital associations by 1962 and wanted individual representation in CHA. This would therefore leave Newfoundland without a voice.

Two organizational meetings of hospital administrators were held in April and May 1962 to discuss how to set up the association. In May, the Newfoundland Hospital Association was officially established, a temporary committee was appointed to draft the bylaws, to explore financial implications for the new organization and to act as the executive until elections could be held. Money was a major issue for the fledgling association, and the Maritime Hospital Association covered the cost of sending a Newfoundland delegate to the November 1962 CHA meeting. The association's first general meeting was held in April 1963 with seven hospitals as members. The delegates also elected a slate of officers, with Sister Mary Fabian of St. Clare's Mercy Hospital becoming the association secretary, a voluntary position.

In 1964, the association appointed its first representative to the CHA board and also held its first educational institute. Member education was considered a high priority, along with continuing education for hospital personnel, the need to lobby for improved salaries and to set up a pension plan for nongovernment health institutions, as well as to improve standards of care. Because there were no paid staff, association work evolved very slowly.

In March 1966, the Newfoundland Hospital Association Act was proclaimed and, in 1967, the association opened a permanent office in St. John's and hired its first executive director, Ralph D. Moore. The association grew rapidly over the 1970s—it established a group purchasing program in 1972—and, by 1976, all hospitals in the province were members. In that same year, Robin J. Burnell became its executive director.

By the 1980s, most provincial governments were reviewing the costs of delivering health services and exploring other options such as integration of services, the closure of hospitals and the establishment of regional health boards. In 1988, the Newfoundland Hospital Association Act was repealed and the Newfoundland Hospital and Nursing Home Association Act was declared to reflect the current role of the association.

Between 1991 and 1992, the provincial health department established regional community health boards across Newfoundland and Labrador. Then, in 1993, the minister of health announced the establishment of a regional health system in the province with thirteen regional boards being set up. In turn, the Newfoundland and Labrador Health Care Association changed its structure to accommodate this shift to regional governance and the chairs of the regional health institution boards became the members of the provincial health association.

Restructuring and repositioning of the provincial health delivery system continued into the early part of the twenty-first century. In 2004, the minister of health announced that there would be four regional integrated health boards in the province. Again, the provincial association reorganized itself to accommodate the new governance structures in the province and is now called the Newfoundland and Labrador Health Boards Association to reflect its membership.

Throughout these changes and shifts, the provincial association has remained committed to a national health association and has been a strong voice at the CHA board table. In 1997–1998, John Baker, who was Newfoundland's member on the CHA board, became chair of the association, only the second time that Newfoundland and Labrador have held this position. Between 1980–1981, Sister Mary Lucy Power (now Dobbin) was the first person from Newfoundland and Labrador to become CHA's chair and the first woman to be elected to the office.

Northwest Territories

In 1965, there were several small hospitals scattered across this large territory; some of the hospitals were owned and operated by church and community groups, and some by the federal government. Two hospital administrators—Reverend Ken Gaetz of Hay River and Peter Verhesen of Fort Smith—recognizing the fragmented nature of the hospitals across the territory, explored how they might organize a hospital association similar to those in the provinces.

With the expertise of the then executive director Murray W. Ross of the Alberta Hospital Association, who had also been a former assistant executive director of CHA, these two men organized a meeting on 25 November 1965 in Hay River. This founding meeting established the Northwest Territories Hospital Association (NWTHA) as an independent, nonprofit organization.[7] One of the association's first objectives was to seek affiliation with CHA. This would enable the territory's hospitals to present a united front when dealing with the federal government and other agencies. Rev. Gaetz was elected its first president and Peter Verhesen became the secretary-treasurer. Both these men continued to provide strong leadership for the association over the next fifteen years.

In 1969, Peter Verhesen became the executive director and editor of the newsletter, *The Capsule*. The association set up education programs, organized an annual general meeting to keep hospitals informed about technological advances and lobbied for the insurance services board to be transferred to the territories from the federal government in the early 1970s.

By the late 1970s, all the territories' hospitals were members of the association and associate membership was granted to Churchill Health Centre in Manitoba. This hospital had been providing hospital and medical services to the Central Arctic population for many years, so it was logical for them to become a member in the NWTHA.

With the support of the provincial members in British Columbia and Alberta, the association formally requested a seat on the CHA's board of directors at the 1976 annual convention. Although the request was denied, CHA did extend an invitation for an association representative to attend CHA board meetings as a nonvoting member later that year. In 1978, the territorial association again applied for membership and this time it was successful. In 1979, Rev. Gaetz became the voting member from the Northwest Territories on CHA's board.

In the early 1980s, the association undertook the groundwork for an employee relations program, the responsibility for which was then turned over to the insurance services board. The association also launched an energy conservation program for its members during this time. Because many of the association activities were being handled by volunteers, by the mid-1980s, the workload was becoming too much for them to complete. In the spring of 1987, the board decided to hire an executive director on a part-time basis to manage the association's activities.

At the same time, the health delivery system in the Northwest Territories was being reorganized under regional health boards. The federal government also transferred all its health care management responsibilities to the territorial department of health in August 1988. The territorial hospital association lobbied the department of health to maintain autonomous regional health boards and represented their interests to government, as well as those of the hospital boards.

By the late 1980s, the long-term care facilities within many of the regional health boards expressed an interest in belonging to the association but were not comfortable with the hospital label. In 1990, the membership of the association unanimously voted to change the association's name to the Northwest Territories Health Care Association. However, many of the health and social services boards, as they were called, were being turned over to communities under the community empowerment initiative, often to local band councils. Then, in 2002, all community health boards were brought under the territorial health department's authority.

The association continued to exist until 2001, when it was disbanded. Today, the Northwest Territories Department of Health and Social Services pays an annual fee to CHA and appoints a voting member to CHA's board of directors.

Yukon

The Yukon Territory has never had a territorial hospital association. For most of its history, its health and social services have been delivered by the federal government. By the late 1990s, the federal government was handing over these services to the territorial government. In 1999, the territorial health department set up the Yukon Hospital Corporation, which owns and operates the hospital in Whitehorse, and the First Nations Health Committee which governs the First Nations health program. In 1999, the Yukon Hospital Corporation applied for membership in the CHA and was accepted as the Yukon member at the annual meeting that same year.

Nunavut

On 1 April 2000, Nunavut was established by the federal government as an independent territory. All existing health and social services boards were integrated into the territorial health department. The Department of Health and Social Services operates all health and outpatient centres, health clinics and the Baffin Regional Hospital in Iqaluit. The territory requested membership on CHA's board and was elected in June 2000. The department appoints a voting member to the CHA board and pays annual dues.

Summary

The hospital council determined from its establishment that its members would be the provincial and regional hospital associations, as well as the Catholic conferences and the Canadian Medical Association. Over the years, this membership changed to the provincial and territorial health and hospital organizations exclusively. These thirteen members make up the CHA federation today.

Endnotes

1. Only the issues from 1937 to 1949 can still be found in the CHA archives at 17 York Street. The board stopped publishing detailed reports in 1953 due to costs.

2. The audited financial statements for the year ending 31 December 1944 show contributions from the provincial associations of $6,500 in total. The council's share of the profit from the journal that year was $6,752 and the journal's reserve fund was listed at $4,500.

3. Not all hospitals in the province were necessarily members of the provincial hospital association. There was still a large contingent of federally owned hospitals, as well as mental and TB hospitals owned and operated by the province, and private hospitals, which were not members of a provincial hospital association despite CHA's urging that all hospitals in every province should join its active member.

4. The following were listed in the 1975 bylaw revisions as active members in good standing, along with the number of votes to which they were entitled: British Columbia Health Association (6 votes), Alberta Hospital Association (5 votes), Saskatchewan Hospital Association (4 votes), Manitoba Health Organizations, Inc. (4 votes), Ontario Hospital Association (14 votes), Association des Hôpitaux de la Province du Québec (11 votes), New Brunswick Hospital Association (3 votes), Nova Scotia Association of Health Organizations (3 votes), Hospital Association of Prince Edward Island (1 vote), Newfoundland Hospital Association (2 votes), Northwest Territories Hospital Association (1 vote), Canadian Medical Association (1 vote), American Hospital Association (1 vote) and the Catholic Hospital Association of Canada (3 votes) (CHA 1975a, 3–4).

5. Murray Ross was hired for this full-time position from the Canadian Hospital Association, where he had held the position of Assistant Executive Secretary for almost 10 years. He was a past president of the AHA and a former trustee and member of the executive of the Alberta Blue Cross Plan.

6. The organizing meeting was actually held in Truro on 15 March 1929 with delegates from New Brunswick in attendance but they decided at the last minute to form their own separate association.

7. Along with representatives from the South Mackenzie hospitals (Rev. Gaetz and Peter Verhesen), there were representatives from the Catholic owned and operated hospitals in Fort Simpson, Fort Rae, Fort Resolution and Fort Smith, the Pentecostal hospital at Hay River and the community hospital in Yellowknife. Murray Ross attended the meeting along with Assistant Executive Director George McCracken of CHA and the executive secretary of the Territorial Hospital Insurance Service.

7

THE ELECTED OFFICERS (PRESIDENTS AND CHAIRS)

"One cannot complete a term as [chair] of an association such as ours without a feeling . . . of very real gratitude and justifiable pride. . . . without having an ingrained sense of loyalty. . . . I have such gratitude—I have such pride—I have such loyalty."

(PORTER 1959, 102)

Over its long history, the Canadian Healthcare Association has been blessed with an outstanding group of dedicated board members who have contributed substantially to the association's progress and success. It is unfortunate that there is not enough space in this book to list the hundreds of individuals who have served on CHA's boards over the past seventy-five years. For this reason, this chapter is limited to describing briefly those who served as either the president or as chairman of the board. Each description gives a brief resume of their career, their achievements during their term and lists any honors that were bestowed on them as a result of their service to CHA. In reviewing the list of the fifty-two people who have held the office of president or chair, every provincial member organization has occupied this position over CHA's seventy-five-year history.[1] (Appendix 3 provides a complete list of the presidents/chairs.)

The Council Presidents, 1931 to 1952

Frederick William Routley, MD, 1931–1935

Dr. Fred W. Routley was among the group of farsighted men and women who established the Canadian Hospital Council in 1931. He was also one of the original members of the advisory committee that was set up in 1927 to determine the activities of the new hospital department at the CMA. He was elected as the council's first president for two consecutive two-year terms. On his departure as president, he was named honorary vice-president in 1935, a position he held until 1944. He worked very closely with Dr. Agnew in criss-crossing Canada during the early days of the council to persuade hospital superintendents and, in turn, the provincial associations and Catholic conferences of the benefits of the council. He assisted Dr. Agnew in ensuring that the council survived in its early days.

In the founding years of the council, the role of president, although voluntary, was a far more influential and administrative position than that of the chair today. Dr. Routley and members of the Executive Committee were entirely responsible for its day-to-day operations and determined exactly what the council would do. Working closely with the other members of the Executive Committee, Dr. Routley ensured that the decisions of the general assembly were carried out, set the agenda and even determined guest speakers for the biennial meetings. He was also one of the three signing members of the council's original letters patent granted in 1936.

Throughout his long career, Dr. Routley was associated with the Canadian Red Cross Society for twenty-seven years, the last eleven as its national commissioner. He also served as secretary-treasurer of the Ontario Hospital Association from its inception in 1924 until his death. In 1950, Dr. Fred Routley was honored for his service to the hospitals of Canada when he was awarded the George Findlay Stephens Memorial Award as its second recipient. Dr. Routley died on 11 February 1951 after a long service to the hospitals of Canada.

Walter Richard Chenoweth, 1935–1937

The council's second president, W.R. Chenoweth, was the superintendent of the Royal Victoria Hospital in Montreal, a position he had held since 1927. He was also a past president of the Montreal Hospital Council. During his term, he spearheaded a resolution through the assembly that exempted all public hospitals from the Unemployment and Social Insurance Act, which would have added an additional financial burden to them during the depression years. He also pointed out to members the precarious financial situation of the council and suggested that it was time to put it on a more solid financial basis if it was to have any degree of stability. During his term, the council was officially incorporated under letters patent, which ensured more permanency for the organization, as well as protecting it legally when the council took over the editorial operation of *Canadian Hospital*, which became the council's official journal. Following his retirement, Mr. Chenoweth regularly contributed articles to the journal.

Father Georges Verreault, 1937–1938

At the time of his election, the Reverend Verreault was the auditor at the Ottawa General Hospital. However, he served as president for only one year, as he was relocated to Rome by his order, Les Missionaires Oblats de Marie Immaculée, to standardize the accounting system of the twenty-five provinces or districts of the order throughout the world. One of his early efforts was to write to the various provincial member associations and conferences, outlining the proposed budget for the council ($6,350) and the desirability of increasing its funding. His major achievement was the preparation of accounting standards for Canadian hospitals. He was instrumental in writing the standards for the original edition of the *Canadian Hospital Accounting Manual* as chairman of the standing Committee on Accounting. These standards were used extensively by the federal health department when developing accountability measures for the national hospital insurance program.

George Findlay Stephens, MD, 1938–1945

Dr. Stephens was elected as one of the initial officers of the Executive Committee of the council in 1931. He took over the presidency of the council on the departure of Father Verreault in 1938 and was reelected to this position in 1939, 1941, 1943 and again in 1945. From 1945 to 1947, he served as honorary vice-president and continued as the chair of the standing Committee on Health Insurance, a position he held for several years while active on the council executive. He holds the distinction of being elected to the position of president in 1939 as the representative from Manitoba and as a representative from Quebec for his next two terms.

Dr. Stephens graduated from McGill University in 1907, pursued postgraduate studies in Montreal, London, Munich and Berlin and then served in the Canadian Expeditionary Force from 1915 to 1919. He became superintendent of the Winnipeg General Hospital in 1920. Elected president of the American Hospital Association from 1932 to 1933, he was the first Canadian to hold this office. He was a charter fellow of the American College of Hospital Administrators and a past president of the Manitoba Hospital Association. Through his efforts, Manitoba was the first province in Canada to implement a Blue Cross Plan in 1939. Dr. Stephens returned to Montreal in 1940 to become the administrator of the Royal Victoria Hospital at a time when the hospital was facing serious difficulties in reorganization and reconstruction.

At the 1941 general assembly, Dr. Stephens talked about some of the achievements of the council, most notably sales tax and custom duty exemptions for hospitals and the cooperation of the hospitals of Canada with the federal government in the war effort. This latter achievement was mainly due to the many trips he personally took to Ottawa to meet with the various federal officials to determine what was needed from Canada's hospitals in the war effort and to ensure that the federal government was aware of the hardships the war was causing for Canada's hospitals.

In his book, Dr. Agnew wrote that "[t]he strain of carrying on the work of the national council as well as of directing his own hospital's undertakings eventually took its toll. In 1945 [Dr. Stephens] suffered a cerebral thrombosis from which he never fully recovered" (1974, 72). He died in 1947, although he had tried to carry on his duties to the end. Dr. Agnew also lamented the fact that Dr. Stephens' services were not recognized by the Canadian government "when the extensive list of civilian recipients of the Order of the British Empire was announced after the second world war" (Ibid.). The American Hospital Association recognized his wartime services by awarding him its much-coveted Award of Merit in 1946.

The Canadian Hospital Council set up an award in his honor in 1949. The George Findlay Stephens Memorial Award was presented annually for "noteworthy service in the realm of hospital administration" to an outstanding leader in Canada's hospital system. (*See* chapter 5 for more details on the award.)

Arthur J. Swanson, 1945–1949

Mr. Swanson not only served two terms as president of the association with his election in 1945, and again in 1947, but returned in 1953 as a member of the board. During his term, the council supported setting up women's aid groups in every public hospital in 1945 and the inauguration of a two-year graduate course in hospital administration at the University of Toronto in 1947. The council also severed its ties with the CMA to become an independent organization and moved into its own new and bigger headquarters in Toronto.

As president, he was involved in many discussions with federal officials, particularly with federal Health and Welfare Minister Paul Martin (senior) about national health insurance. While Mr. Swanson held office, the question of the council restructuring into an association was raised. The council was overwhelmed by the many demands on its staff who were asked to deal with issues from the operation of blood banks in hospitals, to payment of care for indigents, to the best way to clean a floor.

Arthur Swanson had a long involvement with the Canadian Hospital Council. He was the administrator of the Toronto Western Hospital for many years and a member of OHA as well. He was also instrumental in bringing Blue Cross to Ontario. In 1954, he received the George Findlay Stephens Memorial Award in recognition of his contribution to hospital administration.

R. Fraser Armstrong, 1949–1951

Fraser Armstrong was a founding member of the Canadian Hospital Council in 1931 and active in the affairs of the association for over twenty years. He was a member of the committee that recommended the council assume the editorial direction of the journal, *Canadian Hospital*, and adopt it as the council's official organ. He served on the editorial board of the journal for several years and was the author of many articles. For many years, he was the superintendent of the Kingston General Hospital and served a term as president of OHA.

During his tenure as president, Dr. Agnew submitted his resignation as executive secretary of the council. Mr. Armstrong was very involved in defining the criteria to be used to hire a new person in the position, an activity that no other previous president had ever undertaken in the council's history. With the hiring of Dr. Agnew's successor, the role of president of the council changed to one of presiding over a board of directors and dealt with policy and board issues, leaving operational matters to the executive director. Under his leadership, the council protested the federal government's intention to include the hospitals of Canada in unemployment coverage and was successful in persuading the government to exclude hospitals. Mr. Armstrong received the George Findlay Stephens Award in 1957.

Owen C. Trainor, MD, 1951–1953

During his term as president, Dr. Trainor represented the council at meetings with the Canadian Medical Association and the Royal College of Physicians and Surgeons to discuss establishing a Canadian Committee on Hospital Accreditation. He also presided over the council's name change to the Canadian Hospital

Association. With the resignation of Dr. Bradley as executive director, he oversaw the hiring of Dr. Swanson in the position.

Dr. Trainor, a native of Moncton, New Brunswick, moved to Winnipeg early in his career. He did much to strengthen the Manitoba Hospital Association and served as its president in 1945. He was one of the originators of the Western Canada Institute for Hospital Administrators and Trustees in 1946. Dr. Trainor was a member of the CHA board for ten years. He was elected to the House of Commons in 1953 and served as a member until his death in 1956.

The Association Presidents, 1953 to 1977

Angus C. McGugan, MD, 1953–1955

At the time of his presidency, Dr. McGugan was superintendent of the University of Alberta Hospital, Edmonton, a position he held for seventeen years. An ardent nationalist, in his presidential address in 1955, he forcefully made the point ". . . that if this body [CHA] is to become an Association of the hospitals of Canada in fact, as it is in name, you and I and every member of the hospital family in Canada, must cease to think, feel and act in terms of sectionalism, municipalism and provincialism and think, feel and act as Canadians" (1955, 33).

Dr. McGugan was the first Albertan to receive the Stephens Award in 1959. He was also a talented writer who contributed outstanding articles to *Canadian Hospital*, one in which he describes ". . . [t]he province of Quebec [as] the cradle of hospitalization on the North American continent" (1960, 33). During his distinguished career, he was assistant deputy health minister in Alberta and the first president of Alberta Blue Cross.

J. Gilbert Turner, MD, 1955–1957

Dr. Gilbert Turner was the executive director of the Royal Victoria Hospital in Montreal, when he was elected president of CHA, and a leading figure on the Quebec hospital scene. He was instrumental in the formation of the Association des hôpitaux du Québec and announced its creation at the 1957 CHA biennial meeting. He had joined CHA's board in 1951 and was elected president in 1955.

Dr. Turner was a frequent participant in hospital meetings in Canada and the United States and contributed extensively to the hospital literature, especially to

Canadian Hospital. He stressed the need for a strong national association, particularly at a time when the federal government was considering the introduction of national hospital insurance.

Dr. Turner supported the need for a strong voice in the hospital accreditation program and was, in fact, an eloquent champion of it. In 1962, in discussing the lack of participation of smaller hospitals, he questioned how Canadian hospitals could possibly say that they are giving the best in patient care when more than fifty percent of hospitals at the time had not been accredited. Dr. Turner received the George Findlay Stephens Award in 1963.

Donald F. W. Porter, MD, 1957–1959

Dr. Porter was a native of New Brunswick and was appointed executive director of the Moncton Hospital in 1949. He spearheaded the planning of the new Moncton Hospital which opened in 1953. Dr. Porter became a director of CHA in 1951. He presided over the general assembly in May 1959, which agreed that CHA would hold annual meetings of the general assembly from 1960 onward. He believed strongly that all the hospitals of Canada should be united in their support of their provincial associations. To be effective, all hospitals should be members of their provincial or regional associations.

Stanley W. Martin, 1959–1961

Stan Martin was one of the leading lights in the Ontario hospital field. In 1951, he was appointed associate executive secretary-treasurer and comptroller of the Ontario Hospital Association and became its executive director in 1956, a position he held for ten years. Mr. Martin was the first chief executive officer of a provincial hospital association to become CHA's president.

He believed in a strong national association that would put forward the interests of hospitals to the federal government. In order to do so, he promoted the need for CHA to present adequate and accurate statistical data to support its position on issues. He was also a strong advocate for educated and well-trained hospital workers and urged CHA to increase its educational activities. Because he encouraged these activities, he suggested that the association create a special committee on association development to look into these areas.

Judge Nelles V. Buchanan, 1961–1963

Judge Buchanan had been actively involved in the hospital field in Alberta since the 1920s and was also well known at the national and international level. As a trustee on many boards, and the first Canadian to be given an honorary fellowship in the American College of Hospital Administrators, he was described by Stan Martin as an outspoken advocate of the independence of trustees and the autonomy of hospitals. He was president of the Alberta Hospital Association for several years and worked actively in Alberta Blue Cross. In 1965, Judge Buchanan received the George Findlay Stephens Award.

Arthur H. Westbury, 1963–1965

Arthur Westbury was executive director of the Montreal General Hospital when elected president of CHA. His experience in hospital administration extended over a period of forty-one years, thirty-three of which were spent at the Montreal General Hospital; he was named its executive director in 1953 and retired in 1966. Mr. Westbury also served as treasurer and member of the executive of the Association des Hôpitaux de la Province du Québec.

In his report to the 1964 CHA assembly, Mr. Westbury noted that CHA's course in hospital organization and management was so highly regarded that it was being used as part of the basic material for a proposed similar course in the United States.

Charles E. Barton, 1965–1966

Charles Barton was executive director of the Regina General Hospital when he was elected president of CHA. He was a member of the Saskatchewan Hospital Association board from 1952 and served as president from 1957 to 1959. He was also executive director from 1965 until his retirement in 1971.

Mr. Barton was a member of the CHA board from 1959 until he was elected president in 1965. He chaired the CHA Study Committee on the Report of the Royal Commission on Health Services, was an active participant in the Western Canada Hospital Institute and represented CHA on the board of the Canadian Council on Hospital Accreditation.

Judge Chaiker Abbis, 1966–1968

Judge Chaiker Abbis was one of the most influential of CHA's elected officers. The fact that he was elected for a second term of office is evidence of his value to the association. If Dr. Agnew was "Mr. Hospital in Canada," then, Judge Abbis deserves the title "Mr. Trustee in Canada."

During his term of office, Judge Abbis worked diligently to improve relations and cooperation with the federal government. The first mid-year conference of the provincial association presidents and their chief executive officers was held during his tenure. And, at his instigation, the Aims and Objectives Committee of the board was formed to do an aggressive appraisal of the association's objectives and the methods used to attain them in 1966. Judge Abbis's contributions to CHA also included extensive reviews and rewrites of its constitution and bylaws in 1963 which he presented to the assembly for approval. He was then appointed to chair a Special Committee on By-Law revision in 1964. He was appointed again as chair of the Committee on By-Law and Regulations in 1976 and assisted in the draft proposals to change CHA to a corporate structure. Although these recommendations were not accepted by CHA's members at the time, he continued to work on the CHA bylaw throughout 1978.

He was deeply committed to good governance. To promote excellence in governance, he sponsored the American Hospital Association's Chaiker Abbis Forum on Governance in 1984, and annually thereafter, to bring together distinguished trustees from both sides of the border to debate current governance issues. He served as a Canadian delegate-at-large to the American Hospital Association for many years. In 1976, he received the Award of Merit from AHA in recognition of his outstanding service to that organization.

Judge Abbis served on the governing board of the Edmundston Regional Hospital for thirty-four years, eighteen of them as chairman. He was a prime mover in the establishment of the New Brunswick Hospital Association in 1958 and its president from 1958 to 1963. He served on the board of CHA from 1961 to 1968, the last two years as its chairman.

Judge Abbis received the George Findlay Stephens Memorial Award in 1971 and continued his interest in the Canadian Hospital Association and his dedication to good governance well into the 1990s. He attended its annual conference whenever possible and, in 1995, he made a sizeable financial contribution to CHA to publish *Regional Governance: A Resource Guide for Trustees.*

R. Alan Hay, 1968–1969

When he became CHA president, Alan Hay was the executive director of the Ontario Hospital Association, a post he assumed in 1966. Mr. Hay was a board member and former chairman of the Brockville General Hospital and was the first hospital trustee to be appointed to the chief executive position of OHA in its history. He believed that, because OHA was so highly visible in Ontario, it should be careful not to use its power to undermine CHA, which was located in Toronto at the time. He also believed that OHA should use its financial stability to support the hospital system across Canada. An excellent example was his dedication to making Statistics Canada's hospital information statistics useful and usable to all Canadian hospitals. OHA had the resources to produce the statistical reports necessary to do so, and OHA made them available to all interested parties.

During his term as president of CHA, the association embarked on a statistical information project (the forerunner of the Management Information System [MIS] Project), the food supervisors' course was transferred from OHA to CHA and the need for an extension course for nursing home administrators was identified. He also served a five-year term as CHA's delegate to the House of Delegates of the American Hospital Association.

He was presented with the George Findlay Stephens Award at the first ever International Hospital Federation Congress in Canada held in Montreal in 1973. Mr. Hay was chairman of the Canadian Organizing Committee for the congress and played a major role in its success. He suffered a fatal heart attack in June 1981, while on a fishing trip with his wife, Peggy, and his close friend, Chaiker Abbis.

L. Reginald Adshead, 1969–1970

Reg Adshead was administrator of the Foothills General Hospital, Calgary, when he was elected president of the CHA board. He was secretary-treasurer of the Associated Hospitals of Alberta for twelve years and president of the Alberta Hospital Association from 1962 to 1964. For a number of years, he was active in the American College of Hospital Administrators and was very instrumental in establishing the Canadian College of Health Service Executives, which he considered to be the highlight of his year as CHA's president. He later became president of the college. He also expressed concern about the fees being charged for the Nursing Unit Administration Program, which were starting to build up impressive surpluses for CHA. In 1974, Mr. Adshead received the George Findlay Stephens Memorial Award.

Gaston Rodrigue, MD, 1970–1971

Dr. Rodrigue came from Drummondville, Quebec, where he was active in the association of French-speaking physicians, the Quebec Radiologists Association and member emeritus of the Association des Administrateurs d'Hôpitaux du Québec. He was the founding president of the Association des Hôpitaux de la Province du Québec (AHPQ) in 1966 and became a member of the CHA board the same year.

During his term as president, CHA's relationships with the Department of National Health and Welfare were at a low point. At a meeting chaired by Dr. Rodrigue, Health Minister John Munro agreed to designate the assistant deputy minister in his department to deal with CHA on a one-to-one basis. During his term, the decision was also made to construct an additional two floors on the CHA building at 25 Imperial Street in Toronto and to add five floors to the adjacent property owned by CHA.

Dr. Rodrigue died at the age of fifty-six in 1971. At the time, he was the administrator of the Hôpital Ste-Croix in Drummondville, Quebec.

William A. Holland, 1971–1972

William Holland was executive director of the Oshawa General Hospital when he was appointed to the CHA board. During his term in office, he pressed strongly for a reduction in the Nursing Unit Administration Program fees. Under his term as president of the board, a committee was formed to recommend future sources of revenue for the association in relation to its developing role.

Mr. Justice Edward N. Hughes, 1972–1974

Judge Hughes was pressed to serve a second term as CHA's president when the president-designate was unable to accept the office because of a major restructuring being undertaken at his hospital at the time. He was elected as CHA's president representing Saskatchewan, where he was a district court judge in Saskatoon. Judge Hughes worked very closely with Alan Hay to make Statistics Canada's hospital information statistics useful and usable for all Canadian hospitals.

He initiated a joint conference of the CHA, CMA and CNA boards to consider solutions to the rising cost of health services. This conference, dubbed "Health Action '72", was held at Mont Gabriel, Quebec, and was a huge success in bringing the three associations together to suggest recommendations to the federal government. During Judge Hughes' term, the CHA board decided to employ a bilingual associate executive director who might succeed Dr. Brosseau when he retired in 1977. This proved to be a much more difficult task for Judge Hughes and his committee and they did not succeed in their goal. His brief on trusteeship, which was presented to the federal health minister, was viewed for many years as the definitive paper on the role of trustees in Canadian hospitals (CHA May 1972b).

Leo P. Chiasson, PhD, 1974–1975

Leo Chiasson was a professor of biology and chairman of the department of biology of St. Francis Xavier University, Antigonish, Nova Scotia. He was the first CHA president from Nova Scotia. One of the big issues for Dr. Chiasson, which he shared in a letter about his time as president, was the issue of equal representation in a federation at the board table. Voting rights had, unfortunately, become linked with the fee structure. The fundamental arrangement of voting rights in a true federation, that is, equal numerical representation for each constituency—whether large or small—had been lost in the shuffle. The complicated problem of allocating proportionate fees and votes on the basis of population and hospital beds had to be solved. During Dr. Chiasson's term as president, a compromise was reached to which all parties agreed.

George C. Sherwood, 1975-1976

George Sherwood was administrator of the University Hospital in Edmonton when he joined the CHA board. During his term, the major issue was whether to move the association's offices from Toronto to Ottawa. Over his nine-year involvement with CHA, Mr. Sherwood recalled that this matter had come up at least three, if not, four times. The issue would not go away, despite the fact that, on the first go-around, the board almost unanimously agreed that it was a dumb idea which could not be economically justified and which would undoubtedly result in the loss of a number of key staff. On at least one occasion, an ad hoc committee was appointed with responsibility to carry out a full-blown study of the merits—or the lack of them—of a move to Ottawa. Eventually, the board approved the move which Mr. Sherwood opposed.

During his term, the board approved the publication of a journal for trustees and *Hospital Trustee* was launched in 1977. Mr. Sherwood also exerted his presidential prerogative to cancel any commercial exhibition during the 1976 convention (in good part due to strong opposition from OHA). This ban continued until well into the late

1980s. The issue of hiring a bilingual associate executive director was again addressed by the board, with the expectation that this person would become executive director on Dr. Brosseau's retirement. Again, the board failed to find a suitable candidate.

Lucien Lacoste, 1976–1977

Mr. Lacoste was executive director of Hôpital Notre-Dame in Montreal, when he was appointed to the CHA board to represent the Association des hôpitaux du Québec. During his term, he was often unable to attend meetings because of the massive number of strikes taking place in Quebec. As president, the board approved the move of CHA to Ottawa. Dismissed previously for financial reasons, members of the board now believed that CHA should be at the seat of the federal government. It would also be much easier to recruit a new bilingual executive director, if CHA was in Ottawa.

The Association Presidents and Chairs, 1977 to 2006

Gordon Frith, 1977–1978

Gordon Frith was the first CHA president to come from British Columbia, which was the oldest provincial member. He also served one of the longer terms on the CHA board—from 1968 to 1979. Prior to becoming president of CHA, Mr. Frith was the chair of the CHA's national committee on nursing, which was responsible for a very controversial study conducted in 1972–73 on the value of the then newly graduated two-year nurse compared to the traditional three-year hospital-graduated nurse. While the study was hotly contested by the nursing profession at the time, the two-year program did become the norm.

Mr. Frith was chair of the Search Committee to find a replacement for Dr. Brosseau who retired at the end of 1977. From the time of his retirement from the CHA board until his death in 1994, Mr. Frith attended every CHA annual conference, except for one or two he missed because of illness. When he died in June 1994, he and his wife Joyce were planning to attend the conference in Halifax.

William A. Kilpatrick, 1978–1979

Born in Winnipeg, Mr. Kilpatrick received a Diploma in Health Administration from the University of Toronto in 1962. He accepted the position of assistant administrator at The Moncton Hospital in New Brunswick, which he held until 1970, when he became the executive director of the hospital until 1991. From there, he moved to Ontario to take a position as the executive director of the Peterborough Civic Hospital from 1991 to 1997. In that same year, Mr. Kilpatrick retired after thirty-five years in health care.

Mr. Kilpatrick became president of CHA's board in 1978, although he was first appointed to the board in 1972. He was one of the board's more forthright chairs, moving the business of the board forward in quick order. He insisted that a board manual be prepared for the use of new board members and that an orientation session be held. While he held office, he instituted the practice of holding regional meetings of the CHA executive with officers of the provincial member associations.

Prior to assuming the chair, he served as chair of the Finance Committee and contributed considerably to standardize CHA's financial reporting to the board and the membership. He chaired the Study Committee on CHA Headquarters Location from 1976 to 1977 and was very instrumental in the decision to move CHA to Ottawa. Mr. Kilpatrick and his committee also recommended that, even though CHA might rent space for a period, ultimately, it should be located in its own building in Ottawa, a principle that was accepted by the board.

Mr. Kilpatrick pressed CHA hard to seek funding to update, revise or preserve Statistics Canada's Quarterly Hospital Information System (QHIS), which was in danger of being canceled. From this came CHA's proposal for a management information system (MIS), the forerunner of CHA's MIS Project.

Another milestone during his term was the decision to hold a joint convention with the American Hospital Association in Montreal in 1980. He also chaired a committee of the member associations in 1980 to formulate a CHA brief to the federal government's review committee on the health system headed by Justice Emmett Hall. He was appointed chair of the Task Force on the Institute for the Hospital of the Future in 1985 and chaired the board of the renamed Institute for Health Care Facilities of the Future from 1986 to 1989. He had also been on the board of the New Brunswick Hospital Association from 1963 to 1973 and was elected president in 1966.

He was involved in several other health organizations over the course of his career. He was a member of the House of Delegates and the Regional Advisory Board of the American Hospital Association from 1981 to 1988. Mr. Kilpatrick served as chair of the board of directors of the then Canadian Council on Hospital Accreditation from 1982 to 1983 and was on the board from 1979 to 1984. He was also a surveyor for the council from 1985 to 1997.

During his thirty-five years of service in Canada's health system, Mr. Kilpatrick received many prestigious awards. In 1985, he received the Chaiker Abbis Award from the then New Brunswick Hospital Association for his outstanding contribution to the organization and management of health care both provincially and nationally. In 1986, he was recognized for his contributions with a special presentation from the Nova Scotia Association of Health Organizations and, in 1988, he received the George Findlay Stephens Award from CHA. Mr. Kilpatrick also received the President's Achievement Award in 1992 from the Society of Graduates in Health Administration at the University of Toronto for his significant contribution to the field of health administration.

Fred W. Lamb, 1979–1980

At the time of his election as president, Fred Lamb had been a member of the board of CHA for seven years and was president of the Metro-Calgary and Rural General Hospital District No. 93. He was a past president of the Alberta Hospital Association and a proud graduate of the CHA Hospital and Management (HOM) Program.

During his term, the first CHA convention was held in St. John's, Newfoundland. He was also head of the negotiating team working with officials of the American Hospital Association on the joint AHA/CHA convention in Montreal in 1980. Mr. Lamb supported grouping all CHA long-term care activities (i.e., the extension course in long-term care management and the new long-term care directory) under the direction of one committee. He also believed that CHA should appoint a corporate secretary whose responsibility would be to coordinate all activities of the board and the assembly. During his term, CHA prepared a brief to the Hall Review Committee, in consultation with all the member associations who met in Ottawa to review and finalize its content.

Sister Mary Lucy Power, 1980–1981

Sister Lucy (now Lucy Dobbin) was the first woman to chair the board of CHA. She was a member of the congregation of the Sisters of Mercy, Newfoundland, and, at the time of her election, associate executive director of St. Clare's Mercy Hospital in St. John's. She became a member of the CHA board in 1974 and was instrumental in helping to organize the first CHA convention ever to be held in the Maritimes, which took place in St. John's. She convinced the CHA board that a convention in Newfoundland was not only feasible but would be a smashing success. She was right—the turnout was larger than ever for such an event.

In 1980, when she was elected president of the board, she presided over the first (and only) joint convention of the American and Canadian Hospital Associations which took place in Montreal. (Coincidentally, the chair of the American Hospital Association was also a woman, Sister Irene Kraus.) Sister Lucy's determination occasionally kept AHA from steamrolling over their much smaller Canadian counterpart. (There were approximately 2,400 Canadian delegates out of a total of 7,000 who attended the convention.)

Sister Lucy also chaired a special committee on CHA's role and communications. One of the recommendations of this committee was that the annual assembly should be abolished and an annual general meeting (AGM) of the board be held at a time separate from the annual conference. That is, the AGM should take place in conjunction with the national meeting of provincial/territorial member CEOs and presidents held in March of each year. This committee also recommended that CHA become a true federation of the provincial/territorial associations and a special ad hoc committee on the bylaws was appointed.

During Sister Lucy's term, the association embarked on the Canadian Hospital Job Exchange and an additional meeting of the board was added in September to set budget guidelines for the coming year. She also chaired the Long Range Planning Committee which delivered its report in 1983.

Albert (Bert) G. Ayers, 1981–1982

Bert Ayers was appointed to the CHA board in 1978. He had served as chairman of the board of Saskatoon City Hospital and was a past president of the Saskatchewan Health-Care Association. One of his first duties as chair of the board was to chair a committee to investigate CHA's involvement in long-term care, following which a standing long-term care committee was appointed. He was also the first chair of the new Trustee Committee, composed of all trustee members on the CHA board.

Mr. Ayers was a strong proponent of a health council of Canada and took the initiative in proposing and then chairing an ad hoc committee to investigate the possibility of establishing such a council. He invited other national health organizations to join with CHA on this project.

During Mr. Ayers' term, CHA established a communications department, the objective of which was to integrate the association's information-processing procedures and develop a proposal for a communications network. From this, CHA received funding from Supply and Services Canada for a Telidon trial project, which, in turn, led to the creation of InfoHealth. Although years ahead of its time, it unfortunately resulted in a serious impact on the association's finances.

Mr. Ayers was also involved to a considerable degree in CHA's relocation to its permanent Ottawa headquarters at 17 York Street. He did a great deal of groundwork to complete the financing for the reconstruction of the building. During his tenure, the board also agreed to CHA's participation in the AHA's State Hospital Association Review and Evaluation (SHARE) program, a review process that evaluated both the internal operations of an organization and its external relations.

J. David Innes, 1982–1983

Mr. Innes was appointed to the board of CHA by the Ontario Hospital Association in 1981. His first task as a member of the board was to chair an ad hoc committee to revise the association's bylaw on membership. During his term, the association presented a brief to the federal health minister on the Canada Health Act.

His term was not a smooth one. CHA had considerable financial difficulties due partly to the imminent relocation to 17 York Street and CHA was forced to downsize its operations and staff during this time. However, during Mr. Innes' term, the board supported an initiative to launch the first CHA invitational conference, organized along the lines of those of the Conference Board of Canada. Some twenty to twenty-five invited participants were asked to speak extemporaneously and share their views with other participants on a health topic of their choice. Discussions were confidential with no official written report. This concept proved to be very popular for almost eight years but finally died because of lack of interest and funds.

Claire Labrèche, 1983–1984

Claire Labrèche served on the board of the Association des hôpitaux du Québec prior to being appointed to the CHA board in 1981. As a dedicated volunteer and trustee, she was particularly concerned during her term with the establishment of a CHA foundation through which funds could be raised to assist the association in its research activities. The foundation would also serve as a vehicle to keep past presidents/chairs of the association in contact with CHA and take advantage of their knowledge and experience.

During Mme. Labrèche's term, two important documents were finalized: the State Hospital Association Review and Evaluation (SHARE) Report and the Report of the Long Range Planning Committee. The latter report recommended that the association change its name to the Canadian Association of Health Care Organizations (defeated); that an annual report of the association be published (carried); and that the association and its members "develop a formal agreement to establish and operate a communications network for health care organizations in Canada" (CHA 1983b, 16). The Hospital of the Future was also initiated during her term.

Dr. Gustave Gingras, 1984–1985

Dr. Gingras was well known to the association long before he was appointed to the CHA board. As an international expert on rehabilitative medicine, he had founded the famous Institut de réadaptation de Montréal. He was the first past president of the Canadian Medical Association to become chair of CHA. It is somewhat ironic that he came to the CHA board as the representative from Prince Edward Island, when his long history of service was in Montreal. He was the first person from that province to serve as CHA chair.

Even before he was appointed to the CHA board, Dr. Gingras' expertise was sought by CHA to design a questionnaire on long-term care and to write a brief for CHA for presentation to the House of Commons Special Committee on the Disabled and the Handicapped in 1980.

During Dr. Gingras' term, the board dealt with the expansion of CHA headquarters to 24 Clarence Street and seriously pursued the establishment of a health council of Canada. In 1981, the Honorable Emmett M. Hall and Dr. Gingras were jointly awarded the Stephens Memorial Award—the first time in CHA history that this occurred.

Ted I. Bartman, 1985–1986

Ted Bartman was executive director of the Misericordia General Hospital in Winnipeg, when he was elected chair of the board. He was also a graduate of CHA's Hospital Organization and Management (HOM) course. Besides serving as chair of a number of CHA committees in the four years prior to his election, Mr. Bartman also chaired the board of the Manitoba Health Organizations, Inc. and was a member of the board and vice-president of the Catholic Health Conference of Manitoba.

During his term, the board approved the launch of InfoHealth in March 1986, in collaboration with Telecom Canada, even though it was beginning to gobble up larger and larger portions of CHA's resources. The long-term care committee submitted its report to the board, with the committee expressing concern about the association's name. The board agreed to entrench long-term care streams in the national conference and CHA's educational programs.

One of Mr. Bartman's initiatives was to try to identify a role that could be played by CHA's past presidents and chairs. Although a number of informal meetings were arranged to coincide with the annual conference, because of lack of funding, the idea never gained support.

After considerable discussion at the board level, the association entered into a partnership with the Federation of Canadian Municipalities to acquire and construct an addition to 17 York Street at 24 Clarence Street. This would provide much-needed space for the expanding M.I.S. Project and the InfoHealth Project.

Peter Carruthers, 1986–1987

Peter R. Carruthers was the president of the Ottawa Civic Hospital when he was elected chair of CHA's board. During his term, he introduced a board retreat, which was specifically designed to write a vision statement and objectives for the association.

Mr. Carruthers was "all business." He didn't believe that committee or board meetings should last more than two hours and, as a result, he handled board meetings with considerable celerity—often being two or three agenda items ahead of the members of the board.

One of his main concerns was the drain on CHA finances caused by InfoHealth. Every year the association was assuming larger and larger deficits as a result of the project. But the board was still convinced that this project would eventually succeed and continued to support it, despite the losses that CHA was incurring.

Jacques Nolet, 1987–1988

Jacques Nolet was chief executive officer of the Hôpital Louis-H. Lafontaine, a large psychiatric institution in Montreal, and a representative of the Association des hôpitaux du Québec. He joined CHA's board in 1981.

During his term, Telecom Canada agreed to assume management of InfoHealth for the association, although the board expressed some reluctance to relinquish control of the project. Other major initiatives undertaken during his term were the National Conference on the Implications of AIDS for Health Institutions and the first National Conference on Mental Health Services, at which he was a main speaker. The board also restructured its Long Term Care Committee to include representatives from all the provinces. During Mr. Nolet's tenure, CHA prepared a position paper on tax reform.

Margaret (Peggy) Davison, 1988–1989

Peggy Davison never expected to chair the CHA board. But with the untimely death of the incoming chair Derek Hammond, the board member from Newfoundland, she was persuaded to accept the position, so that the rotation of board chairs would be preserved. Mrs. Davison had a long history of voluntary service as a trustee and chair of the Victoria General Hospital in Halifax. Her charm and grace were a great asset to the association and she was in considerable demand to attend provincial meetings across the country where she conveyed what she considered to be her most important message—the value of CHA as the national voice for health care facilities and as the vehicle to facilitate networking and information exchange across the country.

Another of Mrs. Davison's preoccupations was the vital role played by trustees and volunteers in protecting the health care system from government dominance. An action plan and recommendations concerning the association's role in long-term care were approved by the board during her term, and the board approved a policy statement on the role of health care facilities in home care, along with guidelines for organ and tissue donation services in hospitals. A brief on sales tax reform was also submitted to the federal finance minister.

Thelma Sharp Cook, 1989–1990

Dr. Cook was another long-time volunteer in the health sector. She came to the CHA board as one of two British Columbia representatives and was a past chair of British Columbia Health Association. She was a persuasive speaker on behalf of voluntarism and, in 1989, the association's four-member executive committee was composed entirely of trustees. It was only natural, therefore, that governance was a high priority during her term. In fact, the board endorsed a policy statement on health facility governance and approved a special institute on governance as part of the 1990 annual conference.

During her tenure, the board launched a search for a new president and CEO with the retirement of Jean-Claude Martin. In late 1989, Dr. Cook announced the appointment of Carol Clemenhagen as president. The board also approved the report of the strategic planning committee which had been appointed in 1988 to provide clear direction for CHA as it entered the 1990s. One of the first issues to be dealt with in the new decade was the federal government's Goods and Services Tax (GST), a major concern for Canada's health facilities and its members, who urged CHA to lobby strongly in its submissions to government that health care facilities and agencies should receive a zero rating.

Elma G. Heidemann, 1990–1991

At the time of her election to the chair, Mrs. Heidemann was assistant executive director of the Canadian Council on Health Facilities Accreditation (now the Canadian Council on Health Services Accreditation). She was also a trustee and chair of the Ottawa Regional Health Council. She was elected president of the Ontario Hospital Association in 1986 and served until 1987. She had been involved with CHA for a number of years prior to 1990, first, as a consultant to revise the Long Term Care Organization and Management course and, then as a member of CHA's Long Term Care Committee.

Mrs. Heidemann also chaired the Strategic Planning Committee on CHA's future, which submitted its report in 1989. The board set the need to establish national health policy and objectives as one of its major priorities and directed CHA to begin the background work to launch a project that was to articulate needed national health policy reform.

Mrs. Heidemann's term marked the tenth anniversary of the association's Long Term Care Committee with which she had been closely involved. The committee was renamed the Continuing Care Committee in 1989 and, during her tenure, the board directed CHA to implement an integrated approach to continuing care across all CHA departments. In 1990, a national intersectoral long-term care liaison committee was formed to share information and cooperate in lobbying and policy development in this area. Mrs. Heidemann left the CHA board in 1991 to become the executive director of the accreditation council.

André Brousseau, 1991–1992

Mr. Brousseau came to the association as a past president of the Association des hôpitaux du Québec and a trustee. During his term, conflict of interest guidelines were approved for the board and work was accelerated on the National Health Policy Reform Project.

In 1991, the board approved CHA's membership in The Health Action Lobby (HEAL) Coalition to lobby the federal government on sustainable funding for medicare. The board also committed CHA to develop a stress management program for HIV/AIDS caregivers. During Mr. Brousseau's term, the board agreed to change the name of the George Findlay Stephens Memorial Award to the CHA Award of Excellence for Service and Leadership. (While those reading this book will know by now the influence Dr. Stephens exerted during his long service with the association and in the health care field, his name had become less and less known over the years.)

Michel C. Leger, 1992–1993

Mr. Leger is a lawyer and was former chair of the New Brunswick Healthcare Association and mayor of Shediac, New Brunswick. During his term, the board agreed to support the National Health Policy Reform Project—the Vision Project— a major policy undertaking for the association.

During Mr. Leger's term, the board agreed to strategic alliances with the Association of Canadian Teaching Hospitals and the Canadian Long Term Care Association, which were both invited to send observers to CHA board meetings. The board also supported a strategic planning retreat of the national and provincial/territorial association CEOs to look at CHA's goals and objectives for the future.

In his joint annual report, Mr. Leger made the point that ". . . in its relations with other national associations, CHA is perceived positively as an organization that will not hesitate to act in the best interests of its members and the facilities and agencies they collectively represent" (CHA 1993a, 3).

Robert J. Smith, 1993-1994

Mr. Smith was a past chair of the British Columbia Health Association and president of Lion's Gate Hospital, when he was elected to the CHA board in 1988. During his tenure on the board, Mr. Smith served on the Information Services Committee, which was the board advisory committee to the department and chaired the joint

CHA-CNA overview committee for the Nursing Unit Administration Program. He was also chair of the Ad Hoc Expert Advisory Committee on Waste Management in 1989 and chair of the Education Committee from 1990 to 1991. For the next three years, he served on both the Finance and Executive Committees and became chair-elect in 1992.

In June 1993, he was elected chair of the board, after a runoff election at the annual general meeting, when both he and the representative from Alberta were nominated for the position. The rotation of the chair was to fall to Newfoundland for the 1993-1994 term. But Joan Dawe, Newfoundland's member on the board, was appointed deputy minister of health and was asked to step aside as the board was concerned with the conflict of interest that could be perceived, since the association was an advocacy group to government. This meant that the chair rotated to the western region between Alberta and British Columbia.

During his tenure, CHA publicly launched its recommendations and nine key statements for health care in a reformed system. The Vision Report, titled *An Open Future: A Shared Vision*, was released to wide acclaim in Vancouver in June 1993. This bilingual document, the result of two years of consultations with key stakeholders and experts, became a rallying point for CHA's advocacy efforts during the next year. The CHA vision offered confidence and credibility during a time of uncertainty, doubt and even fear about the future of Canada's health system. In his annual report, Mr. Smith stated: "We expect the Vision report to continue to be the benchmark for judging health reform in this country."

On leaving CHA, Mr. Smith also left Lions Gate Hospital in the midst of the regionalization process in British Columbia to work in the private sector. He moved back into the health sector when he became president of the Queen Elizabeth II Health Sciences Centre in Halifax and subsequently the Capital District Health Authority until 2002. He then returned as the CEO and president of the Fraser Health Authority in British Columbia. He was reappointed to CHA's board in 2002 and served until 2004. Mr. Smith is currently a management consultant, member of the faculty of the Sauder School of Business and the Centre for Health Care Management at the University of British Columbia and a director on two national health research and knowledge transfer boards.

W. R. CHENOWETH,

Elected president of the Canadian Hospital Council at the conclusion of its third biennial convention. Mr. Chenoweth succeeds Dr. F. W. Routley, Toronto, who was elected honorary vice-president.

Mr. Chenoweth is superintendent of the Royal Victoria Hospital, Montreal.

Left: Walter Richard Chenoweth, Superintendent of the Royal Victoria Hospital, Montreal, Was Elected President of the Canadian Hospital Council, 1935-1937.

Below:
CHA Board of Directors, 1981-1982, in the Boardroom at 17 York Street, Ottawa.
Seated: Sister Mary Lucy Power (now Lucy Dobbin), Past Chair; A. (Bert) G. Ayers, Chair, 1981-1982; and J. David Innes, Chair-Elect.

Past Board Chairs at the Board Dinner in Victoria, 10 June 2006.
Back Row (left to right): Jean Graham, Alex Taylor, Ken Ezeard, Dan de Vlieger, Ed Bergen (see inset)
Front Row (left to right): Lucy Dobbin, Jacques Nolet, Thelma Sharp Cook, Lorraine Grant, André Brousseau, Elma Heidemann and Mary Lapaine. (Photos courtesy of Eleanor Sawyer)

Garnet Burns, Chair of CHA's Board of Directors, 2006 to 2007.

R. Fraser Armstrong, Superintendent, Kingston General Hospital, Was President of the Canadian Hospital Council, 1949-1951.

Some Members of the Executive of the Canadian Hospital Council at the 10th Biennial Meeting, 28-30 May 1951, Ottawa.
Back row, left to right: Murray Ross, Dr. W. D. Piercy; Percy Ward; R. Fraser Armstrong, retiring president; Dr. A. L. C. Gilday; and Dr. L. O Bradley.
Front row, left to right: Rev. Father H. L. Bertrand; Dr. O. C. Trainor, newly-elected president; and Dr. A. C. McGugan.

James Saunders, 1994–1995

When Mr. Saunders was appointed to the CHA board, he was CEO of the Children's Hospital of Calgary. With health reform initiatives sweeping his province, the hospital was eventually closed during the restructuring and regionalization of the health system.

Mr. Saunders presided over the association during one of its more difficult and exciting periods in recent CHA history and in the history of the Canadian health system. As CHA's member organizations continued to restructure and downsize, many of them were uncertain of their own future within their provincial health system and, therefore, could not make any long-term commitments to CHA regarding their presence at the federation table or in terms of paying fees. This placed CHA in a tenuous position with financial stability always a concern at the board table and throughout most of Mr. Saunders' term as chair.

During the course of the year, the board's Corporate Innovation Committee was mandated to identify and recommend innovations that would enable member input into CHA's policy agenda and priority setting; improve policy development, advocacy, communications, decision-making and coordination; and enhance how the board of directors operated.

As Mr. Saunders stated in his annual report, his principal objective had been to position the association, so it could continue its primary role of serving its members in the evolving regionalized health service environment.

Gaston Levac, 1995-1996

Gaston Levac was CEO of the Laurentian Hospital in Sudbury, Ontario, when he was appointed to the CHA board in 1989 as a representative of the OHA. He served on several committees including the Long Term Care Committee (1989), the Services Committee (1989–1990), the Finance Committee (1993) and the Executive Committee (1994). He was elected chair of the board in June 1995 at the same annual general meeting in which the membership agreed to change CHA's name to the Canadian Healthcare Association/Association canadienne des soins de santé.

As chair of CHA, he oversaw some radical changes in the association as it headed into a period of intense financial strain and transition for its membership. To meet the challenges, the association renewed its corporate identity to more accurately reflect the changing face of its membership, reduced membership fees for the next fiscal year by ten percent, implemented a new board structure and adopted a member-driven priority-setting process to establish the association's advocacy agenda through the newly established CEO Forum. He was the first chair to wear the newly designed ceremonial chain of office which was created in 1995 to replace the gold medallion that had been donated by Dr. Agnew.

With the resignation of Carol Clemenhagen as president in January 1996, halfway through Mr. Levac's term, the board recognized that this would be an opportunity to review the organization's mission and role, as well as its relationship with its changing membership. Mr. Levac often presided over intense and passionate discusions about the organization's future. He was appointed by the board, along with the chair-elect Dan de Vlieger, to consult with other national health organizations in an effort to find cost-sharing efficiencies or even common goals and missions that might eventually lead to integration. The board had also directed CHA staff to implement an intensive financial review of the organization. With CHA's finances constantly strained to the limit, it was almost with a sense of relief that he relinquished his duties as chair in June 1996.

Dan de Vlieger, 1996–1997

Mr. de Vlieger was elected to the chair of the CHA board in June 1996 in Ottawa at a time when the association's survival was under intense scrutiny by it membership and where its financial instability added to the uncertainty. He had been appointed to the board in 1995 as the representative from Saskatchewan.

On taking over the chair, his first priority was to hold the organization together during the 1996 mission and services review that had been directed by the board earlier in the year. He had worked closely with the outgoing chair, Gaston Levac, to seek collaborative arrangements with other organizations that year. At the same time, both the CHA and the Canadian College of Health Service Executives were involved in discussions to determine whether there were opportunities for collaboration or operational integration of some of the programs and services. Mr. de Vlieger also counseled the acting president through a thorough review of CHA's core and ancillary services through close and ongoing consultation with the member chairs and CEOs.

At the critical September meeting, the board received the recommendations from the consultation between the CHA and the college. As a result, both organizations' boards were advised at the time not to pursue this route any further. Discussions at the board table over the recommendations in the "Review of the Mission and Services Report" were often heated and intense. Mr. de Vlieger's skills as a moderator were frequently required to keep board members focused and to take decisions in the best interests of CHA. It was during this same meeting that the OHA member announced its intention to withdraw from membership; OHA was not happy with the direction that CHA was headed in and, as a hospital-based association, did not believe it could support a downgraded organization that no longer carried on ancillary services to support its core work.

By the end of December 1996, not only was Mr. de Vlieger chair of CHA but also the daily contact for CHA's remaining senior staff as Acting President Tim Julien had submitted his resignation effective almost immediately after the December board meeting. The board had failed to approve an operating budget for 1997, rejecting a budget that was based on winding up CHA's operations. Mr. de Vlieger was directed by the board to find an interim president for CHA before the end of January 1997.

No doubt, one of Mr. de Vlieger's most significant achievements and contributions to CHA was persuading Joyce Bailey to come out of retirement—she had been a vice-president at the OHA—to take over as CHA's interim president. He managed to hire her, sight unseen, through a telephone interview in early January 1997. He then worked closely with her during the next few weeks leading up to the March board meeting to settle the organization into carrying out its business and to boost the sagging morale of the CHA staff.

Still not satisfied with the draft budget presented to them at the March meeting, the board set up an Executive Committee Task Force to review the member fee structure and CHA's revenue-generating services. Chaired by Mr. de Vlieger, the Task Force met in Ottawa in May to work with senior staff and the CEOs of CHA's member organizations. In late May, the board discussed the initiatives from the earlier meeting and agreed that these should be used to present a new 1997 budget. The proposed membership fee maintained fees based on population as per the 1996 census and established a minimum and maximum cap to ensure fairness to all members.

By his last board meeting as chair in June, Mr. de Vlieger ensured the board approved the 1997 budget, the new fee structure and urged CHA to now focus on its core business of advocacy, representation and policy development. Mr. de Vlieger must have handed over the chain of office to his successor with a sense of considerable satisfaction. In addressing the board during one meeting, Mr. de Vlieger prophetically stated: ". . . if only one could project into the future, five years from now, there [will] still be a strong national voice to represent the delivery of health care in Canada and . . . CHA will not only have survived but become much stronger" (CHA 1997, 4).

John Baker, 1997–1998

Mr. Baker was appointed to CHA's board as the Newfoundland representative in 1992. In 1995, he ably guided the board and CHA's membership through bylaw changes that included a name change to the Canadian Healthcare Association, streamlined the board structure from twenty to thirteen members and reflected a member-driven policy agenda.

When Mr. Baker was elected as chair of CHA in Halifax in 1997, he noted in his address to the members what his key priority for CHA would be during his term: "I believe strongly that it is time to commit more of our energies to our mission: to advocacy; to policy review; . . . to improving our relationship and influence with federal decision makers" (CHA 1997, 1). During the first six months of his term, CHA was still struggling to stabilize its financial position and to retain its membership in each province and territory. Nor had the organization hired a full-time president and CEO, although the association was considerably stronger at the time of his election under the able leadership of Interim President Joyce Bailey.

By the time Mr. Baker's term as chair was completed in 1998, he was able to report to the membership that a new president had been hired, the financial picture for CHA had improved considerably and, with the hiring of a new director of policy, the association had taken major strides in reestablishing contacts with the federal government. Mr. Baker, along with CHA senior staff, had met with the federal health minister for the first time in several years in October 1997. He presided over board meetings where the focus was no longer on CHA's survival but on a clear, focused and member-driven policy agenda. CHA was no longer invisible at the federal level or on the national scene. As he summed up his term of office at the 1998 Annual General Meeting, he was able to say that, ". . ., our association's visibility has grown immeasurably in the past year. We have been front and centre on every major issue affecting the healthcare system: the budget and funding issues, home and community care, pharmacare, and others" (Ibid.). Given that Mr. Baker had served on CHA's board during one of the most difficult and tumultuous times in its history, it must have given him much pleasure to conclude his address with the words: "Make no mistake—CHA is back." Some of the credit belongs to Mr. Baker's commitment to move CHA forward into a strong and brighter future.

Jean Graham, 1998-1999

Jean Graham was appointed to the CHA board in 1997 to replace the Alberta representative who was unable to complete his term. It was a tumultuous time for the association as it was repositioning itself to meet the needs of its members who were faced with the new financial realities of Canada's health system.

On her election as chair in June 1998, Ms Graham advised the board of her concern over the lack of governance policies for CHA. She believed strongly that there should be policies in place to clearly define how the board should function, including policies on the role of the chair, board members and the relationship between the board and staff. In a memorandum to the board in February 1999, she advised members that, as the chair "tasked with leading our organization towards a solid governance model of leadership, which will ensure stability and growth in our association," she had arranged a governance session for the March meeting. At the direction of the board, and working with CHA staff, she pioneered the development of a policy framework for CHA, as well as the Board Orientation Manual, and worked hard to ensure that the manual was set up in a proper policy format. The manual was formally adopted by the board in October 1999 and is still used today to educate new board members about the association in their orientation session.

Ms Graham also initiated a communications tool called "Board Highlights." It was her practice to write a report after each CHA board meeting for circulation to the Provincial Health Authorities of Alberta Board, whom she represented. This report became more widely circulated and came to the attention of several CHA board members. They liked the idea of a summary of the board discussions and, since that time, the highlights are sent to the board members as soon after each board meeting as possible. This practice enables board members to keep their membership current on CHA activities.

Ms Graham served on many committees, including the Governance and Accountability Committee and the Conference Planning Committee. She also spoke on two occasions at the joint National Healthcare Leadership Conference. For six years, she was the CHA board representative on the CCHSA. In October 2004, she volunteered to chair the board 75th Anniversary Working Group and to put a plan together by February 2005 for the celebrations. In fact, her personal commitment and enthusiasm for a CHA anniversary celebration led to her suggestion to ask for support for the event through a one-time member contribution. With all members providing sponsorship, the Working Group was able to propose several ideas for the anniversary, culminating with a celebratory dinner on Parliament Hill. Ms. Graham was reappointed to serve another three-year term on CHA's board in 2004.

Garth Pierce, 1999-2000

Garth Pierce was first appointed to the CHA board in May 1998 and became chair-elect shortly after. He arrived on the board at a time when the OHA, the member organization he represented, had serious reservations about whether they could continue as a member of the federation. Both Mr. Pierce and David Innes, a past CHA chair, were asked to review the issue of OHA's continuation as a member in CHA and to recommend a course of action to the OHA board, which eventually decided to remain in the organization.

Prior to his first board meeting as chair, Mr. Pierce visited the CHA offices and met with both the president, Sharon Sholzberg-Gray, and the senior management team, one of the few times in which a board chair had done so.

During the March 2002 board meeting, Mr. Pierce and CHA's CEO participated in a press conference on Parliament Hill in which CHA released its document titled *CHA's Framework for a Sustainable Healthcare System in Canada*. All the members of the board attended this special presentation to the national media. Immediately following this, the board met with federal Health Minister Alan Rock to discuss ways in which CHA and the federal health department could work in partnership to attain the goal of sustainability for the health system.

During Mr. Pierce's term as chair, CHA successfully paid off its large mortgage on its building at 17 York Street and he invited board members and CHA staff to celebrate this accomplishment in a brief toast and mortgage-burning ceremony at the same meeting. A major disappointment for Mr. Pierce was the decision by the board to drop CHA's membership in the IHF, an organization that he supported. He believed that the IHF was a better organization with Canada as a member. He was appointed by the board as CHA's participant-observer on the Canadian College of Health Service Executives board. As a Fellow of the college and a past chair of the American College of Healthcare Executives, he represented CHA in this capacity for six years.

Edward Bergen, 2000–2001

Mr. Bergen was appointed to CHA's board in June 1998 as the Manitoba representative. At the time, the association was still struggling to attain financial stability, pay down its considerable long-term debt and retain all provincial member organizations in the federation, including Mr. Bergen's own province where the Manitoba Health Organizations, Inc., had just been dissolved.

In June 2000, he was elected as chair of the board. With his financial background and expertise, it was only fitting that he would focus on guiding CHA to a healthier financial position. In fact, he suggested early in his term of office, and the board agreed, that CHA should develop guidelines for setting up a financial reserve. Mr. Bergen frequently made positive suggestions to assist CHA in presenting concise and transparent financial statements that would inform the board's decision-making.

During his term of office, CHA revised its bylaw on associate memberships in order to accommodate future requests from provincial organizations that were part of the health care continuum and who were seeking a relationship with CHA. The board also encouraged CHA, under both Mr. Bergen's and the CHA president's signature, to make a written presentation to the Fyke Commission review as requested by CHA's Saskatchewan member.

Kenneth (Ken) Wayne Ezeard, CA, CHE, 2001-2002

Ken Ezeard was elected CHA chair in June 2001 at the Annual General Meeting in Winnipeg. Mr. Ezeard was appointed to the CHA board in 1991 and served continuously for over ten years, representing Prince Edward Island in various roles. These included executive director of a large community hospital, a provincial government senior appointment to the crown agency responsible for leading health care regionalization, and latterly as chief executive officer of one of the province's health regions. The significance of this long-standing role is more the reflection of the dynamic changes that were occurring in health care administration in the 1990s and the changes in membership to the provincial and territorial associations and, therefore, CHA.

Kenneth W. Ezeard, Chair, Working Group on the History of CHA, 2004–2006

Among his recollections of his term in office were the opportunities he had to dialogue with and make presentations to various stakeholders to help consolidate the importance of CHA as part of the evolving continuum of health care in Canada. Undoubtedly, the most important event that took place was the 2001 release of CHA's major discussion paper entitled *Private-Public Mix in the Funding and Delivery of Health Services in Canada* on 11 September 2001. By prior commitment, Mr. Ezeard was leading an accreditation survey team in Saskatchewan and could not attend the release of the document in Ottawa that day. Its release was overshadowed by the terrorist events in New York and Washington and the destruction of the World Trade Centre that day.

Despite this tragedy and the related concerns over air travel, Mr. Ezeard flew to Whitehorse two weeks later for a CEO Forum meeting, both in his capacity as CHA chair and as a provincial member CEO. While in the Yukon, he was interviewed in-depth by CBC Yukon and was able to deliver CHA's key messages about sustainability, accountability and integration of the health system. The interview also allowed him to comment on the appropriate private and public mix of services in the system. At the time, the Yukon government was examining ways to initiate CT scanner services in the territory. A useful discussion on the value of CHA to smaller provinces and territories such as Yukon and Prince Edward Island also formed part of the interviews. It was at this Whitehorse meeting of CEOs where Mr. Ezeard suggested the value of CHA's chair attending the CEO Forum.

Mr. Ezeard's first board meeting was unique among board chairs as both the president, Sharon Sholzberg-Gray, and the director of policy and communications were absent from the meeting due to personal situations. After meeting with CHA's senior management team and the president's new executive assistant, Mr. Ezeard proceeded with the November 2001 board and executive meetings as previously scheduled, ably supported by CHA staff and chair-elect, Lorraine Grant. This board meeting also included an orientation session for new board members, policy discussions and a budget review, as well as a meeting with CHA consultants, who were developing a succession and performance evaluation plan for CHA.

Other highlights of Mr. Ezeard's term as chair included a media conference, along with CEO Sharon Sholzberg-Gray, at the Parliament Buildings on 26 November 2001 to announce CHA's Ten Point Plan as the foundation for the upcoming presentation to the Romanow Commission. In April 2002, Mr. Ezeard attended the American Hospital Association (AHA) board of trustees meeting in Washington,

D.C., followed by two days at the AHA Convention. As a result of events of 9/11, security was extremely tight for anyone flying in to Washington's National Airport, which had only reopened a few days earlier. The chair had to undergo four separate personal searches, including checked and carryon luggage, armed air marshals on the airplane and being unable to leave his seat on the airplane for forty-five minutes prior to landing in Washington. Mr. Ezeard believed that participation in this AHA event was worthwhile because it gave him an opportunity during the AHA board meeting to speak about the Canadian health care system, the role of the CHA and to encourage increased dialogue and communication between the two organizations.

Mr. Ezeard also presented to the Romanow Commission on 18 April 2002 in Charlottetown, representing both Prince Edward Island and CHA, and responded directly to questions from Mr. Romanow and his colleagues. In May 2002, at the AGM in Halifax, he passed on the chain of office to Lorraine Grant. Following the meeting, he was immediately escorted to the Canadian College of Health Service Executives AGM, where he received that organization's career achievement award.

Mr. Ezeard's role as chair during 2001–2002 can best be summarized in his own words, "It has been a sincere privilege to represent Prince Edward Island on the CHA board of directors for so many years. Until you take on the role as chair, you do not gain a full appreciation of the importance of the Canadian Healthcare Association to health care both nationally and internationally. I hope in a small way that I have contributed to the increasing value of the Canadian Healthcare Association in the continuum of care across Canada."

Lorraine Grant, 2002–2004

Ms Grant was elected to the chair as the representative from British Columbia in June 2002 for a one-year term. She was persuaded to remain for a second term to provide some transition time for the newly appointed member from Ontario, who was also chair-elect, to become familiar with CHA and the national health care scene. As a result, Ms. Grant has the distinction of being the only chair in thirty years to serve a second term.

During her first meeting with Health Minister Anne McLellan in October 2002 in Ottawa, Ms Grant took the opportunity to visit CHA headquarters. While on-site, she met all the CHA staff and toured the building before meeting with CHA's President Sharon Sholzberg-Gray. She maintained regular contact with CHA's president through weekly phone conferences from thereon in which she offered wise counsel and advice to the CHA president on a number of internal and member relations' issues. She also attended the CEO Forum, an advisory committee of the CEOs of the provincial and territorial member organizations, which met the day before each scheduled board meeting to discuss issues of mutual interest and concern and to make recommendations to the board or to respond to specific board recommendations or requests. Ms Grant, in turn, extended an invitation to each of the member CEOs to attend CHA board meetings. She also made a point at the end of each board meeting to write a note to the CHA president thanking all CHA staff for their work and support leading up to and including board meetings.

Ms Grant's two-year term in office was one of the busiest and most hectic times for the association. At her first board meeting in November 2002, the board agreed to extend for one year the strategic alliance with the then Association des hôpitaux du Québec (AHQ), which was not in a position financially to rejoin CHA as a full participating member. The board also agreed that patient safety and quality care had become a priority activity for the association with the issue high on the national health care agenda in the coming months. In addition to system funding, reform and sustainability, which were the anchors of CHA's policy agenda for the coming year, the board also added governance. Roundtable reviews from each board member showed the alarming increase of provincial ministerial intrusion into both governance of the system and its management through appointments at the ministry level. The board also agreed at this meeting to develop a policy statement on CHA's vision for home, community and long-term care, as well as a detailed policy document on facility-based long-term care.

In February 2003, both the Romanow Commission and the Kirby Senate Committee reviews of Canada's health care system were released and CHA was much in demand to respond to the recommendations of both reports. Agendas for CHA's board meetings were heavily focused on key advocacy and representation activities around these two reports.

Among other key activities, Ms Grant presided over the board reviews of a draft document, written in partnership with the Canadian Comprehensive Auditing Foundation (CCAF), which included principles on governance, accountability and system effectiveness. The other major issue on the agenda focused on patient safety and CHA's work with the Royal College of Physicians and Surgeons to draft bylaws to set up the Canadian Patient Safety Institute, which was launched in December 2003.

Because of her long-standing association with the Canadian Association of Health-Care Auxiliaries—she had served on its executive for several years—Ms Grant informed the board that the member from Ontario had withdrawn its membership in the organization and the national association was facing major financial stressors and an uncertain future in late 2003. CAHA was an associate member in CHA and Ms Grant represented them at the board table (the organization had sent a participant-observer in previous years to board meetings). The board requested that CHA do what it could to assist in raising the profile and highlight the work of CAHA among its member organizations.

In addition to her weekly talks with CHA's president, Ms Grant also worked closely with the chair-elect, Mary Lapaine, to smooth her transition to the chair. In the second year of her term, the board reviewed the financial policies in the board orientation manual to ensure conformity to actual practice. And the board also agreed to proceed with the publishing of a history of CHA to celebrate its seventy-fifth anniversary in 2006.

When Ms Grant left the board in June 2005, she made a lasting impression on all CHA staff, when she arranged with the Chateau Laurier Hotel in Ottawa to send fresh scones with strawberry jam and real whipped cream to the association to thank each CHA staff member for the support they had given her during her term on the board and as CHA's chair.

Mary Lapaine, 2004-2005

Mary Lapaine was elected to the CHA board in Edmonton in 2003 as the representative from Ontario. She had been chair of the OHA board from 2002 to 2003 and has a long history of volunteer work in the Ontario health system.

In 2004, she was elected as chair of the board in Quebec City. Because of her proximity to Ottawa, Ms Lapaine was able to visit the CHA offices on several occasions and, along with the CEO, she was present for several face-to-face meetings with government officials and for CHA's presentation to the federal Standing Committee on Finance.

The highlight of Ms Lapaine's term was being present and an observer in the Conference Centre, along with CHA president Sharon Sholzberg-Gray, at the First Ministers' Meeting on Health held in Ottawa in September 2004. This was the first time that CHA had been present as observers during crucial negotiations on health care financing between the first ministers. When the report was finally released, many of CHA's advocacy positions were included.

During her term as board chair, she was delighted to host the federal minister of health, Ujjal Dosanjh, who was invited to a lunch session that included both board members and the CEOs of the provincial/territorial member organizations. Ms Lapaine is particularly pleased that the board did extensive review of aboriginal issues during her term, as this was another area of considerable interest to her. In 2005, as past-chair, she was appointed to chair a committee to revisit the CHA's mission and vision statements. She also chaired a committee on the changeover of the CHA conference secretariat to the Canadian College of Health Service Executives.

Alex Taylor 2005-2006

Alex Taylor was chair of the Saskatchewan Association of Health Organizations (SAHO) when he was elected to the CHA board in 2002. In 2005, he became the chair of CHA's board. One of the highlights of his term was to preside over discussions between CHA and the Canadian Association for Community Care (CACC) regarding the integration of the latter organization with CHA. In reporting to the board, he noted that meetings had been open and frank and boded well for a successful integration process in the future. He was correct; in June 2006, both the CACC and CHA boards approved the merger.

At the end of his term in June 2006, CHA officially launched its seventy-fifth anniversary celebrations with a special board dinner to honor past chairs of the association. Mr. Taylor, retired from the active ministry of the United Church of Canada in 2001, continues to be involved in the health system as a hospital volunteer and with the Regina Emergency Services. He is also a member of the board of the Regina Qu'Appelle Health Region and the Regina Scottish Society.

Garnet Burns, 2006-2007

Mr. Burns was appointed to the CHA board as the member for Nova Scotia in 2001. He was elected chair of the board in June 2006. He is the chair of the Nova Scotia Association of Health Organizations and vice-chair of the Capital District Health Authority.

Long involved in health care as a volunteer in his province, Mr. Burns served on the board of the Central Regional Health Board from 1996 to 1999. He was chair of the Hants Community Hospital in Windsor, Nova Scotia, from 1993 to 1996, having served on its board since 1988, and chair of the Hants Community Hospital Foundation. Mr. Burns became chair of CHA's board as the organization was beginning the celebrations of its seventy-fifth anniversary. One of the highlights of his term of office was to preside at the by-invitation-only dinner on Parliament Hill in October 2006 and the launch of this book on CHA's history.

Summary

This chapter has described the fifty-two individuals who were elected as presidents or chairs of the Canadian Healthcare Association. It is also important to remember, however, that there were many other volunteers—several hundred, in fact, over the course of seventy-five years—who served on the hospital council executive, on the association board of directors and on its dozens and dozens of standing and ad hoc committees. These men and women devoted many hours, traveled great distances and worked tirelessly to provide direction for the association throughout its history.

Endnote

1. A breakdown of the list of past presidents or chairs shows the following representation: British Columbia 4, Alberta 7, Saskatchewan 5, Manitoba 4, Ontario 13, Quebec 9, New Brunswick 4, Nova Scotia 3, Prince Edward Island 2 and Newfoundland/Labrador 2. No one from any of the territories has ever held the position.

8

THE LEADERS WHO MANAGED THE ASSOCIATION

"Leadership is a verb, not a noun. Leadership is action, not a position. Leadership is defined by what we do, not the role we're in.

(CLEMMER 1999, 22)

During the last seventy-five years, the Canadian Healthcare Association has been privileged to have had many experienced, knowledgeable and committed staff, who have become recognized leaders in their respective fields of expertise. The position of chief executive officer (CEO) has been filled by ten men and women over the course of CHA's history. These men and women have brought their own unique backgrounds, education and abilities to the management and leadership of the organization.

The Canadian Hospital Council, 1931 to 1952

Dr. George Harvey Agnew (1931-1950)

There is little doubt that there would not be a national health association today without Dr. Harvey Agnew, who was dubbed "Mr. Hospital in Canada" by a hospital journal in its tribute to him in 1971. His leadership, first, on behalf of the Canadian Medical Association (CMA) Department of Hospital Service and, second, on behalf of the Canadian Hospital Council, spanned twenty-two years.

He started his career as a young intern during World War I, serving part of his internship at the Ross Memorial Hospital in Lindsay, Ontario, and later moving to Toronto Western Hospital. He was eventually offered a position at a teaching hospital in

199

Great Britain after the war. He also worked temporarily in the Bellevue and Allied Hospital System in Harlem. His internship in New York City included a four-month stint riding an ambulance and daily visits to the narcotics wing of a prison before he returned to Canada to begin practice at Toronto Western Hospital.

From the day he joined the Department of Hospital Service until the day he died, he devoted all of his working life—and probably a great deal of his personal life—to the hospitals of Canada and the United States. In fact, when he died in 1971, he was working on a history of Canadian hospitals. The book was published in 1974 under the title *Canadian Hospitals, 1920 to 1970: A Dramatic Half Century* and still remains one of the best sources of information about the history of Canada's hospitals during that period.

Dr. Agnew began his long term of leadership in 1928, when the CMA, recognizing the need for a national coordinating body for hospitals, established the Department of Hospital Service. Dr. Agnew was appointed associate secretary of the CMA and full-time secretary of the department. He worked tirelessly with the existing provincial associations and hospitals, travelling thousands of miles across Canada, to explain the purpose of the department, why it was important and how it could benefit hospitals in Canada. In fact, the very first issue that the department tackled under his leadership was that of tariffs and the need for an exemption for Canada's hospitals.

To promote the work of the department, and later the hospital council, he attended hospital meetings, association conventions, wrote letters to federal government officials, worked with physicians, nurses and hospital superintendents to resolve conflicts, and found the time to write about the hospital field in his many editorials published in *Canadian Hospital*.

It was due to his foresight and hard work in contacting many hospital superintendents across Canada and inviting them to the founding meeting in 1931 that the Canadian Hospital Council was established. He became its first secretary, a part-time position he held until 1945, when he left CMA and took on the responsibility of managing the council full-time until 1950. From 1938 until 1950, he was the editor of *Canadian Hospital* and became well-known throughout the hospital field for the opinions he expressed in his column "Obiter Dicta."

As both the editor and an author for the journal, there were very few subjects that Dr. Agnew was reluctant to address. In 1930, he tackled the relationship of the medical profession to the hospital. He suggested joint meetings of the medical staff, trustees and hospital superintendents, and the creation of a medical advisory committee of three to five people. He also supported cooperative purchasing, some form of health insurance and believed in the hospital as a health centre, the health headquarters of the community.

Working with the federal Department of Pensions and National Health during the late 1920s, he helped to compile the first hospital directory which listed the various types of hospitals in Canada. Dr. Agnew was responsible for compiling the data on the type of hospital and the number of beds set up at the time. The federal department agreed to publish this directory in an effort to improve hospital statistics in Canada. He was an avid supporter of setting up standards for Canadian hospitals and worked tirelessly to persuade both hospital superintendents and physicians to accept the American-based accreditation program.

In 1947, he established a two-year graduate course in hospital administration at the University of Toronto and was head of the department until 1962. Committed to education for hospital management, he was named chairman of the council's Committee on Education in 1951. Under his guidance, the committee established the first extension course in hospital organization and management (HOM) in North America (*see* chapter 12 for more details). He spoke to each class of HOM students for the next twenty years and contributed substantially to the extensive revision of the course in 1969. Dr. Agnew was also at the initial meeting of representatives to establish the Nursing Unit Administration Program in 1961.

In 1949, he announced his intention to leave the position of executive secretary of the Canadian Hospital Council in order to pursue a consulting career. He joined the firm of Neergard, Agnew and Craig of Toronto and New York in 1950. Dr. Agnew participated in the first annual convention of the Canadian Hospital Association and was elected president of the Ontario Hospital Association in 1954-1955. In 1958, he established the hospital consulting firm of Agnew, Peckham and Associates Limited and was its board chairman. This firm still carries his name today.

The honors that were bestowed on Dr. Agnew are extensive. He was elected president of the American Hospital Association in 1938 to 1939 and was president of the American Society of Hospital Consultants from 1953 to 1955. He received CHA's George Findlay Stephens Memorial Award in 1953, became an honorary charter fellow of the American College of Hospital Administrators and was named the first honorary member of the Canadian College of Health Service Executives in 1971, the year he died.

Dr. Harvey Agnew—a physician, a scholar, an author, an editor, a painter (in oils), a photographer, a caricaturist, a consultant, a teacher and lecturer—was quite possibly the most significant and influential leader in the Canadian hospital field in the twentieth century. For more than forty years, he worked on behalf of hospitals to improve their position locally and provincially by helping to establish provincial organizations where these did not exist and to give them a national presence through the CHA. Without his dedication and commitment and the endless hours of mostly unpaid time that he devoted to establishing the hospital council, it is very unlikely that it would have survived during these crucial early years.

Dr. Leonard Orville Bradley (1950-1952)

In 1950, Dr. L.O. Bradley (known as Brad) was hired as the full-time executive secretary of the Canadian Hospital Council. Before taking the position, he had been an associate professor of hospital administration at the University of Toronto.

Dr. Bradley was born in Saskatchewan, graduated in medicine from the University of Alberta in 1938 and completed his internship at the Royal Alexandra Hospital in Edmonton. He was awarded the Mead Johnson Fellowship in Pediatrics at the Minneapolis General Hospital and continued on to a second fellowship in the same specialty at the University of Minnesota Hospital in 1940. For the next five years, he served as a medical officer in the RCAF and, in 1946, he became assistant to the superintendent of the Royal Alexandra Hospital in Edmonton. He later enrolled in the School of Business Administration at the University of Chicago and, on graduation, was appointed associate professor at the University of Toronto.

From 1952 to 1956, he was administrator of the Calgary General Hospital and executive director of the Winnipeg General Hospital from 1956 to 1967. In 1967, he became the president-elect of CHA and, at the same time, he was appointed president of the Minneapolis Medical Center.

During Dr. Bradley's term as executive secretary of the hospital council, the Hospital Organization and Management (HOM) course was launched. He was also instrumental in introducing the *Canadian Hospital Accounting Manual (CHAM)*, which set up accounting standards and was eventually used by most of the hospitals in Canada. He was involved in the preliminary organization of the Canadian Council on Hospital Accreditation and, in 1969, he became its executive director, a position he held until 1974.

Although Dr. Bradley was with the council for only two years, he continued to be actively involved for several more years. In 1952, he was appointed to the Committee on Education and eventually became its chairman. He also served on the board of directors and, in 1966, he was named president-elect of CHA. However, before he could take over the office, his appointment as the president of the medical centre in Minneapolis prevented him from serving his term.

Dr. Bradley was also elected the first president of the Canadian College of Health Service Executives in 1970. In 1980, he received the George Findlay Stephens Memorial Award from the association. The citation noted Dr. Bradley's far-sightedness and "the innovative and progressive measures he has brought to the health care system."

Dr. Bradley continued to attend CHA conferences, especially when they were held in Alberta, and board dinners for as long as his health permitted. He remained passionate and committed to the health care field during his lifetime and was always interested in what was happening at CHA. Dr. Bradley died in 2005 in Calgary.

Dr. Arnold L. Swanson (1952-1954)

In 1952, Dr. Swanson succeeded Dr. Bradley as executive secretary of the association. At the time of his appointment, he was deputy medical superintendent of the Provincial Mental Hospital and Crease Clinic of Psychological Medicine in Essondale, British Columbia.

Born in Alberta, Dr. Swanson attended McGill University Medical School and interned at the Montreal General Hospital. He served for two years with the Royal Canadian Medical Corps, following which he joined the medical staff of the British Columbia Mental Health Services. In 1948, he was chosen to attend the course in hospital administration at Northwestern University in Chicago, from which he received a master in hospital administration. He spent the summer of 1949 inspecting hospitals for the American College of Surgeons.

In relating his own personal recollections about the issues facing the CHA during his term, he recalled that the greatest challenge for hospitals in 1952 was the polio epidemic. CHA, and Dr. Swanson, spent considerable time trying to assist the federal government, and the medical and nursing organizations, in procuring respirators and placing them in hospitals where they were most needed. He remembered visiting the Winnipeg Municipal Hospital and seeing several survivors still on rocking beds and in respirators—and all of them very young.

Dr. Swanson was also involved in the development of the hospital accreditation program in Canada. Up until this time, accreditation was conducted by the American accrediting body. Dr. Swanson believed that Canadians were quite capable of establishing their own accrediting organization and standards, and undertaking surveys and evaluations of Canada's hospitals. At the second meeting of the Canadian Commission on Hospital Accreditation, he and Dr. Arthur Kelly, general secretary of the Canadian Medical Association, served as joint secretaries and hired the first two surveyors in Canada for the new organization. Dr. Swanson also became a part-time surveyor for the commission.

During Dr. Swanson's term as executive director, he recalled that one of the longest business meetings of the Canadian Hospital Council was held in 1953 in which members debated changing the name of the council to the Canadian Hospital Association. Both the name change and the issue of accreditation preoccupied members, particularly, whether the latter was affordable for hospitals.

Dr. Swanson left CHA in 1954 to become the administrator of the new University of Saskatchewan Hospital in Saskatoon. He later served as executive director of Victoria Hospital in London, Ontario, and the Queen Street Mental Health Centre in Toronto. In 1969, he became the second Canadian to be elected president of the American College of Hospital Administrators. In 1975, he became the executive director of the Canadian Council on Hospital Accreditation, the organization which he worked so hard to establish in Canada. He also served as president of the Saskatchewan Hospital Association.

The Canadian Hospital Association, 1953 to 1977

Dr. W. Douglas Piercey (1954-1966)

Dr. Piercey became the fourth consecutive physician to lead the association when he was appointed executive director in August 1954. A native of Nova Scotia, he obtained his medical degree from Dalhousie University. He became the superintendent of the Ottawa Civic Hospital, where he had long been regarded as one of the leading hospital administrators in Canada. A past president of the Ontario Hospital Association (1949-1950), he had also chaired the executive committee of the Blue Cross Plan. At the time of his appointment as executive director, Dr. Piercey had been a member of the CHA board for three years and its second vice-president since 1953.

Dr. Piercey believed that the association should be a true national organization representing the interests of all hospitals in Canada. To promote his philosophy, he suggested that one of the main objectives of the association should be to strengthen the lines of communication between the member organizations and the national office located in Toronto at the time. To foster this, he instituted a monthly newsletter, which was sent to all members and other interested groups across Canada.

During his term of office, the CHA purchased a building at 25 Imperial Street in Toronto as its national headquarters. Under Dr. Piercey, the distance education courses offered by the association underwent a rapid expansion with the startup of the Nursing Unit Administration Program in 1961, in partnership with the Canadian Nurses Association, and the departmental management course in 1965.

Dr. Piercey, often described as one of the least pretentious of men, was also passionate about horticulture and won many prizes for his floral exhibits. On one occasion, the CHA board of directors approved the expenditure of a considerable sum of money to redecorate and refurnish his rather shabby office. However, within a few weeks, every available surface in his office was covered with old kitchen pots and pans in which he was growing seedlings for next year's garden.

Dr. Piercey remained at CHA until 1965, when, following two stays in hospital, he resigned on the advice of his physician. He did continue as an editorial consultant for the association journal until the end of the year. He died in 1972 and, in his will, he bequeathed a thousand dollars to the association, which was used to start an audio cassette library.

Dr. Bernard Louis Persillier Brosseau (1966-1977)

In 1966, recognizing the bilingual nature of the CHA membership, the board appointed Dr. Bernard Brosseau as its executive director. Known as Barney by his friends, he had held a number of positions in the army, in government and in several associations prior to coming to CHA.

Born in Montreal, he obtained his medical degree from the University of Montreal and served with the Royal Canadian Army Medical Corps between 1932 and 1962, first as a member of the reserve and, in 1941, as a full-time medical officer. He won the Military Cross during the closing stages of World War II and was made an officer of the Order of the British Empire for his service as commanding officer of the 25th Field Ambulance during the Korean War.

He was a graduate of the hospital administration program at the University of Toronto School of Hygiene and spent six months at Western and Sunnybrook Hospitals in Toronto gaining postgraduate experience in hospital administration. Following his retirement from the armed forces in 1962, he joined the Ontario Hospital Services Commission as the director of the hospital services branch. In 1963, he was appointed commissioner of hospitals in Ontario. Dr. Brosseau was the director of hospital services for the College of Physicians and Services of the Province of Quebec before becoming the executive director of CHA in 1966.

During his eleven years with the association, Dr. Brosseau initiated a number of important projects. These included the launch of the magazine *Hospital Trustee*, for which he had been instrumental in acquiring a startup grant from the W. K. Kellogg Foundation. Annual conventions with exhibits were established by the association during his tenure, as well as regular meetings with the minister and senior officials of the federal Department of Health and Welfare Canada. Under his leadership, the Research and Statistics Department was started, the Education and Publishing Departments were expanded, and CHA's headquarters in Toronto were also expanded to accommodate CHA's growing staff.

Dr. Brosseau was fluently bilingual in both English and French. He was equally capable of writing in both languages and his editorials in *Canadian Hospital*—later the renamed *Dimensions in Health Service*—were widely read. At his direction, the association adopted a policy of providing information and services in both English and French. This dual ability, however, did cause him some difficulties during his term. Sometimes, it seemed as if the English-speaking membership found him to be too French and the French-speaking membership considered him too English.

During Dr. Brosseau's term as executive director, a number of important national symposia and conferences were held including one on computer applications in the health field, group purchasing and treatments for drug users. He managed to successfully negotiate a supporting grant from Health and Welfare Canada for each conference. He was also instrumental in organizing two successful conferences on hospital-medical staff relations in collaboration with the Canadian Medical Association and the Canadian Nurses Association. In 1973, CHA hosted the International Hospital Federation (IHF) Congress in Montreal, the only one ever held in Canada at the time. Dr. Brosseau sat on the IHF council of management.

His leadership style was heavily influenced by his military background and, while always correct in his bearing and conduct, he often appeared distant to staff. He never called a staff member by his or her first name, or vice versa. Sometimes, his correctness was off-putting to people. Yet, in spite of his formal manner, he was thoughtful and fair to CHA staff.

Before he retired from CHA in 1977, Dr. Brosseau oversaw the association's move from Toronto to Ottawa. In addition to his work in the IHF, Dr. Brosseau was very involved in accreditation and standards. He was one of the more active and well-respected surveyors in the accreditation program and, in 1978, he was appointed the assistant executive director of the council. He was vice-chairman of the Sectional Committee on Health Care Technology of the Canadian Standards Association for many years and also a member of the Standards Council of Canada. He died suddenly in June 1988 and was awarded the Canadian Standards Association Order of Merit posthumously that same year.

The Canadian Healthcare Association in Ottawa, 1978 to 2006

Jean-Claude Martin (1977-1989)

Jean-Claude Martin was appointed as the first nonphysician executive director of the association in March 1977. Born in Montreal, he received a bachelor in pharmacy in 1956 and a master in hospital administration in 1962 from the University of Montreal. From 1956 to 1962, he served as a lieutenant-pharmacist in the Royal Canadian Army Medical Corps, where his path crossed with that of Dr. Brosseau.

At the time of his appointment, he was the chief executive officer at Hôpital du Sacré-Coeur in Montreal. Mr. Martin had risen progressively through the various levels of hospital administration in that city and had helped to establish the Montreal Joint Hospital Institute, which was a shared services organization, sponsored by the four McGill teaching hospitals, and one of the first such organizations of its kind in Canada.

Mr. Martin was already involved with CHA as chairman of the annual convention, which was being held in Quebec City in 1977. One of his first responsibilities as the incoming executive director was to find rental space for the association, which he managed to do by the end of the summer in downtown Ottawa within walking distance of Parliament Hill. In addition, he had to hire new staff to fill the various positions in the association as only three CHA staff had agreed to move to Ottawa. By

Left:
Dr. G. Harvey Agnew,
Secretary-Treasurer, 1931 to
1947, and Executive
Secretary, 1947-1950,
Canadian Hospital Council.

Right:
Dr. Leonard O. (Brad)
Bradley, Executive
Secretary, Canadian
Hospital Council, 1950-1952.

Left:
Dr. Arnold L. Swanson,
Executive Secretary,
Canadian Hospital Council/
Association, 1952-1954.

Right:
Dr. W. Douglas Piercey,
Executive Director,
Canadian Hospital
Association, 1954-1966.

Left:
Dr. Bernard (Barney) L.P.
Brosseau, Executive
Director, Canadian Hospital
Association, 1966-1977.

Right:
Jean-Claude Martin,
President, Canadian
Hospital Association, 1977-
1989.

Left:
Carol Clemenhagen,
President, Canadian
Hospital/Healthcare
Association, 1990-1996.

Right:
Tim Julien, Acting
President, Canadian
Healthcare Association,
March-December 1996.

Left:
A. Joyce Bailey, Interim
President, Canadian
Healthcare Association, 1997.

Right:
Sharon Sholzberg-Gray,
President of the Canadian
Healthcare Association,
1998 to present.

the end of the year, all key positions had been filled and the move of CHA headquarters was completed by the end of January 1978.

With CHA now located in Ottawa, Mr. Martin was able to establish cordial relationships with various federal government departments and with other national health organizations which had also established their headquarters in Ottawa. He also brought a much less formal style of management to the association and would not hesitate to remove his jacket, roll up his sleeves and pitch in to do both heavy-duty (furniture moving) and support tasks (photocopying and sorting).

Among his accomplishments, he first pushed for a national health council in 1978 and also spearheaded a campaign to raise funding to define a management information system (MIS) to set up and provide national financial guidelines to collect and disseminate statistical information on Canada's hospitals. Mr. Martin also believed in the value of staff both working together and getting to know each other under informal circumstances. In 1978, he convened the first annual senior staff retreat, which included some educational aspects, some priority setting for the future and some time set aside for socializing. Although not universally popular with all staff, nevertheless, his enthusiasm and conviction usually resulted in some positive outcomes for everyone who participated.

In 1982, the CHA became a true federation with membership in each of the provincial and territorial hospital and health care associations. The emphasis for the organization was on representation of the members' needs and concerns at the federal level. In this same year, preliminary discussions were held on the hospital of the future project, which eventually led to the establishment of the Institute for Health Care Facilities of the Future. In 1983, a communications committee was set up to investigate CHA's involvement in the development of a national health communications network, which eventually became InfoHealth/InfoSanté.

To strengthen CHA's links with both federal government departments and other national health care organizations, Mr. Martin hired a vice-president of public affairs in 1984 in this newly created position. He was also a keen believer in the value of evaluation, and CHA undertook an exhaustive self-review through the American Hospital Association State Hospital Association Review and Evaluation (SHARE) project in 1982. In 1988, the board embarked on an in-depth strategic planning exercise at his urging.

Originally elected to the board of governors of the International Hospital Federation in 1985, Mr. Martin became the first Canadian president of the federation in its sixty-year history, serving from 1989 to 1991. A long-time representative to the House of Delegates of the American Hospital Association from 1977 to 1989, he became one of the few Canadians to receive an honorary life membership in 1989. He was also made an honorary life member of the Canadian Association of Hospital Auxiliaries in 1989 in appreciation for the assistance and support he gave the organization during his years as president of CHA.

Not all of his visions and future thinking were successful. Nor were all his years at CHA easy ones. Funding problems plagued the association from the very early years of his appointment as executive director and the shifting needs of the membership often ran counter to his visions. His vision for a national health council never received any support from either the federal or the provincial governments, despite support from a number of national health organizations. And the InfoHealth Project ultimately cost CHA considerable money and never realized a return on the members' or CHA's investment of time and money, despite the ongoing commitment of both the majority of board members and provincial and territorial member organizations.

Nevertheless, it is interesting to note that his visionary thinking did eventually result in some of these projections being developed. The Management Information System (MIS) Project, launched by CHA during Mr. Martin's presidency, merged with other organizations to become the Canadian Institute for Health Information. The Health Council of Canada was set up in late 2003 and InfoHealth, initiated in 1983, was reincarnated as Canada Health Infoway.

One of his major achievements was the relocation of the association in its own headquarters building at 17 York Street in the Byward Market area of Ottawa. Close to Parliament Hill, and a very short distance from the American Embassy, this heritage building has provided the association with easy access to its key stakeholder groups—parliamentarians, particularly those involved in health care funding issues, parliamentary committee members, federal ministers and senior federal officials in the many departments that impact the health system in Canada.

Mr. Martin stepped down as president of CHA at the end of 1989 after twelve years but continued with the organization on a contractual basis to establish a CHA foundation until the end of 1990. (*See* chapter 10 for more details about the foundation.) He lectured part-time at the University of Ottawa in the Department of Health Administration and eventually returned to Montreal where he continued to consult to various health organizations in Quebec. Over the years of his retirement, he continually supported CHA activities through his attendance at conferences, whenever possible, and it was his outline for the history of the association that was adopted for this book. In June 2006, he received the CHA Award of Excellence for Service and Leadership, only the third CEO to receive CHA's highest honor.

Carol Clemenhagen (1990-1996)

Carol Clemenhagen was the first woman to be appointed to the position of president of CHA and, at thirty-six years old, the youngest. She was a vice-president at the association for six years prior to her appointment to its highest executive position.

Born in Buckingham, Quebec, Ms Clemenhagen obtained a bachelor in political science and sociology (with distinction) from Carleton University and a master of health administration from the University of Ottawa.

In 1977, she began her health administration career at the Department of Epidemiology and Community Medicine at the University of Ottawa. From there, she joined the administration of the Ottawa General Hospital and, in 1984, she became the vice-president of public affairs at CHA.

In January 1990, Ms Clemenhagen took office as president and CEO of CHA at a time when the association was in serious financial difficulty. She focused internal management on untangling liabilities and rebuilding a base for financial stability, presiding over a small organization with a big agenda. She managed to keep the full-time complement of thirty-five staff intact and the budget balanced, with all the association's programs fully operational and some even expanding. Fully bilingual, Ms Clemenhagen emphasized the need for CHA to function in both official languages and improved the association's French-language capacity.

One immediate concern for the hospitals of Canada in 1990, and for Ms Clemenhagen in the early months of her presidency, was the implementation of the Goods and Services Tax (the GST). Ms Clemenhagen negotiated an eighty-three percent rebate rate for hospitals, the highest in the public sector. In collaboration with Ernst & Young, she coauthored the widely used book *Goods and Services Tax: A Question and Answer Guide for the Health Care Sector*.

CHA's advocacy agenda during Ms Clemenhagen's presidency generally focused on Health Canada. Recognizing the growing role of the Department of Finance in health policy decisions at the federal level, she invited both the federal Finance Minister Michael Wilson and Health Minister Perrin Beatty to address the membership at CHA's 1991 Annual General Meeting. The dual thrust worked out very well and, from that point onward, CHA's advocacy agenda has included both federal departments.

One of the major accomplishments of Ms Clemenhagen's presidency was the National Health Policy Reform Project, a two-year effort undertaken by CHA to articulate its vision for Canada's health care system. The nine vision statements and seventy-two health reform recommendations, which remain remarkably pertinent today, were released with considerable publicity for CHA in June 1993. The resulting bilingual reports titled *An Open Future: A Shared Vision* (*Un avenir à bâtir : une vision commune*) served as an historic touchstone in CHA's policy and advocacy base.

During this time, health care reform was also highly topical in the United States. In 1993, Ms Clemenhagen was invited by Congressman Stark of California and Senator Wellstone of Minnesota to present seminars on Canadian health care for congressional and senate staff in Washington, D.C.

Throughout her presidency, she maintained an active policy agenda for CHA, developing health care management reports, guidelines and position statements on subjects such as quality assurance, credentialing, HIV/AIDS, the reuse of disposable medical devices and blood borne pathogens. In 1991, CHA became a founding member of The Health Action Lobby (HEAL), along with several other national organizations. Ms Clemenhagen also negotiated a joint annual conference partnership with the Canadian College of Health Service Executives in 1994, which was extended to the Canadian Long Term Care Association in 1995. And, during Ms Clemenhagen's presidency, the membership agreed to a name change for CHA to the Canadian Healthcare Association in June 1995.

CHA worked hard to bring national attention to the negative impact on health service delivery that the 1995 federal budget cutbacks to cash transfers for health would have. The culmination of this dogged communications effort was probably the 1995 joint conference in Calgary where CHA's call to action to renew the federal commitment to health made the front page of the *Globe and Mail*.

During the last years of Ms Clemenhagen's presidency, there was intense pressure on the CHA member organizations from the fallout of health reform that was sweeping the country. Provincial hospital and health associations faced considerable uncertainty about their future. In turn, they could not guarantee that they would continue as fee-paying members of the CHA federation. A dramatic part of association life at this time was witnessing just how quickly a previously large and powerful provincial member association could be restructured into a small secretariat for regional health authorities.

In early 1996, Ms Clemenhagen announced her resignation from the presidency of CHA to join the then Medical Research Council (MRC), Canada's national medical research funding agency. Retired these days, Ms Clemenhagen lives with her spouse on the St. Lawrence River in the hamlet of Rockport, Ontario. She continues to be active in health care as a member of the board of directors of the Kingston General Hospital and chairs its research committee. Ms Clemenhagen also serves on the board of the Ontario Hospital Association.

Tim Julien, CA, CAE (March-December 1996)

Tim Julien was appointed to the position of acting president in March 1996 during a major transition year for CHA. A chartered accountant, he had been hired as the vice-president of finance and administration in November 1990, reporting directly to the president and to the Finance Committee of the board. He was also responsible for managing building operations at 17 York Street.

In June 1991, he became vice-president of management services with responsibility for information systems and technology, CHA Press, distance education and marketing CHA's products and services. In January 1995, as the only remaining vice-president in the organization, he added the additional internal activities of corporate services, communications and media relations, journal publishing and conference management to his long list of responsibilities. He was also a trustee on the board of the Ottawa General Hospital.

One of the first tasks Mr. Julien undertook in his role as acting president was to reorganize the senior management group and realign the departments and services under each director. He also abolished his former position of vice-president in the restructuring process. At his first board meeting in March 1996, the board asked him to focus particularly on the ongoing financial difficulties that CHA was experiencing, partly due to the restructuring and downsizing taking place in the provincial membership across the health delivery system. To assist with the review of CHA's programs and services and their future viability, he contracted with the firm of Deloitte and Touche to review and recommend actions for the future; the report was to be presented to the September board meeting.

Provincial and territorial members, whose own continued existence was being questioned, began to raise similar questions about CHA such as: Is there a need for a national voice to speak on behalf of the membership? What is the business of CHA? What are its core services? How much should the membership pay for these core services? These questions came to the fore of the board agenda at the June meeting in which both board members and the CEOs of the member organizations asked that Mr. Julien prepare a review of both the core services and its ancillary services, with input from the membership, for presentation at the September board meeting. This would parallel the financial review already underway.

In conjunction with this, an opportunity had also arisen to examine whether there were possibilities for amalgamation, integration or partnerships with other national health organizations. In March 1996, the board mandated the chair and chair-elect to explore opportunities and options with other national health organizations for partnerships or, at the very least, for sharing services and programs. They were to report back at the June board meeting. When the Canadian College of Health Service Executives also announced that it would be seeking a new CEO, Mr. Julien was asked to work closely with the acting president of the college over the summer to explore integration options; both acting presidents were to report back to their respective boards in September on the outcome.

The September 1996 board meeting was a crossroad for CHA. First, neither the CHA nor the college board wished to pursue any further discussions on a merger, after each board had an opportunity to review the "Report of the CHA/CCHSE Task Force." Both boards did ask the two organizations to continue to explore how they might share programs and services. After a long summer of consultation with the CEOs of CHA's member organizations, the senior staff of CHA, board trustees and other national health organizations, Mr. Julien presented the report "Review of Mission and Association Services" to the board for discussion and recommendations on CHA's future. The board had barely begun its deliberations, when the Ontario Hospital Association announced its intention to pull out of CHA by the end of 1996.

With continuing and serious financial shortfalls projected for the future, because members could not commit to ongoing membership at their current fees, the CHA federation now had to face the possibility that their largest member would not be a part of CHA's future. This would not only add to CHA's already unstable financial position but would also deal a serious blow to CHA as one of the few remaining national organizations with representation across the country.

The board took several major decisions at the September meeting and directed Mr. Julien to downsize programs and services as much as possible in an effort to stabilize the finances of CHA. Shortly after this meeting, CHA laid off more than a third of its workforce and staff were informed that various services such as CHA Press and distance education would be seeking buyers for these operations. Failure to find a buyer would mean that these services would be wound down by the end of 1997 and mid-1998.

To say that Mr. Julien's time as acting president was difficult is most definitely an understatement. CHA staff were demoralized by the layoffs and the news of further cuts to come. Keeping the organization focused on a day-to-day basis was extremely difficult. Mr. Julien maintained a fairly laid-back management style throughout his brief tenure as acting president. He kept his door open to all staff during these stressful months and always maintained his sense of humor during these trying times. He particularly liked the summer months and saw this season as a time for a more casual dress code. It was not uncommon to see him working away at his desk in a shirt and tie, knee-high socks and his favorite business shorts.

In early December, he advised the board chair and CHA staff that he would be leaving CHA at the end of the year to become the chief financial officer for the Heart and Stroke Foundation of Canada, a position he held until early 2006.

A. Joyce Bailey, MScN, FCCHSE (January-December 1997)

Joyce Bailey was asked to take over as interim president of CHA early in 1997. She had just recently retired as vice-president of community hospitals at the Ontario Hospital Association (OHA) and agreed to accept the position on the condition that she would commute between Ottawa and Toronto weekly. A nurse by profession, she had received her training at The Wellesley Hospital where she had held a number of senior positions. In 1982, she became the president and CEO of the hospital and remained in this position until 1989.

Ms Bailey joined the OHA in 1990 and served as vice-president until 1996. She was active as a hospital surveyor for the Canadian Council on Health Services Accreditation, a strong supporter of the Canadian College of Health Service Executives and received her fellowship from the college in 1987 and served as chair of the board from 1987 to 1988.

One of Ms Bailey's major tasks on arriving at CHA was to put the organization back on a sound financial basis and to deal with a demoralized staff, as well as the rumors circulating around the capital of CHA's imminent demise, which were adversely affecting CHA's reputation. One of the first decisions she took was to expand senior management to include an experienced person from within CHA's Finance Department. Ms Bailey worked closely with the department to improve financial controls and internal processes in the coming months.

On taking over the position of president, Ms Bailey also had to deal with the instability within the CHA federation membership. Because of her close ties with the OHA, she had been asked to work closely with the organization to persuade them to continue as a member of CHA. She arranged meetings both in Toronto and Ottawa between senior members of both organizations and opened up the lines of communication with CHA's largest member. Before the end of the year, OHA agreed to continue as a member.

During her first month on the job, the Association des hôpitaux du Québec (AHQ) had informed CHA of its intention to withdraw from membership at the end of 1997 because of their inability to pay future member fees. (Unlike other CHA members, the Quebec member's fee was paid by the provincial government.) Along with the CHA past-chair, she met with the CEO and the chair of AHQ to discuss how it might continue its relationship in the future with CHA. AHQ did commit to fulfilling its financial obligations to the end of 1997.

In focusing her efforts on the finances of CHA, at the board's direction, she worked through the first months of her presidency to put together a realistic budget to cover all contingencies in the event one of CHA's members had to withdraw from the federation, not an easy task as the British Columbia Health Association was also about to shutdown its operations and was uncertain about its future status. Along with the CHA board's Task Force, which had been set up to review the fee structure, she presented a revised fee structure to a special board meeting, conducted by teleconference in May, that won the unanimous support of the board. By the time of the November board meeting, the subject of CHA's finances had finally moved to the bottom of the agenda and the board was once again able to focus on setting its policy agenda for the coming year.

By mid-1997, with CHA's financial situation stabilized, Ms Bailey focused on the advocacy and representation side of the organization. The past year had been a difficult one for CHA's reputation and it was important to strengthen this side of the organization. The number one priority for the membership at the time was for CHA to lobby the federal government to reinvest in health care after years of cutbacks. The country was in the midst of a federal election in the spring of 1997, so it was important to the membership that CHA focus its efforts on influencing the various federal parties about shoring up the federal contributions to the Canada Health and Social Transfer (CHST).

In July 1997, Ms Bailey reorganized CHA's policy and communications areas. She hired a new director to take over the policy and advocacy role and to strengthen this core area. She set up a Public Affairs Department to focus on getting CHA's message out to its various publics and to increase its visibility and credibility.

Among her final tasks while interim president, she worked closely with the board Search Committee to find her permanent replacement and advised staff that a new president would be taking over the position at the beginning of 1998. When Joyce Bailey departed from CHA at the end of the first week in 1998, she left a much stronger financial organization than she had found. In fact, the organization ended 1997 with a surplus. In projecting another surplus for 1998, she suggested to the board that it consider paying off CHA's $400,000 mortgage sooner rather than over the proposed eight years.

Ms Bailey had reestablished CHA's voice at the national level by repositioning the policy and advocacy division of the organization, had persuaded CHA's largest member to remain in the federation and had worked closely with several other members to assure them that CHA was now a financially viable organization and worthy of their ongoing membership and support.

In 1998, the board of directors asked Ms Bailey to represent CHA on the board of the Canadian Council on Health Services Accreditation. She was elected chair of the council's board in 2004. Today, Ms Bailey is enjoying her retirement but remains involved in health care as vice-chair of the board of the St. John's Rehabilitation Hospital in Toronto. She also serves on its foundation board and was appointed in 2000 by the OHA as the pensioner-observer on the board of the Hospitals of Ontario Pension Plan (HOOPP).

Sharon Sholzberg-Gray, 1998 to Present

Sharon Sholzberg-Gray has been the president and CEO of the Canadian Healthcare Association since 1998. She is a lawyer by profession and an association manager by occupation. Prior to joining CHA, she was the coexecutive director of the Canadian Association for Community Care (CACC) from 1995 to the end of 1996. Prior to that, she had been the executive director of the Canadian Long Term Care Association from 1989 until its merger with HomeSupport Canada to form the CACC. She was also cochair of The Health Action Lobby (HEAL) for seven years.

She is a member of the Quebec bar and holds degrees in science and law from McGill University, as well as a graduate diploma in public law from the University of Ottawa. Ms Sholzberg-Gray has been active in a wide range of community organizations and has served as a member on various national boards. She has written and spoken extensively about Canadian legal, health and social issues.

Ms Sholzberg-Gray took up her duties as president of CHA in January 1998 after a particularly challenging time in its history. The board, with the full support of its membership, had decided that membership fees would be used to support core activities, which would be the main focus for the organization. These activities included policy development, advocacy, communications and representation of its member interests at the federal level to both government and other national health organizations. Ancillary programs such as distance education, publishing and conferences would be self-supporting and, over the years, some of the revenue generated by these programs has been used to support core services. Ms Sholzberg-Gray's main priorities in the first two years of her presidency were to ensure that the CHA's primary focus was on the core services of the organization with a secondary focus on ongoing financial stability. (The latter had been achieved somewhat by the end of 1997.)

The year 2000 was a particularly significant year for Ms Sholzberg-Gray's presidency for a number of reasons. CHA's financial status remained stable to the point where it had surpluses in the late 1990s and was able to pay off the $400,000 mortgage on its headquarters building at 17 York Street by 2000. She was able to negotiate a strategic alliance with the Association des hôpitaux du Québec (AHQ), which was no longer a member of CHA due to its inability to pay member fees. This strategic alliance remains in effect today.

Almost immediately on her appointment as president, Ms Sholzberg-Gray was effective in raising CHA's public profile. She has been regularly interviewed by both the print and electronic media, delivering CHA's message on both national newscasts and on popular public policy programs. She has often been cited in the media as CHA's chief spokesperson. In the first year of her term, it was vitally important that CHA increase its profile to convey its funding and health system renewal messages to both government and the public. It was also important for key stakeholders to recognize CHA's new name, which it had adopted in 1995. The Canadian Hospital Association had been a recognized and recognizable brand name. But it was somewhat more difficult to explain who the Canadian Healthcare Association represented and what it did.

Ms Sholzberg-Gray has worked extremely hard as CHA's president to explain that CHA today represents a broad continuum of care from acute, long-term and home care to community care and a full range of other services such as public and mental health. This is more complex for CHA's various publics to understand. However, at the federal level, she has made considerable progress. CHA is accepted as the voice of Canada's broad continuum of care, which she regards as one of her major achievements.

One of Ms Sholzberg-Gray's greatest strengths is her considerable understanding of the complexities of Canada's health system funding arrangements. She has an uncanny ability to see through the bureaucratic language to convey complex messages into simple terms. As a result, she has addressed key issues around sustainability, public-private funding and delivery, accountability, safety and quality, privacy and health human resources, among many others. Through her informed discussion of these issues, CHA has continued to play an important role in shaping macro health policy in Canada. In fact, often CHA's wording in its policy documents, position statements and briefs to federal departments and committees has been adopted by others both in- and outside government. CHA's words such as cash floor, escalator and targeted funding have often appeared in other organizations' comments when talking about health system renewal.

Some of the key events in which Ms Sholzberg-Gray participated on behalf of CHA occurred in 2001. In May, CHA released its Policy Brief on accountability entitled *Towards Improved Accountability in the Health System*. Then, on 11 September 2001, CHA scheduled a press conference on Parliament Hill to release its next Policy Brief titled *The Private-Public Mix in the Funding and Delivery of Health Services in Canada*. Unfortunately, the terrorist attacks in the United States that same day overshadowed CHA's release of the document. But there was considerable followup later in the fall on CHA's position. Following on these events, Ms Sholzberg-Gray presented to the Romanow Commission. This brief was based on CHA's ten-point plan titled *A Responsive, Sustainable, Publicly Funded Health System in Canada: The Art of the Possible*. In November 2001, at the request of the board, Ms Sholzberg-Gray was asked to present a history and overview on funding Canada's health system to inform the board and clarify CHA's positions at the next board meeting.

She was no less busy in 2002 when CHA presented to the Standing Senate Committee on Social Affairs, Science and Technology, more commonly known as the Kirby Committee, in March; the basis for this briefing was again the CHA ten-point plan. CHA was invited to appear before the committee once more in June to comment on principles outlined in its final volume of recommendations. Ms Sholzberg-Gray also appeared before the Romanow Commission in April and was invited by the commission to participate in stakeholder consultations in June. When the Kirby and Romanow Reports were released in 2002, CHA, through Ms Sholzberg-Gray, was a credible and impartial voice for the health system in providing feedback.

In February 2003, the Federal/Provincial/Territorial First Ministers' Meeting released the Accord on Health System Renewal in the wake of reports from the Kirby and Romanow reviews. While other health organizations were praising the 2003 Health Accord, CHA was unique among them in forcefully articulating its ongoing concerns. CHA believed that, while the accord had made some progress in addressing problems facing Canada's health system, it fell short of what CHA thought was necessary. As well as pointing out the positive aspects, Ms Sholzberg-Gray delivered the message on behalf of the membership that funding in the accord to "shore the core" was inadequate. As time passed, a consensus among several other national organizations occurred and, in 2004, the new prime minister, Paul Martin, announced another First Ministers' Meeting for September, confirming CHA's message that the 2003 accord had not done the job.

Another key accomplishment for Ms Sholzberg-Gray also occurred in 2003. She was asked to play a major role in the establishment of the Canadian Patient Safety Institute, an autonomous nongovernmental agency created to promote patient safety issues across the continuum of care. Along with Dr. Michael Brazeau, CEO of the Royal College of Physicians and Surgeons of Canada, she cochaired the federal/provincial/territorial and stakeholder process that led to the creation of the institute. She also drafted the bylaws and recommended a slate of candidates for the founding board of the institute, along with Dr. Brazeau. The issue of public health also came to the forefront in 2003 with the SARS crisis. CHA advocated for the creation of a public health agency and a chief public health officer for Canada, which eventually occurred.

Ms Sholzberg-Gray regards 2004 as a watershed year both for CHA and her personally. The year was action-packed from the June 2004 federal election, where health care was touted as a top priority, to the September First Ministers' Meeting, which resulted in the 2004 Health Accord, to the release of the first annual report from the Health Council of Canada. Throughout the year, perhaps more so than ever, CHA's input was repeatedly sought by a wide range of audiences including senior government officials, policymakers, other national health organizations and the media. Ms Sholzberg-Gray was continually asked to present CHA's position and policies, which were not only sought after but often repeated or quoted by others. During the June election, she was interviewed by the media on health issues and asked to communicate CHA's position on the various party health platforms.

Following the election, CHA entered into an intense period of government relations activity as a prelude to the First Ministers' Meeting. Either alone or as members of the Group of Four, which included CHA, along with the Canadian Medical Association, the Canadian Nurses Association and the Canadian Pharmacists Association, CHA met with the new health minister, Ujjal Dosanjh; the Clerk of the Privy Council; and key officials in the prime minister's office, Finance Canada and Health Canada.

For her personally, one of her most significant accomplishments in 2004 was to secure credentials for all the Group of Four representatives, thus enabling them to be present in the meeting room at the Conference Centre in Ottawa in September during the first ministers' deliberations. This historical on-site presence facilitated CHA's role as an honest broker among all levels of government. This period was marked by extensive media interviews and coverage of CHA's position. Ms Sholzberg-Gray took part in media scrums, live television and radio commentary, and print interviews. She believes that the combined effect of CHA's presence on-site, along with her board chair, and CHA's advocacy efforts leading up to the meeting resulted in a better agreement. Still she knows that much remains to be done and leads CHA in continuing to press the federal government on behalf of its membership.

During this extremely busy year, CHA released a joint publication, with CCAF (formerly the Canadian Comprehensive Auditing Foundation) entitled *Excellence in Canada's Health System: Principles for Governance, Management, Accountability and Shared Responsibility*, in response to provincial and territorial member organizations' concerns about both government and public perceptions around the governance and management of Canada's health system. CHA also released its fifth brief in its Policy Brief Series on facility-based long-term care delivery.

While her main focus has been to develop policy based on the board's priorities and with input from the membership, CHA continued to successfully deliver several distance education programs and position itself for the future with a new name—CHA Learning—in 2001. The department remained financially healthy over the course of her term, generating revenues that contributed to the association's financial stability. This enabled CHA to keep up to date with current technology, including developing its own Web site.

Although there were glitches in the partnership with the Canadian College of Health Service Executives and the Canadian Association for Community Care, the three partners nevertheless planned, implemented and delivered the successful National Healthcare Leadership Conference annually, with healthy profits for the partners during Ms Sholzberg-Gray's term as president.

During these years, publishing continued to face challenges in the North American publishing environment, although it began to identify niche areas such as long-term care in which to focus its efforts. Still the Publishing Department was able to contribute to the debate on health reform by publishing books such as Dr. Nuala Kenny's *What Good Is Health Care?*, as well as working with the Policy Development Department to publish CHA's Policy Brief Series. Ms Sholzberg-Gray's term included the fifty-year anniversary publication of the *Guide to Canadian Healthcare Facilities* in 2003 and publication of the history of CHA to celebrate its seventy-fifth anniversary.

Being president of a nonprofit advocacy association continues to be a challenging occupation for Ms Sholzberg-Gray. Internally, the small staff is asked to accomplish much for CHA and its membership. Organizations such as CHA are continually asked by their membership to demonstrate they are value added and worth the fees that members pay from their scarce resources. Ms Sholzberg-Gray believes that CHA plays a crucial role in Canada as the collective voice for a high-quality accessible health system. She will continue to do her part to ensure that CHA's voice is heard.

Summary

While this chapter has highlighted the background, abilities and contributions of the men and women who have led CHA during its past seventy-five years, they would not have achieved their successes without the many staff who have worked in the association since its early establishment in 1931.

These staff members have made many contributions over the years to the success of CHA. Whether they worked in the mailroom or in customer service, or as program directors in distance learning, as analysts in research and policy development, as editors and writers in publishing, or as corporate secretaries, administrative and executive assistants or at the senior management level, each individual has helped CHA to fulfill its mission and vision throughout the course of its history. And each of these staff made it possible for the leaders of the association to achieve their own goals and make their own unique contributions to CHA.

Part III

CHA AND OTHER NATIONAL HEALTH ORGANIZATIONS

This part of the book will focus on the many relationships that CHA has established with other national health organizations throughout its seventy-five years. Because of the nature and size of Canada's health care system, CHA could hardly function alone and independently over the years without interacting with many other organizations.

Some of these represent health professionals such as physicians, nurses and other allied health professionals who work in hospitals and, in many cases, require linkages with those representing the institutional component of the system to resolve problems and improve health delivery. Some health organizations simply shared common goals, while others partnered with CHA to create a new program, deliver a conference or present a joint brief to a key federal department.

Chapter 9 describes CHA and its historical national health partners. It begins with an overview of the Canadian Medical Association, CHA's oldest Canadian partner and its founding organization. Each health organization is briefly described from its own early beginnings with a brief overview of where the organization is today. The chapter then outlines CHA's long-term relationship with that organization, the areas in which they shared common goals and issues on which they differed. The chapter also includes both the American Hospital Association and the International Hospital Federation because of the role they have played with CHA over the years as a partner.

Chapter 10 presents the seven health organizations that were founded by CHA outright either as spinoffs of special projects or that were set up in partnership with other health organizations to meet some need in the health system. As the health care system evolved, the need of CHA's members changed. Driven by this, CHA established health organizations that could fill voids in the health system. Again, the chapter follows a set format by moving through each of the key historical periods in CHA's history and describing key events that led to the founding of these health organizations. It also outlines the organization as it exists today or discusses the events that led to its demise.

9

CHA AND ITS HISTORICAL PARTNERS

"What all of these strategic partnerships . . . have in common is that they require a win-win relationship in which each partner contributes something of significant value and gains something of significant value in return.

(HESSELBEIN ET AL. 1999, 265)

The Canadian Healthcare Association has established relationships with many health organizations on the national scene over its seventy-five-year history. Some of these relationships grew out of early connections in which the organization played a key role in setting up CHA and ensuring that it got off the ground. Other organizations developed linkages with CHA based on shared goals, mutual interests or the need to resolve problems that pertained to Canada's hospitals. These relations have continued over the course of CHA's history. This chapter looks at some of the key historical partners who have been inextricably linked to CHA over the years.

Canadian Medical Association (CMA)

The historical linkages between the hospital association and the Canadian Medical Association (CMA) reach back to the founding days of the Department of Hospital Service in 1928. The CMA itself was founded in 1867, the same year that the Canadian confederation came into existence. CMA is a professional membership organization of individual physicians and is one of the oldest and most influential medical organizations in Canada today.

By the 1900s, the hospital had become the centre of choice in which physicians practiced medicine. After World War I, physicians increasingly chose the hospital to test their medical knowledge, practice their surgical skills and further their medical careers. They became hospital superintendents, visiting physicans with privileges or joined the medical staff of the hospital outright, working in surgical units, caring for patients on public wards and in private rooms, and developing medical specialties where access to surgical units, laboratories and outpatient clinics allowed this. Decisions taken by physicians in hospital determined the extent of treatment, the type of care and how long a patient could expect to occupy a hospital bed. These decisions impacted on hospital costs as doctors ordered treatment and care, performed surgery, delivered anesthesia and conducted other diagnostic tests as more and better technologies emerged.

The interests of the medical profession in the operation of hospitals were crucial to both the hospital and its medical staff. Many physicians had become concerned with the lack of standards for hospitals in everything from construction, to laboratories, to the delivery of patient care at the bedside. As such, this had led to the establishment of the Department of Hospital Service in 1928. The CMA hired Dr. Harvey Agnew as its associate secretary to direct the activities of the hospital department and to focus on hospital matters specifically. This left the CMA to take up the cause of quality care and better training for interns in hospitals.

Occasionally, Dr. Agnew addressed the matter of medical/hospital relationships. Speaking in Vancouver in August 1930 to a joint hospital association meeting, he commented on the relationship of the medical profession to the hospital by noting:

> . . . that every decade we are going to see the interests of the hospital and the medical profession thrown closer together; . . . each is quite dependent upon the other; . . . each has a definite responsibility to the other; and . . . the medical profession as a whole is taking a much more active and intelligent interest in the general problem of its workshop [the hospital] than ever before (17).

This summary of the linkages between the hospital and the medical profession set the framework for some of the ongoing issues that would be raised over the following decades between the council and the CMA.

One area in particular that needed attention was how the medical staff should relate to the hospital and its staff. Dr. Agnew suggested "the creation of a medical advisory committee of three or five" physicians who would be appointed by the medical staff with advisory responsibility only (1930, 16). Most physicians were independent professionals who were granted privileges to practice in the hospital. To ensure a better working relationship between the medical staff and the hospital, medical advisory committees were eventually established. This organizational structure provided a forum where hospital physicians could discuss and resolve problems, and make recommendations to the administration and the governing board of the hospital. These committees were mandated by the board to develop the necessary standards of medical practice and its specialties in the facility, to evaluate the competence of practising physicans and to make recommendations to the board on the renewal of physician privileges.

Not only was the CMA one of the founding members of the Canadian Hospital Council in 1931, but it also sponsored Dr. Agnew's efforts to organize the founding meeting. The CMA was generous in providing assistance to set up the early council office and the delegates at the founding meeting accepted ". . . the offer of the Department of Hospital Service of the [CMA] to make use of its facilities . . . " (Burcher 1931, 12). The CMA also allocated "part of the annual grant of the Sun Life Assurance Company . . . [to be] used in furthering the aims and objects of the Canadian Hospital Council . . . (Ibid.). The council operated out of CMA headquarters and used CMA's stenographic and secretarial services, accessed the Blackader Library, as well as the hospital information files that had accumulated over the years. It would have cost considerable money if the council had to set up these services on its own. In assisting the council further, the CMA took over much of the work involving any studies that were requested by the delegates, because the council had minimal staff in the person of Dr. Agnew as part-time secretary-treasurer. Most of these studies were published as council bulletins over the years and CMA periodically contributed money to cover the printing costs (CHC 1941, 21).

At the 1933 Biennial Meeting, the council devoted part of its agenda to the discussion of medical issues, led by the chairman of the Committee on Medical Relations, Dr. Alfred Haywood, who was superintendent of the Vancouver General Hospital. On presentation of his report, there was a round table discussion among the delegates about medical staff problems. CMA was present as a voting member at all meetings throughout the 1930s and 1940s, and the assembly meetings usually included a discussion about a medical issue. Intern training in the hospital and hospital standards were two key issues that periodically appeared on the agenda. From time to time, the delegates would direct the council to set up joint meetings with CMA to work out solutions to these problems.

In 1945, the hospital council separated from the CMA to become an independent organization. The council moved out of CMA headquarters in Toronto to its own offices and officially became independent in January 1946. However, it could not have made even this transition without, yet again, the financial assistance of the CMA, which transferred the Sun Life annual grant and permanently loaned the Blackader Library and library fund to the council. In return, CMA lost the services of their long-time associate secretary, when Dr. Agnew left CMA to become the full-time council managing secretary.

By 1951, the issue of hospital standardization was becoming crucial, especially with the rapid expansion of hospitals under the federal grants program for hospital construction. A new American commission was being set up to deal with this issue and delegates had directed the council to study this matter. The CMA and the CHA, along with the Association des Médecins de Langue Française du Canada and the Royal College of Physicians and Surgeons, worked jointly throughout the 1950s to set up an all-Canadian accreditation program, which was successfully launched in January 1959. Both CMA and CHA held seats on its board and worked together to ensure its survival throughout its early years.

For both organizations, the big issue of the 1960s was the introduction of universal hospital insurance and the impact this had on each association. In 1963, the CMA invited the CHA to form a joint committee to approach the federal government to request a review of the hospital insurance act (CHA 1964a, 5). Although this committee was formed to deal specifically with this particular issue, the CMA, CHA and CNA had been meeting for many years to discuss many health-related issues— everything from hospital disaster planning to intern shortages.[1] The original focus of the liaison committee had been on nursing issues but by the mid-1960s, discussions were wide-ranging on a multitude of issues and CHA's board reaffirmed its commitment to the continuation of the CMA/CNA/CHA Liaison Committee in 1965.

In 1968, the three health organizations agreed to change the name of their committee to the Joint Committee of the CHA-CMA-CNA. The composition and terms of reference of this committee were formalized and approved by each association's board. Its purpose was to discuss issues of mutual concern, recommend solutions, initiate studies, make joint approaches to government and report back to their boards. And, throughout the decade, CMA continued to send a voting delegate to the CHA assembly. In turn, CHA sent representatives to CMA's annual meeting. Usually, the president or executive director represented CHA and delivered a detailed report to the board, which became part of the board record, with considerable board time spent on discussing mutual CMA-CHA issues. (*See* chapter 13 for additional cooperative efforts between the three associations.)

In the 1980s, a new issue confronted both national associations, namely, medical malpractice and the alarming increase in the monetary compensation being awarded as a result of physician liability in health care facilities across the country. A 1985 editorial in the CHA journal *Dimensions* noted that ". . . the situation is now reaching alarming proportions with recent judgements allocating substantial awards" (Martin, 6). The editorial concluded by suggesting that a working group be formed with representatives from the health professions and institutions ". . . to study available data, evaluate the need of the sector and propose . . . solutions" (Ibid.).

The CMA, through its involvement in the Canadian Medical Protective Association (CMPA), a mutual defence organization for physicians who practice in Canada, was also involved in this critical issue. The federal government had appointed a national working group to study and make recommendations pertaining to liability insurance. Since many of the malpractice lawsuits involved physicians and their actions in a hospital, input and cooperation from both the CMA and CHA was essential in reaching solutions. Numerous bilateral discussions were held between the two organizations and, at a meeting on 18 April 1986, agreement was reached on recommendations to be presented in a joint brief to the federal working group.

In the 1990s, the CMA and the CHA frequently worked together to issue joint statements, along with other national health organizations, on such matters as resuscitative interventions (1995) and to publish books on subjects such as clinical guidelines. In 1991, both organizations were among the founding members of The Health Action Lobby, commonly known as HEAL, which lobbied the federal government to restore federal funding for health care to its pre-1990 levels. In 1994, the CMA and the CHA signed an agreement in which CHA would assume full responsibility for the inventory management and distribution of more than three hundred CMA book titles.

Throughout the late 1990s and continuing today, both CMA and CHA have worked together to present joint policy positions to the federal health minister, other officials at Health Canada and to various parliamentary committees. In September 2004, both the CMA president and the CHA chair, along with William Tholl, the secretary general of the CMA and Sharon Sholzberg-Gray, president of CHA, were among a select group invited to attend the First Ministers Meeting on Health at the Conference Centre in Ottawa.

Today, both CMA and CHA, along with the national nursing and pharmaceutical associations, make up what has commonly become known as the G4—the four national health organizations that speak out on issues concerning Canada's health care system. Throughout CHA's history—either as founder, supporter, partner and, occasionally, opponent—the CMA has been involved in some way with the association and this relationship will no doubt continue into the future as both organizations work together to improve Canada's health system.

American Hospital Association (AHA)

From the very early days in the 1900s, Canada's hospitals were members of an American hospital organization, since none existed in Canada at the time. Founded in September 1899 from a meeting of eight hospital superintendents, who met in Cleveland to discuss common interests and concerns, this informal gathering led to the establishment of the Association of Hospital Superintendents, which, in turn, became the American Hospital Association of United States and Canada in 1906.

In the absence of a Canadian national association of hospital superintendents, many of them—especially from large institutions and teaching hospitals—decided to join the AHA and developed strong relationships with their counterparts in the United States. In fact, Canadian hospital superintendents were successful in convincing the AHA to hold their 1931 annual meeting in Toronto in September.[2] This 1931 meeting was also the inaugural meeting of the Canadian Hospital Council.

The relationship between Canadian hospital superintendents and the AHA was so interwoven that the complete agenda for this meeting was reprinted in the September pages of *Canadian Hospital*, followed by detailed reports of the meeting and its attendees. The article also included pages of photographs of the elected officers of the AHA and other health organizations that were at the meeting, indicating the importance of this organization to Canadians on matters involving AHA. Not only did the journal feature a great deal of information about the AHA, it encouraged Canadian administrators to join the association.

The AHA was not only the largest such organization of its kind in North America at the time, it was also one of the reasons why Dr. Agnew and other founding members of the council decided against setting up a similar hospital association in Canada in 1931. They knew they could not compete with AHA in organizing educational sessions and commercial exhibits.

Changes in the operation of the AHA were clearly of interest to the council and each biennial meeting included an item on its activities, many of which impacted Canada's hospital superintendents. In 1937, Dr. Agnew reported to the delegates that the AHA was implementing constitutional revisions and would create a board of trustees that year to act as the executive council in future for the association. To elect members to this board, the new structure would include a House of Delegates representing all parts of the United States and Canada. In accordance with this change, AHA members in each province would be entitled "to name at least one delegate to the House of Delegates—possibly more, if they have a large membership" (CHC 1937, 17).

The AHA invited the council to name the Canadian delegates. But the council declined because it did not pay membership dues; these were paid by individual hospitals or their superintendents. In 1939, the AHA announced a reduction of twenty-five percent in its membership fee for Canadian hospitals as the governing board was aware of the fact that not all the activities and actions undertaken by AHA, particularly in the area of hospital legislation, had any effect on Canada's hospitals.

The importance of the AHA to the council was such that the board of directors had set up a Committee on Association Relations in 1951, initially, to study and report on setting up a Canadian standardization program, which included relations with the Joint Commission on Hospital Accreditation. In 1953, the council's board agreed that this committee should continue for the exclusive purpose of exploring and developing a working relationship with the AHA (CHC 1953b).

By 1954, the AHA had again increased its fees for Canadian hospital membership. Several provincial associations raised the issue through their representatives on the CHA board, which directed CHA to ask AHA for associate membership. Discussions continued between the two associations and, in late 1955, the two organizations reached an agreement. AHA decreased Canadian hospital membership fees and invited provincial associations to become affiliate members. AHA would also coordinate the collection of hospital statistics through CHA and CHA would recommend the Canadian representative to be appointed by AHA to the Joint Commission on Accreditation of Hospitals.

In 1968, the AHA changed its constitution and bylaws again and signed an agreement with CHA, whereby all Canadian hospitals could receive all AHA membership privileges. The AHA granted special institutional membership to CHA and, in turn,

CHA granted the American association active membership. At the time, CHA paid the membership fee for Canadian representation to AHA and, as a courtesy, AHA made every effort to ensure that all contact with Canadian hospitals was first made through the CHA. CHA would also select a representative to the House of Delegates. The proposed amendments now made it possible for a representative from Canada to be eligible for election to the board of trustees and to become an officer of AHA.

When CHA amended its bylaw in 1975, it made provisions for other organizations to become active members. As a result, AHA was named an active member, entitled to name its own delegate and alternate to CHA's Annual General Meeting, where it had one vote under the bloc voting system. Then, in 1981, under a newly amended bylaw, AHA was given associate membership only. By the early 1980s, both organizations had abandoned the practice of appointing representatives to each other's boards.

For many years, both associations continued to exchange information about hospital activities in their countries. AHA often permitted CHA access to some of its services, including exclusive reprint rights of its trustee series in the 1977 launch of the *Hospital Trustee* magazine. In 1982, CHA also acquired access to the Share Hospital Association Review and Evaluation (SHARE) program, which CHA used to evaluate its internal operations and external relations.

When the AHA advised CHA in 1979 that it would be holding its annual meeting in Montreal in 1980, CHA agreed to work with the AHA in partnership to cohost the conference. While the conference was successful for both organizations, and for CHA's members in Ontario and Quebec, such a large event did tie up CHA's resources for months in planning and on-site management. When AHA approached CHA to undertake a similar arrangement in 1986, CHA declined. Between the late 1980s and the mid-1990s, CHA also distributed AHA publications through its Publishing Department in a mutual distribution arrangement between the two organizations.

Many of CHA's elected officers played key roles in the AHA over the years. In 1933-1934, Dr. Agnew was elected as a trustee and both Dr. George F. Stephens (1934-1935) and Dr. Harvey Agnew (1938-1939) were elected presidents of AHA. Other CHA presidents such as Stanley Martin, Alan Hay and Justice Chaiker Abbis were involved at different times in the governance of the AHA. In 1989, after having served for twelve years as the CHA representative in the AHA House of Delegates, Jean-Claude Martin was made a Life Honorary Member of AHA on his retirement from CHA. To this date, CHA continues to send a member of its board, usually the chair and, occasionally, the president, to AHA meetings. Until CHA stopped delivering an annual conference, the AHA chair was always invited to attend.

Canadian Nurses Association (CNA)

The development of modern nursing began with Florence Nightingale and the creation of a School of Nursing at St. Thomas Hospital in 1860 in London, England. The first Canadian School of Nursing was founded at the General and Marine Hospital in St. Catharines, Ontario, in 1874, thus, establishing links with hospitals. In fact, student nurses provided unpaid labor for hospitals as more and more of these training schools were set up in Canadian hospitals.

In 1908, representatives of sixteen organized nursing bodies met in Ottawa to form the Canadian National Association of Trained Nurses (CNATN). This body became the Canadian Nurses Association (CNA), a federation of all the provincial nursing associations, in 1924. Today, the Canadian Nurses Association is the national professional voice of Canada's registered nurses. It supports these nurses in their practice and advocates for healthy public policy and a quality, publicly funded, not-for-profit health system. It is a federation of eleven provincial and territorial nursing associations and represents more than 126,000 registered nurses.

In 1932, the CNA and CMA's Committee on Nursing cosponsored a study that was conducted by Dr. George M. Weir from the University of British Columbia. This report became the master plan for the future development of hospital nursing in Canada. Until the 1950s, all nurses in Canada received their training in nursing schools that were based in and operated by hospitals. Then, as now, among the health care professions, the nursing sector is still the largest in the health care field.

Almost from the establishment of the council, nursing issues of one type or another could be found either on the agenda of the General Assembly or the subject of a report, a study or a resolution from the delegates. In fact, the record of the Fourth Biennial Convention in 1937 shows, that among the various committees, a nursing committee was established by the delegates to study nursing issues and report back to the delegates at each assembly. Issues such as the length of the nursing work day in hospital, the curriculum for hospital nursing schools and what clinical duties nurses should be allowed to undertake in hospital were among some of the issues addressed at council biennial meetings in the 1930s. The records of these meetings also indicate that representatives from the CNA were invited to address the delegates on these issues as part of the discussion or to present reports.

Throughout the 1940s, nursing shortages in hospitals, the use of nursing aides and their training, graduate studies for nurses and how to enhance the exchange of information on nursing between the two organizations were frequently discussed. The 1947 biennial convention of the council included resolutions on "the urgent and immediate necessity for a thorough study and analysis of the . . . factors in the constant and increasing shortage of nurses, . . ." (CHC 1947, 100), as well as on the waste of nurses' time on tasks that could be handled by others and on improving nurses' pay. A full report on the future of nursing and nursing education was presented to the 1949 biennial meeting of the council.

In 1952, the council approved participation in the Canadian Commission on Nursing. It comprised two representatives from the CMA, the CNA and the council, and would study and recommend ways to improve nursing shortages at the local, provincial and national level. At the time, the CNA was conducting nursing surveys and collecting data on nursing shortages through their various provincial associations. Although the commission met regularly, it does not appear to have accomplished much mostly due to the lack of funds. The leadership on most nursing issues was left to the CNA.

In October 1955, the CNA, members of CHA's Committee on Education and faculty from the University of Toronto School of Nursing were invited to a meeting in Toronto with representatives of the W. K. Kellogg Foundation. The foundation believed that an extension course on nursing administration was needed. This was the beginning of the joint Nursing Unit Administration Program, cosponsored by both the CNA and the CHA but coordinated and operated by CHA, specifically for nurses to improve their administrative knowledge and skills. (*See* chapters 10 and 12 for more details.)

A major issue that set both organizations on a collision course was the CNA decision in 1959 to undertake a pilot project to reexamine the whole field of nursing education and, most particularly, to develop "a program of accreditation for schools of nursing" (CHA 1961a, 2). At the time, schools of nursing were hospital-based. CHA was fully committed to these nursing schools and the notion of training at the bedside. On the other side, CNA was moving toward nursing education being conducted in accredited learning centres such as colleges, where the focus was more on academic training. In the end, hospital schools of nursing were closed and training was moved to colleges. The two organizations did maintain open communication through membership on the CMA/CNA/CHA Liaison Committee.

As other organizations moved toward more professional standards and demanded higher education, the boundary issue over the scopes of practice between nurses and physicians took on more significance. This pulled CHA into the debate as the members of both the CNA and the CMA practiced their professions within the hospital. In 1966, CNA continued its membership in the newly named Joint Committee of the CHA-CMA-CNA. Along with meetings of this joint committee, there were also bilateral meetings of the CEOs, as well as joint projects and presentations. But the issue of nursing education continued to keep both organizations on opposites sides; the point was driven home quite clearly to CHA in 1966, when the membership passed a resolution directing CHA to continue to ensure that hospital-based nurse training was retained as one of the principal methods of preparing nurses for practice. In 1982, CHA's board requested that a report be prepared on nursing shortages in high-skilled areas. Once again, both organizations were on opposite sides in the debate.

By 1987, the CNA again examined the requirements for nursing education for its members. As more and more professions had entered into the health care field, many of them with university degrees, the CNA announced that they intended to develop a position on nursing entry to practice with the expectation that all nurses would be required to have a baccalaureate degree by the year 2000. CHA, speaking on behalf of its members, advised CNA about the impact this would have on salary expectations and on hospital budgets. The board advised CHA to consult with its provincial members and to continue to meet with CNA to ensure that the hospital viewpoint was clearly represented.

Over the years, the two organizations had worked together through a joint board committee to review, revise and oversee the Nursing Unit Administration Program. As more and more nurses moved to university training, enrolment in the course continued to decline. In 1992, CHA informed CNA that it could no longer support the program and, after more than twenty-five years of cosponsoring and delivering the program with CNA, CHA withdrew from its partnership arrangement.

Both the CNA and the CHA were among the founding members of The Health Action Lobby (HEAL) Coalition in 1991. In fact, the secretariat was set up at CNA and both organizations worked closely together to ensure its success. Today, the CNA is one of the four major health organizations—known as the Group of Four or G4—along with CHA, that lobby the federal government on funding and sustainability of Canada's health system. While the two organizations have not always been on the same side of every issue, they have worked closely together over CHA's seventy-five-year history to ensure that their mutual points of view are known. Both organizations interact frequently on nursing human resource issues, organize conferences and lobby the federal government on improving the health system.

International Hospital Federation (IHF)

Several American and European physicians organized an international hospital congress in Atlantic City, New Jersey, in 1929. According to Dr. Agnew's description, this was so successful that a second meeting was held in 1931, which resulted in the establishment of the International Hospital Association (1974, 101). The council sent at least two officers to each biennial congress to represent Canadian hospitals and to report back to the delegates.

In 1939, the council, along with the Ontario Hospital Association and the AHA, cosponsored the Sixth Biennial Congress of the International Hospital Association (IHA). This meeting was scheduled for Toronto that year. As the council reported to the 1939 assembly, it had spent considerable money translating documents and programs for this meeting. But, with the outbreak of World War II, the IHA had cancelled its participation in the Toronto meeting and the activities of the international organization disappeared from the record of the council's assembly meetings as the country became preoccupied with the war effort.

In 1947, the hospital council assembly delegates supported the establishment of the International Hospital Federation (IHF), which was created in 1948 to succeed the IHA. Periodically, over the next few years, reports of IHF activities were recorded in the minutes of CHA's board meetings or in the record of the biennial meetings of the assembly. These were usually reports from the officers who attended the international meetings of the hospital federation. Throughout the 1950s, IHF frequently invited CHA to become a member. Finally, CHA joined the federation in 1961 and elected representatives to its board of directors throughout the 1960s.

Since the IHF was mostly concerned with the delivery of health care to third-world countries, and a major portion of its funds were devoted to supporting these countries, CHA's participation over the years was more in giving time and money than in receiving benefits. However, IHF activities were considered of sufficient importance over the years that some CHA member organizations supported the attendance of Canadian hospital representatives at IHF meetings and made substantial contributions to pay their expenses.

In 1973, CHA hosted the IHF Annual Congress in Montreal, the only one ever held in Canada. At the time, Dr. Brosseau, CHA's executive director, was a member of the IHF management council and was instrumental in arranging the event. In 1982, CHA's board invited the IHF to hold its 1986 Study Tour in Canada, which CHA organized on its behalf. The tour was conducted in western Canada in June and July 1986. More than 200 visitors from around the world were hosted by hospitals in Calgary, Edmonton and Vancouver. CHA's senior staff undertook considerable work to provide translation services and to accompany these groups in their travels. Elected to its board in 1985, CHA's president, Jean-Claude Martin, was the first Canadian to be elected president of the IHF in 1989.

When the new secretary-general of the IHF took over his duties, he decided to redesign the IHF journal. Much of the redesign and all editorial work was undertaken by CHA staff in the Publications Department between 1988 and 1989. In fact, Secretary-General Errol Pickering visited the CHA offices to review and approve the proposed new journal format.

Less and less contact occurred between the two organizations in the 1990s. Then, in the late 1990s, CHA's membership in the IHF and the cost to the organization became an issue, especially as CHA's financial position was being closely monitored throughout this period. In 1998, the Executive Committee recommended that CHA review its membership in the organization. It is important to remember that the membership at CHA's board table had shifted signficantly, so that the majority of members represented the interests of a broad continuum of care and not just those of the hospital. In 1999, CHA's president, Sharon Sholzberg-Gray, presented a report to the board indicating that membership in the IHF had no impact on CHA's policy agenda.

Nonetheless, the incoming chair, John Baker, as well as those board members who specifically represented hospital interests at the board table (i.e., Ontario),

believed that CHA should retain its membership, if only because of Canada's reputation in international circles for delivering quality care in a publicly administered
health system. It was necessary to resolve this issue as the IHF was considering
holding its biennial congress in Vancouver in 2001. There were serious financial
ramifications and commitments for CHA's British Columbia member if CHA intended to cut its ties to the IHF.

In June 2000, the CHA board voted to end its membership in the IHF. In a letter
from the IHF to the CHA's president, the association and its board were asked to
reconsider their decision. The IHF was so concerned about Canada's withdrawal
that they also wrote to the federal minister of health, seeking his assistance to persuade CHA to reconsider. At the February 2001 board meeting, members voted to
stand by their initial decision to withdraw from the federation. Today, Canada is
virtually the only Western nation not represented in the IHF.

Catholic Health Association of Canada (CHAC)

Representatives from the Ontario and Maritime Conferences of the Catholic
Hospital Association of the United States and Canada were founding members of
the Canadian Hospital Council in 1931. As these provincial conferences expanded
across Canada, they joined as members and sent delegates to council assembly
meetings throughout the 1930s. Many representatives from the provincial Catholic
conferences also served on the Executive Committee and several individuals were
council officers between 1931 and the late 1940s.

In 1939, the Catholic Hospital Council of Canada (CHAC) was founded as the
national voice of Catholic hospitals, although the provincial conferences continued
as members and sent delegates to CHC meetings. CHA's records are silent on interactions between the two organizations, no doubt because provincial conferences
voiced their concerns through delegations at the council's biennial meetings where
they shared many common issues with lay public hospitals.

In 1954, the Catholic Hospital Council changed its name to the Catholic Hospital
Association of Canada, reflecting a similar name change by CHA. In 1958, the CHAC
asked CHA to consider making a joint presentation to the federal health department
asking for a change in the Hospital Insurance and Diagnostic Services (HIDS) Act
regarding the exclusion of depreciation and interest on capital debt. In January
1959, both organizations met jointly with Health Minister J. Waldo Monteith, who
advised the delegation that there would be no change in the legislation at that time.

When the accreditation council was established in 1959, the CHAC was assessed a fee to pay for one of the five seats held by CHA which sat on the accreditation board. In 1960, the Catholic association protested this additional fee, as it was already paying for membership through its provincial conferences. The CHA board agreed that this practice should be abandoned. In future, CHA would pay all fees and ensure that one of the five seats was delegated to a representative from a Catholic hospital.

In 1968, as a result of some of the recommendations of the Aims and Objectives Committee, CHA informed the national Catholic association that it might be preferable for it to become the active member, with the provincial conferences relinquishing their active status. The CHAC board was to discuss the issue. But it took several years for the change to be implemented and it did not happen without considerable opposition among the assembly delegates.

In 1975, with a change in the bylaw, the CHAC was granted active membership in the Canadian Hospital Association. This membership was changed to affiliate status under the bylaw change in 1981. Historically, the two organizations have found ways to work together to resolve problems and to present the views of their respective hospitals at the federal level. There has been a regular exchange of information over the years on subjects of common interest and, according to board records, a number of bilateral meetings have been held as necessary between the two organizations on subjects such as the recognition of pastoral services in hospitals, setting standards for training pastoral care workers and formulating codes of ethics.

The two organizations have also collaborated, along with other national health organizations and the Canadian Bar Association, to develop joint statements on resuscitative interventions (1995), terminal illness (1996) and on resolving ethical conflicts in health facilities (1999). While there are no formal committees set up between the two national organizations today, more informal communication takes place at meetings and through networking as needed.

Canadian Association of Health-Care Auxiliaries (CAHA)

The official record of the Canadian Hospital Council's biennial meeting in 1937 lists delegations from the Ontario Hospital Aids' Association, the first such mention of a volunteer group attending council meetings. In 1941, the executive director of the Canadian Nurses Association reported to the council's delegates that recruiting voluntary ward or nursing aides was proving to be a successful way to provide much-needed assistance for nurses in Canada's hospitals. By this time, hospitals were reporting serious nursing shortages due to the recruitment of nurses for the war effort. Volunteers in the hospital were essential to support patient care at the bedside.

The National Council of Women's Hospital Auxiliaries was founded in May 1951 during the eleventh biennial meeting of the Canadian Hospital Council in Ottawa. At the time, executive members of five provincial auxiliary associations formed the nucleus of this organization. However, several other provincial associations had indicated their intention of joining this national organization as well.

The national auxiliary council was "to serve as a clearing house and guide for all hospital auxiliaries and . . . its objective was the eventual representation of all provinces" ("With" 1951, 62). Funding for the council was set up through personal contributions of the founding members. One of its first official acts was to apply for associate membership in the Canadian Hospital Council; this was approved by the hospital delegates in 1953.

The national auxiliary organization ratified its constitution and bylaws in 1953, held biennial meetings, and elected its officers for a two-year term, similar to the constitutional format of the hospital council. The early years were difficult ones for the national association as it worked with its members to consolidate into a cohesive organization, with voluntary and often uncertain funding. Dr. Swanson, the executive director of CHA, raised the issue of support for the organization at the December 1953 meeting and the board agreed that, while it would not offer financial assistance outright, nevertheless, CHA would support this fledgling organization in every other way.

Recognizing the valuable services rendered to hospitals by the national council, CHA agreed in 1962 to provide it with both secretarial assistance and office space at 25 Imperial Street in Toronto. In 1963, the council approached CHA for assistance in redrafting its constitution and requested a seat on CHA's board. Although the board rejected the latter request, it did direct Dr. Piercey, CHA's executive director, to assist the council in rewriting their bylaws. In 1964, the council changed its name to the Canadian Association of Hospital Auxiliaries (CAHA).

By the late 1960s, CHA was supporting the auxiliary association in the amount of almost $2,000 annually through secretarial support, printing services, inventory and distribution of fundrasing items such as pins, cards and other items, as well as handling all its finances and board documents. In fact, a motion had been passed at the 1963 general assembly reaffirming the membership's support of a national association of auxiliaries and confirming CHA's assistance to the organization, assistance which continued uninterrupted for over thirty-four years. CAHA continued to press CHA for a seat on its board of directors and CHA continued to reject this request.

As both organizations entered the 1970s, the members of CAHA once again sought guidance and support from CHA as the organization was coming under considerable criticism. By 1971, the members were questioning CAHA's role and what value it provided to its membership for the fees they were paying. In fact, Dr. Brosseau, CHA's executive director, supported the recommendations of the 1967 review of CHA and its activities, undertaken by Judge Chaiker Abbis, in which Judge Abbis suggested that the national auxiliary association be disbanded and taken over by a committee of CHA. CHA would charge a small fee per bed to all provincial auxiliary associations to support the expenses of this national consulting committee. Dr. Brosseau believed that this committee would be far more effective than the current organization, especially with the withdrawal of the auxiliary association in Quebec.

CHA board records indicate that it endorsed a proposal to move toward a national auxiliary committee under the CHA umbrella but no action was ever taken. And CAHA continued to flounder. By 1972, CHA's board asked the organization to prepare and present a detailed plan on how CAHA could assist its members. If its provincial members approved the plan, then CHA would assist the association in preparing an application for a national health grant to develop its national program (CHA 1972a, 3-4). In 1973, Alberta withdrew its membership and Newfoundland still remained outside the organization. There was now considerable competition for volunteers coming from the professional sector in the form of directors of volunteer services, who were intent on setting up their own national organization.

With the arrival of Jean-Claude Martin in 1977 as the executive director of CHA, support for CAHA was considerably enhanced. Mr. Martin always held the national auxiliary organization in high regard for the work they did to support Canadian hospitals through their fundraising efforts, and annual agreements for cooperation were reviewed and signed throughout his tenure. CHA provided secretarial support directly through the president's office and a member of his staff provided support at their annual meeting, which still took place at the time of CHA's meeting. CHA also provided consultation and support for the CAHA journal, maintained their inventory of fundraising items through the Circulation Department and attended their annual meeting.

By the early 1980s however, the national auxiliary association was again in serious trouble with only five provincial members remaining. CHA increased both secretarial support inhouse and worked closely with their national executive to win back their provincial members. In 1987, CHA's board unanimously approved a resolution on auxiliary membership on hospital boards either through appointment or election as voting members. By the late 1980s, several of the provincial members had rejoined CAHA, a credit to both Jean-Claude Martin's belief in a strong national auxiliary organization and the efforts of his staff throughout the decade to recruit and enhance the services that CAHA provided to its provincial members.[3] In fact, in 1989, CHA's board formally approved a memorandum of agreement between the two organizations to formalize what was officially being done for CAHA.

Worried about its own fiscal survival and with the shifting of health delivery to regionalized systems in the early 1990s, CHA was unable to contribute as much time and support to the auxiliary as it had in the past. Nevertheless, the two organizations did hold bilateral meetings of the executive and CAHA's board approved a five-year strategic plan in October 1990 to address its need for financial stability. The Canadian Association of Health-Care Auxiliaries, as it was now called, also worked closely with the Canadian Association of Directors of Volunteer Services in Healthcare to draft guidelines for volunteers working in all Canadian facilities.

CHA's board granted CAHA participant-observer status in 1995, with the appointed representative expected to pay their own expenses; the first representative joined the CHA board as a nonvoting member in June 1996; this continued until the late 1990s. The association was also included in the consultation and review process of the CHA's mission and services in mid-1996 and in the 1997 CHA draft budget. In 1996, CHA and the Canadian College of Health Service Executives welcomed the auxiliary association, along with the Canadian Home Care Association and the Health Care Public Relations Association, as partners at the joint national health-care conference in Ottawa-Hull.

But, by the end of the decade, the two organizations had drifted further apart, such that in 1998, "the board directed staff to write a letter to CAHA to reaffirm the importance of a continuing relationship between the two organizations" (CHA 1998b, 2). President Sharon Sholzberg-Gray contacted the then vice-president of

CAHA, Lorraine Grant, to arrange a meeting. Although CAHA wanted to continue to have a permanent national office at 17 York Street, with the space donated by CHA, space limitations in the building did not allow for such an arrangement, although CAHA continued to send a participant-observer to board meetings. Then, when Lorraine Grant, who was chair of CHA's member organization in British Columbia and a member of the CAHA executive, was appointed to CHA's board in June 1997, she reported to the board on CAHA's activities.[4]

By 2003, the survival of CAHA had once again become a major issue when Ontario withdrew its membership. With the retirement of Lorraine Grant from the board in 2005, there is no participant-observer from the organization on CHA's board. Ongoing relations between the two organizations will most likely depend on CAHA's ability to survive as a financially viable organization in the future.

Royal College of Physicians and Surgeons of Canada (Royal College)

The Royal College of Physicians and Surgeons of Canada is a national organization established in 1929 to oversee the medical education of specialists in Canada. Its mission is to support medical specialists in providing high standards of quality care. Little has been recorded in the historical records of the hospital council about interactions between the two organizations. However, in 1952, the Royal College did write to the hospital council suggesting that hospital administrators could be added to the list of specialties for which the college granted certificates. CHA's board deferred the matter for discussion to a later date.

It was the issue of hospital accreditation that drew the college into a partnership with CHA in 1953. After a long debate at CHA's annual assembly meeting, the delegates agreed to join with the CMA, the Association des Médecins de Langue Française du Canada and the Royal College to set up the Canadian Commission on Hospital Accreditation, initially a study group, which recommended setting up a Canadian accreditation program. The two organizations worked on the commission, along with the other members, to launch the accreditation council in 1959. The Royal College continues to hold two seats on the council board.

In the early 1980s, both CHA and the Royal College foresaw the need for a national health council to develop standards for Canada's health system. In 1982, CHA sought the Royal College's support for its proposal for a health council. But the college favored an institute of medicine that would admit nonphysicians as members and sought private funding to launch it. By 1986, the Royal College was proposing a Canadian Institute of Health and sought CHA's support, although the association was still pursuing its own proposal. Both organizations were having difficulty defining how membership would be selected and how their mutual bodies would be funded. Neither proposal was successful but eventually a health council was established by the federal government in 2003.

As health care safety concerns began to emerge both at the international level and within various countries such as the United States and Australia, the Royal College recognized the need for open discussion and hosted a one-day forum at its annual conference in September 2001. More than fifty leaders from government and both health and nongovernmental organizations took part in the roundtable discussions; the result was the establishment of a National Steering Committee on Patient Safety. CHA was one of the attendees at the formation of this committee as its board and members had already identified patient safety and quality care within the health delivery system as priority issues for the association. With the release of the Steering Committee's report in 2002, one of the key recommendations was to establish a Canadian Patient Safety Institute.

In 2003, as identified in the Health Accord and the budget, the federal government agreed to set up an institute. While the Federal/Provincial/Territorial Advisory Committee on Governance and Accountability was directed to oversee an implementation plan, the CEOs of both the Royal College and CHA were selected to hire a lawyer, draft bylaws and recommend a slate of candidates for the founding board of the Canadian Patient Safety Institute, which was launched in December 2003.

Canadian Pharmacists Association (CPhA)

The Canadian Pharmaceutical Association (CPhA), as it was originally called, was founded in 1907 by fifteen pharmacists to represent their interests to the federal government. In 1924, the organization was incorporated by letters patent and, today, represents more than eight thousand individual pharmacists. CPhA was the last of the major health organizations to move to Ottawa from Toronto; in 1997, its members voted to change its name to the Canadian Pharmacists Association.

As the use of therapeutic drugs increased tremendously after World War II and as the number of pharmacists working in hospitals also increased, the significance of their role in the hospital gained greater recognition particularly where issues impacting the hospital were concerned.

Searches through the records of CHA's business meetings through the 1930s and 1940s show little interaction between the two associations. Then, in the May 1955 board minutes, it is interesting to note that CHA had received a letter from the secretary-manager of CPhA advising CHA that it had formed the Committee of Interprofessions to discuss issues of mutual importance among the various health organizations. As directed by the board, CHA's executive director, Dr. Piercey, notified the pharmacy association that CHA would work with them when the need arose.

In November 1997, the pharmacists' association, along with CHA and several other national health associations, cosponsored the National Conference on Pharmacare. This conference focused on international experiences with public pharmacare programs and the lessons that could be learned for Canada in light of the National Forum on Health recommendation that the federal government set up a national pharmacare program for Canada. Both CHA board and staff members attended the conference.

By 2002, issues around the pharmaceutical industry had been identified by CHA's board as part of its advocacy agenda. In 2003, with the inclusion in the Health Accord that year of a catastrophic drug fund, the board asked CHA staff to invite both the brand name and generic associations to provide an overview of the industry and the role each played in containing costs and monitoring appropriate utilization. In 2004, the board directed CHA to work with the Canadian Pharmacists Association to find ways to improve the safety, appropriateness and use of drugs. Both organizations continue to work together today on these issues and are both members of the Group of Four key health organizations.

Association of Canadian Academic Healthcare Organizations (ACAHO)

The Association of Canadian Teaching Hospitals (ACTH) was set up in the early 1960s to represent Canadian teaching hospitals that were affiliated with a medical school or faculty of medicine. Medical students and residents, as well as other health professionals, spend much of their time during their years of studies in health care facilities. They require space and supervision, access to and use of the facility's equipment and technology, and practice their skills and medical knowledge at the patient's bedside.

In order to solve problems that may arise between the needs of faculties and those of the health facility, lines of communication were vital between both CHA and the teaching hospitals association. In 1970, CHA's board directed the executive director,

Dr. Brosseau, to open up discussions with ACTH. Dr. Brosseau had been invited on two prior occasions to attend the ACTH annual meeting as an observer. Over the years, CHA continued to send a representative to their annual meeting, which was held in partnership with the Association of Canadian Medical Colleges (ACMC), representing all the Canadian schools or faculties of medicine. In 1970, for the first time, CHA published a list of all the ACTH members in its *Canadian Hospital Directory*, a practice that has continued for more than thirty-five years.

In 1978, CHA invited ACTH to consider associate membership in the organization. ACTH was also negotiating with CHA's Research Department to undertake research on their behalf. Then, in 1982, ACTH was asked to send a representative to the CHA's Research Committee, which was the board's advisory committee to the Research Department.

As the cost of accreditation surveys continued to increase throughout the 1980s, ACTH became more and more concerned about the lack of input from teaching hospitals into the survey process. In 1987, it surveyed the accreditation process among its members, who were extremely critical of how the accreditation surveys were conducted. In 1989, ACTH formally asked CHA to allocate two of its five board seats on the accreditation council to it. CHA declined to do so but reiterated their commitment to ensure that at least one of their representatives on the board came from a teaching hospital. In 1990, CHA invited the chair of the ACTH to join its Sub-Committee on Accreditation in order to ensure that teaching hospitals' concerns about the accreditation survey process were reported to the accreditation board.

In 1993, ACTH and CHA agreed to send a participant-observer to each other's board meetings; these observers would have no voting status. In 1996, ACTH was one of five national associations approached by CHA's chair and chair-elect at the direction of the board to discuss a potential partnership, alliance or merger during its intensive year of evaluation and review.

The ACTH was disbanded and replaced by a new organization under a new constitution and bylaws in 2002. It is now called the Association of Canadian Academic Healthcare Organizations (ACAHO), with its own independent board, and no longer sits at CHA's board table. In 2003, ACAHO organized a fall invitational meeting to look at the future of academic health sciences centres in Canada. CHA was invited to take part in this meeting. Today, both ACAHO and CHA engage in advocacy and representation efforts on behalf of their members, many of which are shared by both organizations.

Canadian Standards Association (CSA)

The Canadian Standards Association (CSA) was charted in 1919. It is a not-for-profit, nonstatutory, voluntary membership association that engages in standards development and certification activities serving business, industry, government and consumers in Canada. CSA works in Canada and around the world to develop standards that address areas such as enhancing public safety and health.

The early years of the council were dedicated to ensuring that standards for the hospital were developed, implemented and monitored to ensure the safety of those working and being cared for in hospital. Early council CEOs and its boards worked with various national bodies to ensure quality in the hospital, including the CSA, the Medical Research Council, the National Research Council and the Department of National Health and Welfare.

In 1954, the general manager of the CSA wrote to CHA advising that it was setting up a Committee on Hospital Hazards. CSA requested that CHA appoint several members to this committee. Unfortunately, CHA couldn't afford to pay expenses for several appointments but it did agree to appoint at least one member to the committee. The first mention of ongoing representation between the two organizations appears in the May 1959 minutes of the board meeting in which Dr. Douglas Piercey, CHA's executive director, is appointed as CHA's representative on the CSA board; this appears to have been a permanent and ongoing appointment over the next few years.

As more and better equipment and technologies were developed over the years for use in the hospital—especially during the late 1960s and early 1970s—the need for national standards to protect both health care providers and patients became critical. For many years, CHA had been concerned about product and service standards in the health field, particularly with respect to hospital equipment and systems. On more than one occasion, it requested that specialists in the Department of National Health and Welfare consider providing an information and evaluation service for various types of hospital equipment.

When CSA decided to establish a health technology service in the 1970s, CHA enthusiastically supported the project and designated two hospital administrators to represent it on the Sectional Committee on Health Care Technology. In addition, it agreed to designate hospital technical personnel to serve on appropriate technical subcommittees and working groups. When the Sectional Committee was reorganized and renamed the Steering Committee on Health Care Technology, a CHA representative was elected vice-chair and member of the executive committee.

The activities of both developing and publishing standards were considered an essential service for hospital safety and improved care throughout the 1970s and 1980s by CHA's member organizations. These activities are still considered extremely important today and CHA appoints a member to the CSA board and Steering Committee. In many instances, the names of technical experts to sit on various committees and subcommittees are recommended by CHA's member organizations. Oftentimes, the member CEO is able to provide a name or list of names of people both capable and willing to serve as representatives.

Each year, more and more technology and techniques are developed to streamline the delivery of health care both in- and outside the health facility. It is imperative that standards be developed, implemented, monitored and updated in areas such as tissue and organ transplant, for medical devices and their reuse—a major issue for health facilities during the late 1990s and still high on the agenda today. These and other emerging issues will no doubt keep both organizations interconnected for many years to come.

Canadian Long Term Care Association (CLTCA)

In the 1970s, several long-term care administrators and provincial associations determined that there was a need for a national long-term care organization in Canada to provide a forum for the discussion and resolution of issues in this sector of the health system. In 1977, a founding meeting was called in Toronto at the Ontario Nursing Home Association meeting to discuss establishing a national organization. In 1979, the nonprofit corporation, called Canadian Long Term Care Association (CLTCA), was set up under a constitution and bylaws as an independent organization to improve long-term care services in Canada. The first part-time staff was hired in 1981 and a full-time manager came on board in 1984 and set up a permanent office for the association. As a relatively young organization on the national scene, most interactions with CHA have taken place since CHA's move to Ottawa.

CHA was pressed by its membership early in the 1980s to become involved in the long-term care sector in Canada. In fact, in 1978, CHA's board directed staff to negotiate the rights to a long-term care directory that was being created by a former staff member. Then, in 1979, as proposed by CHA's Manitoba member, the

membership approved a resolution for CHA to become more involved in supporting the needs of long-term care facilities in Canada. CHA's board approved the formation of the Long Term Care Committee. It was therefore inevitable that the paths
of the CLTCA and CHA would cross sooner or later.

In 1979, one of the first decisions of the CHA's Ad Hoc Committee on Long Term
Care was to contact the newly formed national long-term care organization and
review the status of long-term care both nationally and across the provinces.
CLTCA appointed a representative from one of its members to sit on the CHA committee. Both organizations collaborated on the First Conference on Long Term
Care which took place in 1980. Considered successful, the CHA committee, with
input from the CLTCA, planned a second conference for 1982, with the organizations sharing any surpluses.

In the early 1980s, discussion took place with the CHA president regarding the possibility of CLTCA joining CHA as an associate member. CHA also invited the CLTCA
to work with them to investigate ways in which CHA's current long-term care distance education programs could be expanded to meet the growing needs of the
long-term care sector. (*See* chapter 12 for more information.) CLTCA expressed its
intention of working in close cooperation with CHA, whenever possible, and in
1981, endorsed a survey questionnaire that was being designed by CHA to collect
information about the long-term care field. For the next several years, CHA's Long
Term Care Committee was inactive as the CLTCA picked up the responsibility for
moving this agenda forward.

When CHA reactivated the committee in 1985, with Elma Heidemann as chair, part
of the discussion involved looking at the relationship between CHA and the national long-term care association. It would appear, however, that much of the activity
of this committee proceeded without input from CLTCA. In early 1986, CHA moved
ahead to establish long-term care sessions at its annual conference and to entrench
long-term care courses in its distance education programs. For the most part, CHA
was becoming a competitor to the CLTCA in this sector of the health care system.

A joint meeting of the Executive Committees of the two organizations was scheduled
in September 1986, with a member of CHA's Long Term Care Committee also present
at the discussions. Cordial relations were established between the two organizations
at the time. Issues such as funding, portability, bed blockers, education, research and

evaluation and accreditation in long-term care were identified as areas of mutual interest to both organizations. In 1987, Elma Heidemann spoke to the board about the need for CHA to enhance its relationship with CLTCA.

Because the long-term care association was a very small organization, it had become increasingly apprehensive about CHA's expansion in the long-term care field. More often than not, it sought the advice and assistance of the CCHSE to advance its agenda rather than working with CHA. In 1987, CHA set up a bilateral meeting of the executive of both organizations to open up communications between the two organizations and members of each board attended the other's annual conference.

Throughout the late 1980s, CLS, as it was called with the adoption of its bilingual acronym in 1986, moved its policy agenda forward through representation of its members' interests on the national scene. CLS encouraged long-term care senior managers to enroll in CHA's Long-Term Care Organization and Management course and it also joined with CHA, CMA and CNA to establish national definitions for types and levels of long-term care.

By the early 1990s, regionalization of the health system in every province except Ontario was impacting both CLS and CHA. With long-term care facilities falling under these regional health authorities in many of the provinces, the membership of CLS was now seriously affected, similar to CHA. In June 1991, CLS, along with CHA, and several other national health organizations joined together to form The Health Action Lobby (HEAL) to request stable funding for Canada's health system.

CHA invited CLS to send participant-observers to its board meeting in March 1993 and CLS endorsed CHA's Vision Report that same year. Eventually, after long discussions between the two organizations, CLS and CHA signed a strategic alliance agreement in March 1994, committing the two organizations to work together on issues of mutual interest. In April 1994, the CLS moved into rental space at 17 York Street as a first step to build closer linkages between the two organizations. In 1995, CLS joined both the CHA and the Canadian College of Health Service Executives at the joint conference in Calgary and it continued to send participant-observers to CHA's board.

In 1996, a merger of CLS and HomeSupport Canada to form the Canadian Association for Community Care (CACC) was formally approved. And, in late 1997, CHA hired the then co-executive director of CACC as the new president of CHA.

Over the next few years, both the presidents of CACC and CHA worked together, along with the CEO of CCHSE, to set policy regarding the delivery of the joint annual National Healthcare Leadership Conference. In June 2006, CHA and CACC completed negotiations to integrate the two organizations under the umbrella of CHA. CACC will cease operations on 31 October 2006.

Other National Health Organizations

The list of CHA's partnerships and interactions with various national health organizations over its seventy-five-year history is quite extensive. Almost as soon as some organizations were established, one of their first actions was to seek an affiliation, partnership or associate membership with CHA. This was particularly true in the late 1950s and early 1960s as new health occupations entered the health field and attempted to establish their jurisdictional boundaries. Among the many organizations that were associate members in CHA by 1955 were the Canadian Dietetic Association, the Canadian Council of Blue Cross Plans and the National Council of Women's Hospital Auxiliaries of Canada. Other organizations seeking a similar arrangement were the Canadian Society of Hospital Pharmacists, the Canadian Association of Medical Record Librarians and the Canadian Physiotherapy Association. By 1966, when the Aims and Objectives Committee was set up to look at CHA's future role, the area of associate membership was under review.

Among other key organizations with whom CHA has worked closely is the Canadian Public Health Association. Both organizations partnered throughout the 1980s to ensure the celebration of Canada Hospital Day—later renamed Canada Health Day—on May 12 each year. (*See* chapter 16 for more information on this event.) CHA also collaborated over the years with the Canadian Society of Hospital Pharmacists to resolve issues regarding their scopes of practice within the hospital. In 1995, CHA and the Canadian Home Care Association (CHCA) signed a two-year strategic alliance agreement, which entitled both organizations to send participant-observers to each other's board meetings. Neither did so mostly due to staff and time limitations. However the home care association did set up its head offices at 17 York Street where it remains today. CHA also worked very closely with the Canadian Centre for Philanthropy and the Institute of Donations and Public Affairs Research (IDPAR) in the early 1980s to look at fundraising activities in hospitals. CHA enjoyed a close working relationship with the Canadian Institute of Child Health, which for many years rented space in CHA's building.

Summary

CHA has been very fortunate to have maintained long-standing and amicable partnerships with many of the oldest, most respected and influential national health organizations in Canada over the course of its history. In the case of the Canadian Medical Association, the relationship has been similar to that of a mother and child, with CMA offering much support until the child can set out on its own. CHA has certainly managed to leave its home in the CMA and strike out on its own. Where other historical partnerships have developed, these have been based on mutual goals and objectives in solving issues that arose around Canada's hospitals.

The dynamics of CHA's historical partnerships have shifted over time and will continue to do so as the needs of all the partner organizations evolve and move forward to meet their individual organizational needs. Nevertheless, CHA has joined with some of its traditional and more influential partners to take its place as an equal among equals in influencing Canada's health care system.

Endnotes

1. Records are available of the first joint meetings which were originally held between the Canadian Nurses Association and the Canadian Hospital Council. These minutes go back as far as 1946. The first record that includes all three associations is dated July 1947.

2. The American Hospital Association has held its annual meeting in Canada only five times in its history: Toronto in 1908, 1931 and 1939 and Montreal in 1920 and again in 1980.

3. Special recognition for CAHA's increased visibility and growth during this period should be given to Joan Roche, who was the director of administration and, later, corporate secretary for CHA. She worked closely with both Jean-Claude Martin and the CAHA executive to support this group of volunteers and ensure their organization did not collapse during this time.

4. Board minutes indicate that, when Lorraine Grant joined the board in 1997, no one else from CAHA sat at the table as a participant-observer. When Ms. Grant left the board in 2005, CAHA did not send anyone to represent them.

10

FORGING NEW HEALTH PARTNERS

"Over the years, CHA has often started programs that have sometimes gone on to. . . develop their own. . . separate organizations. For example, the whole concept of management information systems (now a mandate of the Canadian Institute for Health Information) began as a CHA initiative. . .

(BURNELL 1995, 7)

Over the course of the Canadian Healthcare Association (CHA)'s history, it has been instrumental in setting up new health organizations. Seven such organizations either created by CHA on its own or through collaboration with other national health organizations are presented in this chapter. Sometimes, these were forged through collaboration and partnerships with CHA's traditional partners such as the Canadian Medical Association (CMA) and the Canadian Nurses Association (CNA). In other instances, new organizations were set up directly by CHA to fill an identified need in Canada's health system either at the request of its own membership or by some other group. Occasionally, the establishment of another health organization resulted from the decision of others to withdraw from the field and hand over responsibility to other organizations. Whatever the process, the result has been the creation of new health organizations with whom CHA has established new partnerships.

Canadian Hospital Council, 1931 to 1952

The first two decades of the council's existence were devoted to establishing a stable and enduring organization and to ensuring its own survival. Its early years were

spent strengthening its ties with its various provincial members, Catholic conferences and other national health organizations as they came on the scene and
sought affiliation of some type with the council. There were little or no financial
and human resources available to the council to create and spin off new health
organizations during this time. The first two decades required all of the hospital
council's resources to ensure its continuation as a viable national health organization in its own right.

Canadian Hospital Association, 1953 to 1977

By 1953, the Canadian Hospital Association (CHA) had proven to be an important
organization in resolving emerging problems in Canada's health care system. As its
provincial member organizations began to play more powerful roles on behalf of
their provincial hospitals, in turn, they increased their expectations and requirements for services, programs and policy direction from CHA. Occasionally, this
required CHA to explore and eventually launch other health organizations to fill a
vacuum at the national level.

Canadian Council on Health Services Accreditation (CCHSA)

The Canadian Council on Health Services Accreditation (CCHSA), as it is called
today, describes itself as an organization that assesses quality in health care. Health
services organizations achieve accreditation by undergoing an objective evaluation
of the care and quality of services they provide to clients and then comparing these
findings against a set of national standards. Accreditation is also an educational
process that benefits staff, improves communications and collaboration, and provides an organization with access to valuable advice from other health care professionals. By participating in accreditation, organizations demonstrate to clients,
communities, stakeholders and partners their commitment to quality.

The need for some kind of standards in Canada's hospitals was recognized early on
by both the CMA and Canadian hospital superintendents. The role of providing a
hospital standards program was filled in 1919 by the American College of Surgeons.
The program focused on setting standards for physicians in the diagnosis and treatment of patients in hospital. To implement this accreditation program, the college
recruited the very capable Canadian, Dr. Malcolm T. MacEachern. According to Dr.
Harvey Agnew in his book, it was the work of this man that ensured the accreditation

program and the development of standards for hospitals were successful for American and Canadian hospitals.

Canadian physicians were particularly hostile to any form of oversight of their work in hospitals. It was the support of the CMA in 1921, which wholeheartedly approved the American standardization program, that eventually led to its acceptance in Canadian hospitals and to setting up the Department of Hospital Service. But the program was a hard sell from the moment it was launched. Without the persistence of CMA and Dr. Harvey Agnew, secretary of the hospital council, and Dr. Malcolm MacEachern from the American College, who travelled back and forth across Canada to visit and inform hospital medical staffs about the program, it would probably have faltered and failed. This would have left the field wide open for governments to move in and set up what would have undoubtedly been both a compulsory and more costly program.

The issue of standards was raised at the council Executive Committee meeting in May 1949, when Dr. Agnew reported that "[h]ospitals, governments and other associations are constantly asking us for definitions, standards, et cetera" (CHC 1949a, 228). He suggested that the council work out some standards but the executive members believed that this would be a costly undertaking for the council. It would require a subcommittee of experts with special knowledge from several areas in the health field and at least an annual budget of $50,000. Some people had even suggested that the council take over the standards program from the American College.

The American College of Surgeons had carried on the standardization program for more than thirty years at considerable cost. When Dr. MacEachern announced his retirement in the late 1940s, the college decided to seek the support of other health organizations to carry on the program. In 1951, several American health and medical organizations formed the Joint Commission on Hospital Accreditation and, in 1953, invited the CMA to send a Canadian representative.

At the same time, Canadians were looking at how they might form a similar program. In 1950, the CMA set up the Committee on Accreditation of Hospitals. It expanded quickly into the Canadian Commission on Hospital Accreditation with four members from CMA, four from the hospital council and two from the Royal College of Physicians and Surgeons. CMA's representation included one from the Association des Médecins de Langue Française du Canada (AMFC) and the council's representation included a member from the Catholic Hospital Council of Canada.

The commission was designated as a study group and was not empowered to create an independent organization. It was to carry on an accreditation program in Canada and set standards on behalf of and in cooperation with the American Joint Commission. Its members did not have the funds to operate an independent program at the time, although the intent was to eventually set up a separate Canadian commission.

The support of Canadian hospitals for the accreditation program in the 1950s was as difficult to attain as it had been in the 1920s from Canadian physicians. From its earliest days, the commission operated with little or no funding. In fact, estimates to set up an independent body in 1952 ran somewhere around $75,000 annually and each member approached its own constituency to seek funding. Although the delegates at CHA's 1953 general assembly unanimously voted to support the establishment of an all-Canadian accreditation program, they were not prepared to set up an independent organization at the time; the problem once again was lack of funding.

Two individuals in particular—Dr. Leonard O. Bradley and Dr. Arnold L. Swanson—both executive directors of CHA between 1950 and 1954, were very much involved in the development of the Canadian accreditation program. Both men had conducted surveys—Dr. Bradley in 1948 and Dr. Swanson in 1949. Both men eventually became executive directors of the accreditation council—Dr. Bradley from 1969 to 1974 and Dr. Swanson from 1975 to 1982. In an issue of *Canadian Hospital*, Dr. Swanson described the development of the Canadian Commission on Hospital Accreditation and threw out the following challenge:

> Are Canadian hospitals as good as or better than those of other countries? Have we capable trustees and administrative officers? In short, have we the knowledge and ability necessary to establish our own system of standardization for the inspection and evaluation of our own hospitals? The Canadian Commission on Hospital Accreditation firmly believes that affirmative answers may be given to each of these questions—with one proviso. The success of our own program will depend on the positive support of Canadian hospitals (1952, 35).

In the meantime, Dr. Swanson and Dr. Arthur Kelly, general secretary of the CMA, acted as joint secretaries for the accreditation commission and hired the first two surveyors in Canada in 1955. By this time, CHA had succeeded in persuading its membership to pay some fees, which the provincial members collected from public hospitals. But all Canadian accreditation reports were still sent to Chicago for a decision by the Joint Commission on a hospital's accreditation status. The process continued this way until 1959, when the Canadian Council on Hospital Accreditation (CCHA) was launched (Agnew 1974, 35-38).

At the 1957 CHA assembly, the delegates finally passed a motion "[t]hat this Assembly approve an all-Canadian program of hospital accreditation to become effective on January 1st, 1959." Although the delegates had approved the program in 1953, the members had been concerned about the cost of the accreditation program, as well as the inadequate representation of hospitals on the commission at the time. CHA held five seats and the other medical organizations held seven seats altogether, giving medical organizations the majority on the commission. These issues would come up throughout CHA's history, as members and Canadian hospitals continued to express their concerns about the increasing cost of the program and the loss of a hospital voice at the board table.

In 1956, as protection against liability, the accreditation commission was incorporated as the Canadian Council on Hospital Accreditation under its own constitution and bylaws and officially launched on 17 January 1959. The council's purpose at the time was to set standards for Canadian hospitals and evaluate their compliance. The accreditation program was voluntary, free from government intervention, national, bilingual and not-for-profit. The original membership was composed of the three national associations that created the study commission in 1953. CHA appointed five of the ten representatives to the board of directors of the new organization. Its representation comprised the members of the board Committee on Accreditation, which had originally been set up by the board in 1946 as the Committee on Standards to explore how the council would develop these in the event the members requested action in this area. This committee reported to each board meeting on the accreditation council's activities and received direction from the board on issues for resolution at the accreditation council's board meetings.

Federal Health Minister J. Waldo Monteith delivered the keynote address at the inaugural meeting of the accreditation council in Toronto and noted that the purely Canadian accreditation program coincided closely with the introduction of public hospital insurance: "Here are two important health projects beginning more or less at the same time, independent yet complementing each other, and having the opportunity of growing together towards a common goal" ("A Major" 1959, 49).

The council experienced ongoing problems with financing even as early as 1960. It struck a special committee to review options for funding alternatives including raising member fees, asking for donations from foundations and insurance companies, inviting other national medical organizations to become members and applying for a grant from the Department of National Health and Welfare. CHA objected to approaching the federal government for financial assistance as it was concerned that funds such as these could be subject to government control.[1] The other issue that was raised at the CHA board in 1960 was that of nonmember hospitals such as defence, veterans and TB facilities requesting to be surveyed. These facilities were not members of the provincial association and thus were not paying a share of the survey fee.

The accreditation council then raised the possibility of charging a survey fee to hospitals in 1964. CHA was already paying $20,000 annually for its five seats and the board opposed the implementation of such a fee. However, in a resolution at the 1964 assembly meetng, the members directed CHA to provide adequate financing for the council and CHA's board agreed to cover the $10,000 shortfall both that year and again in 1965. In 1965, the CHA assembly voted to accept a fee for the survey process in principle. But the fee per survey was not to exceed a maximum of eight hundred dollars.

In 1968, CHA requested that its lawyers review the constitution and bylaws of the accreditation council. The association wanted increased representation on its board at least equal to that of the other member organizations. CHA's representation on the Executive Committee of the council had been reduced to one person only, who was to be a medical person. The association was concerned about the dominance of the council by the medical profession, when survey fees were being paid by hospitals through their provincial associations. CHA also opposed the council's move to Ottawa. These problems led to various meetings between the council and CHA in order to resolve the issues and to ensure both the CMA and the council that CHA was not antiphysician as had been charged by the accreditation council's executive director. Relations between the council and CHA were somewhat strained as a result but became more cordial by the end of the decade, although another request by CCHA for a survey fee increase in 1969 was not well received by either CHA or its membership.

Over the next decade, the CHA board continued to receive reports on the activities of the accreditation council and to debate—often extensively—periodic requests that survey fees be increased to meet the council's growing administrative costs. CHA supported a fifteen-percent increase in the fee in 1970 and the board directed Dr. Brosseau to write to CCHA inquiring when it might develop survey standards for small hospitals. In 1972, CHA supported the CNA's request for a seat on the board of the accreditation council and a member fee increase in 1975.

The CCHA submitted its document titled "Development, Concepts, Role, Main Objectives, Policies and Functions of CCHA" to the CHA board in 1975 for review and comment. Dr. Brosseau recommended that the board accept the document. Although there were concerns about government intrusion into the accreditation survey process in both Manitoba and Quebec at the time, Dr. Brosseau believed that this could be worked out. CHA should focus on "what he considered one of the great achievements of Council—the development of standards—for example the recently developed standards for mental health institutions" (CHA 1975b, 11). CHA's board—as the parent organization—accepted the document and its recommendations. One of these recommendations was for surveys to be undertaken by survey teams of three people.

In late 1976, the council published a new *Guide to Hospital Accreditation* for implementation in January 1977. The guide revised existing standards and added a number of new ones, as well as revising the survey questionnaire. In 1978, the council began work on refining standards for accreditation of long-term care facilities and, in 1979, CCHA moved to Ottawa to join the many other health organizations that had set up headquarters in the capital.

Through much of the 1980s, the issues of accreditation appeared less often on CHA's board agenda. CHA was preoccupied with several major projects during this time and, with both organizations located in the same city, opportunities to communicate were much easier to arrange. As an autonomous organization, the CCHA made major changes to adapt its constitution and role to the changing environment of the decade. For example, in 1980, the Canadian Long Term Care Association joined the council's board and, in 1981, the composition of its board changed again, when the Association des Médecins de Langue Française du Canada withdrew as the CNA became a member. The accreditation council changed its name to the Canadian Council on Health Facilities Accreditation (CCHFA) in 1988 to recognize the much broader focus of the health system. By the end of the decade, the council had successfully accredited almost 1,300 health facilities.

The 1991 proposed thirty percent increase in accreditation fees did not go over well either at the CHA board or among its member health/hospital associations, which were facing cutbacks in provincial funding to their health systems. As the largest member on the council board at the time, with five members at a cost of $60,000 annually, CHA's board opposed the increase. Eventually, through negotiations at both the chair and CEO levels, CHA managed to reduce the fee to fifteen percent.

In 1992, the accreditation board expanded to accept representatives from the Association of Canadian Teaching Hospitals, the College of Family Physicians of Canada and the Canadian College of Health Service Executives. As restructuring and regionalization of the health system continued throughout the 1990s, and with the focus shifting to services and programs delivered outside facilities, the council changed its name again to the Canadian Council on Health Services Accreditation (CCHSA) in 1995. It also launched its client-centred accreditation program where the focus is on patient care in the facility.

Throughout the history of the council's development, CHA has played a major role by supporting its work, ensuring that its members' points of view are articulated at the council board table and by cooperating with CCHSA both to promote an afford-able accreditation process and to ensure that the system delivers the best quality care it can. Two of CHA's past CEOs became CEOs of the accreditation council; many of its board members have been appointed over the years to serve on the accreditation board and some have become chair of the organization. In one instance, a CHA past board chair, Elma Heidemann, became the CEO of the council between 1991 and 2004. To this day, a report on the strategic directions and other activities regarding accreditation in the health system is a standing item on the CHA board agenda.

Nursing Unit Administration (NUA) Program

In 1955, officers of the W. K. Kellogg Foundation suggested to CHA and to the Canadian Nurses Association (CNA) that they would favor the development of an extension course for nurses in supervisory positions to teach them the basic prin-ciples of organization. An exploratory meeting was held at the School of Nursing, University of Toronto, with representatives from the school, CHA and CNA. Questionnaires were sent to all directors of nursing in Canadian hospitals to assess the need for such a program. Feedback was positive and indicated that a program would be most beneficial.

CHA and CNA established a joint committee in the fall of 1959 to discuss and design a program that would improve nurses' management skills. Although the pro-gram was under joint sponsorship, the operation of the program would be carried out by CHA, which would manage the three-year Kellogg grant. There was an over-whelming demand for the program, which was first offered in 1961 with more than three hundred students registered. In 1963, the course material was offered in the

French language and, with the termination of the three-year grant, fees were increased to accommodate the loss of the grant.

With no formal arrangement in existence between the two organizations, in 1964, CHA's board directed Dr. Brosseau, the executive director, to draft a mutual agreement to be ratified by both boards. The program was governed by the joint committee with the chair rotating between each organization every two years. Each board appointed four members to the committee with each group reporting to its mutual board. CHA provided financial services for the program and leased office space to the program's staff.

By 1965, the program was not only self-supporting but was making considerable profits. Both organizations decided to conduct an evaluation to be financed by the unexpended balance of the Kellogg grant. The results of the evaluation indicated that the program was well received by both nurses and administrators, so both organizations recommended to their boards that the program continue.

Based on its successes, in 1968, CHA's board again directed the executive director to negotiate a new agreement with CNA, so that surpluses would be split equally between the two organizations. Since both organizations needed to determine how these surpluses would be used, three subcommittees were set up. One subcommittee would review the terms of reference of the joint committee, one would draw up the terms of reference for a trust fund and one would explore other educational opportunities.

Both organizations had received several requests from other countries to develop a similar program. The joint committee held discussions with the Canadian International Development Agency (CIDA) in 1974, with CIDA agreeing to support an international version of the program. Since the program was not suitable for every country, criteria were developed and a pilot project was set up in Lebanon. Its success led to three-year projects being introduced in Zaire, Haiti and Botswana, supported by CIDA.

The NUA Program and its staff moved to Ottawa at the same time as CHA and continued to rent office space at CHA's headquarters. Once again, based on its ongoing success, the two sponsoring organizations developed revised terms of reference for the joint committee in 1979, which more or less confirmed both CNA and CHA as the parent organizations of what was now called the Nursing Unit Administration Joint Committee. The committee was responsible for the management of the extension course, hired the director of the program and approved its annual budget. The committee was to meet once a year with the chair alternating between the two organizations as in the past.

By 1991, the program began to experience a serious decline in its enrolment. Because of this and the potential financial liability that carrying the program posed to it, CHA's board approved a procedure permitting it to give a one-year notice to the CNA of its intent to withdraw from the nursing management program by the end of August 1992. The program continued under the aegis of the CNA until 1993 when it was transferred to McMaster University in Hamilton.

Canadian College of Health Service Executives (CCHSE)

As a national association, the Canadian College of Health Service Executives (CCHSE) provides the opportunity for professional support and contributes to the advancement of health services management. The college is an educational and professional association of some 3,000 members from all sectors of health services in Canada. Its professional designations of Certified Health Executive (CHE) and Fellow (FCHE) offer the only credentials available to health service executives in Canada. Its vision is to lead and promote the profession of health service management through its mission of strengthening its membership, enhancing collaborative relationships, providing excellent programs and offering value-added services to its members (www.cchse.org).

For a number of years, the desirability of establishing a Canadian organization of hospital administrators was discussed with increasing enthusiasm by Canadian administrators. But the real push to launch such an organization came from CHA's own graduates of the Hospital Organization and Management (HOM) course. They had formed the Students' Association of Alumni from HOM and wished to expand across Canada. In 1954, the students' association wrote to Dr. Arnold Swanson, CHA's executive director, requesting CHA's support.

Dr. Swanson sought direction from the board. At the time, many of Canada's hospital administrators were members of the American College of Hospital Administrators (ACHA). CHA's board declined to support the organization for two reasons: 1) it believed that hospital administrators were already well served by the ACHA and 2) the establishment of such an organization would require the development of professional standards which was a slow process.

The board directed Dr. Swanson to write to the students and advise them that: "If, in the course of time, a professional association of administrators in Canada appears to be indicated and feasible, the Directors of C.H.A. would desire to be kept informed and to co-operate with the new organization" (CHA 1954). In November 1955, the Alumni Association again approached CHA for its support and this time CHA's board agreed, subject to a review of its draft constitution and bylaws. Little is recorded over the next few years about this initial effort to create a professional Canadian body to represent the interests of hospital administrators.

The issue came up again in the final report of CHA's Aims and Objectives Committee, submitted at its assembly in 1967, which recommended that a special committee be established to study the feasibility of forming an organization of individual hospital administrators in Canada. In September of that year, CHA's board established the Committee to Study the Feasibility of a Canadian College of Hospital Administrators. This committee spent two years investigating the need for and feasibility of such a body.

In May 1969, the committee presented its recommendations to CHA's board, which approved setting up either an association, institute or council. The committee recommended that the organization focus on both developing acceptable minimum standards and educational programs for hospital administrators but with no power to grant diplomas or degrees. CHA was to be the founding organization until the body could stand on its own. The board also agreed that membership would be on an individual basis and not based on the federation model.

When the American College changed its membership criteria, many Canadian hospital administrators were no longer eligible and a Canadian organization that played a similar role was now a necessity. At a joint meeting of CHA's Executive and Finance Committees in October 1969, the members supported forming yet another committee to determine the structure of the organization, establish classes of membership, and describe the aims and objectives of this body. The report was to be completed and presented to CHA's board by early 1970. This committee also drafted the provisional bylaws for the Hospital Administrators Council of Canada and included a registration form for founding the council; this form was sent to all hospital administrators across Canada to determine the level of interest in establishing a professional organization. CHA's board ratified the bylaws and recommended a founding date for June of that year.

The process was now moving quickly toward establishing this new organization for Canada's hospital administrators. In June, both the CHA board and assembly members approved the launch of the council. Through their membership applications, more than 900 health administrators indicated their desire to see such an organization formed and more than 350 members gathered in Edmonton on 2 June 1970 to approve provisional bylaws and to elect Dr. Leonard Bradley, former executive director of CHA, as its first president. Justices Chaiker Abbis and Edward Hughes, both past chairs of CHA, as well as Dr. Brosseau, CHA's executive director at the time, were instrumental in reviewing, revising and writing the bylaws for the administrators' council.

At its board meeting in December 1970, the name was provisionally changed to the Canadian Council of Health Service Executives. Applicants for membership were required to hold a senior management position in a hospital or extended care facility; health educational program; regional, provincial or national hospital or health association; health department or plan; or could be a senior health consultant. In organizing the council, CHA's board obligated the association to manage its

The first executive and board of the Hospital Administrators Council of Canada at the founding meeting in Edmonton in June 1970. Standing (left to right) Sister B. Poirier, Montreal; F. S. Whittington, Albernie, B.C.; Dr. B. L. P. Brosseau, Executive Director of the Canadian Hospital Association which was instrumental in developing the Council: J. Carter, Winnipeg. Seated, (left to right) R. E. McDermit, Regina; Reg Adshead, Calgary, Immediate Past President of the CHA; Dr. L. O. Bradley, first President of HACC; and Dr. W. R. Slatkoff, Montreal. Missing members of the board include H. Frowd, Lunnenburg, Nova Scotia, and Ken E. Box of Toronto.

finances and to act as the secretariat. It was also headquartered at CHA's offices in Toronto. Dr. Bradley encouraged the college to become independent as quickly as possible but, until it did, CHA's board monitored and approved its finances.

At its first annual meeting in 1971, its name was changed again to the Canadian College of Health Service Executives (CCHSE) and the college presented its first honorary membership to Dr. Harvey Agnew, CHA's founding executive secretary. In 1972, following Dr. Agnew's death in late 1971, the college established the G. Harvey Agnew Memorial Lecture to be given at its annual conference. It was intended as a way to recognize and honor Dr. Agnew's service to the Canadian health care field. The first lecture was given by Stanley W. Martin CHA's president from 1959 to 1961.

In 1978, when CHA moved to Ottawa, the college moved as well and shared office space. The college also moved into CHA's permanent headquarters at 17 York Street in 1983, where it remained until 1991. The proximity of the two associations during these years enabled them to collaborate on projects, exchange information on issues of mutual interest, and discuss concerns and resolve problems on a daily basis, if necessary, because of their shared location.

The college and CHA have collaborated in many areas over the years. Through an agreement with the college, students enroled in CHA's Health Services Management distance learning program have an opportunity to earn their CHE designation, while completing the CHA program requirements. In turn, CHA recognizes the college's certification activities in its programs. The college has also partnered with CHA Press to publish books and papers. Both organizations became partners in 1986 in managing joint conferences at the same time and in the same city for the benefit of their mutual delegates. The first single joint conference was held by both partners in 1994 and, today, both the college and CHA remain the founding partners of the National Healthcare Leadership Conference. They both appoint participant-observers to each other's board, under a reciprocal agreement signed in 1996. The two organizations also worked together that year to explore options for integration of the organizations at the direction of their mutual boards, at a time when both organizations were seeking new CEOs and financial stability.

During the last thirty years, the relationship between the two national organizations has been cordial and based on the need for both to cooperate and communicate with each other. But, because of their shared and mutual members—the college's administrators manage the health system that CHA speaks on behalf of—there have been some divergent views and opinions that inevitably caused friction between the two organizations. Both CHA and the college are members in organizations such as the HEAL Coalition and the college has supported CHA's proposals such as a health council for Canada. Today, both organizations send a representative to each other's board meetings as a participant-observer in order to keep each other up to date on activities, programs and developing issues, and to maintain good relations between the two organizations.

Health Computer Information Bureau (HCIB)

As computer technology slowly began to impact society, including the hospital specifically and the health care sector generally, the federal government became concerned about the proliferation of this technology within hospitals, how it was being used and whether it was part of the reason for rising hospital costs beginning in the early 1970s. In fact, this new computer technology was mentioned several times in the report of the 1969 Task Force on the Costs of Health Care as a factor in increasing costs in this sector.

In 1969, federal representatives from the Department of National Health and Welfare approached CHA to determine if it would be interested in developing a conference on computers in health. Sponsored by a grant from the department, CHA delivered the first National Symposium on Computer Applications in the Health Field in March 1970. (For more details about this symposium, refer to chapter 13.) One of the resolutions adopted during this symposium by the more than two hundred delegates in attendance "called for the establishment of a national committee to determine priorities for computer applications and to encourage and steer the development of projects to meet these goals" ("Focus" 1970, 30).

In turn, the federal steering committee recommended that an abstract service and bureau be set up to collect information from Canada's hospitals about the use of computers. The federal health department encouraged CHA to take the lead in setting up the bureau and suggested it apply for funding from the health grants program. However, when CHA initially submitted a proposal, the Advisory Committee on Health Grants turned it down; eventually, the funding was approved, when CHA appealed to the health minister for support.

The Health Computer Information Bureau (HCIB) was set up in 1972, cosponsored by the CHA and the CMA. CHA was designated as the secretariat to administer

funding and hired a project director in 1973. The bureau was to collect and catalogue information on computer applications and their use in Canadian hospitals
and disseminate this information to hospitals and other interested parties. In its initial stage, the director of the bureau travelled extensively across Canada, consulting with hospitals to determine their level of support for the project. Based on
positive feedback, by April 1974, offices were set up in Ottawa and staff had been
hired. A trial issue of the catalogue was published in late summer 1974 and CHA
applied again for funding to operate the bureau from 1975 to 1976.

In March 1975, the HCIB published the first complete volume of the catalogue,
titled *Health Computer Applications in Canada*, and Dr. Brosseau advised CHA's
board that the federal health department had agreed to fund the bureau for another year. The expectation was that the bureau would eventually become self-sustaining through sales of the catalogue and an abstract service. By mid-1975, HCIB had
published its second volume of computer applications and CHA was hopeful that
the bureau could be set up as a separate corporation with an expanded board that
would include representation from the provinces.

From the very beginning, the bureau struggled financially to become a viable and
stable organization. Each year it had to apply for funding from the Advisory
Committee on Health Insurance, which, in turn, collected a portion of the grant
from the provinces. Each year, the money became tighter and tighter as the federal health department began withdrawing direct funding to many projects that it had
supported in the past. These were difficult years with inflation seemingly out of
control and steps such as wage and price controls being implemented to bring
costs under control.

While there appeared to be a need to look at how computers were being utilized in
hospitals and to determine whether they added to or reduced hospital costs, most
hospitals were struggling to get their own costs under control and could not support a subscription service, one of the ways in which the bureau had planned to
become self-sustaining. However, the hospitals did provide information on their
financial and clinical computer applications to the bureau, which were catalogued
and published.

In March 1977, the six-person advisory board that governed the HCIB was replaced
by a twelve-member management board with members from the federal and
provincial governments, the Canadian Organization for the Advancement of

Computers in Health (COACH), the Association of Canadian Teaching Hospitals (ACTH), the Association of Canadian Medical Colleges, as well as CHA and CMA. CHA's executive director, Dr. Brosseau, chaired the board and CHA continued as the secretariat to manage the funding grant.

By this time, the bureau had catalogued nine hundred computer applications and published abstracts on almost three hundred. An evaluation of the bureau and its service was conducted over the summer of 1977. Although it was expected that it would receive ongoing funding, one of the provinces declined to pay its share of the bureau costs earlier that year and, once more, the bureau struggled to survive on reduced funding.

In late 1978, the federal health advisory committee agreed again to fund HCIB until the end of January 1979. CHA sought additional sponsorship from both COACH and CMA but neither were willing to provide funds. To cut costs, the bureau was reduced to a one-person operation and moved into CHA's headquarters at 410 Laurier Avenue in Ottawa late in 1979. Now managed by an executive committee of representatives from COACH, CMA and CHA and unable to generate sufficient money to support itself, both CHA and CMA withdrew their support due to the ongoing deficits. The Health Computer Information Bureau ceased operations at CHA on 1 September 1980 and the responsibility and assets of the bureau were transferred to COACH.

CHA in Ottawa, 1978 to 2006

With the move to Ottawa, CHA was able to build closer relationships with both the federal government and other national health organizations. The association— either alone or in partnership with others—launched new health organizations during the 1980s to improve the financial position of CHA itself or to assist its members in improving the delivery of health care in Canada.

Institute for Health Care Facilities of the Future
CHA played a key role in implementing a project that led to a recommendation for the establishment of a hospital of the future forum. In 1982, CHA invited several national organizations to an informal luncheon to discuss the idea of a hospital of the future and its role in the health system. From that early meeting, an ad hoc committee was formed to plan the project and find funding.

In September 1984, CHA's Department of Research and Development staff, under the guidance of an external Advisory Committee made up of eight specialists, with the financial support of the National Research Council of Canada, prepared and published a document entitled *Exploring the Future of Hospitals in Canada: A Definition Study*. The document became the framework for a hospital of the future project. The report made one recommendation only that: "*a national hospital of the future forum be permanently established. The primary objective of this forum must be to define and examine sensitive, key issues which relate directly to the future of hospital services*" (CHA 1984a, 28, italics in original). The final chapter of the report outlined what this forum, as it was called in the report, would do and what approach it would use in looking at the hospital of the future.

Although it was recognized at the onset of the project that the forum would eventually function as an independent national body, initially, CHA played a leading role in getting the project started. CHA's board also recognized that the association would need to be involved in funding the project or finding the funding to launch the institute. The association also organized and delivered two national conferences—in Ottawa in 1984 and in Toronto in 1985—to inform and sensitize the health care community about the need for a research project on the future of health care facilities.

The first meeting of the Task Force to Develop the Health Institution of the Future Forum—as it was named at the time—was held at CHA's offices in Ottawa in September 1985. Seventeen organizations from the voluntary and private sectors, from government, consumer groups and research agencies were invited to attend and to appoint a representative to the task force.[2] William A. Kilpatrick, a past chair of CHA's board, was named as chair of the task force. In October 1985, CHA presented the project concept to the members of the Institute of Donations and Public Affairs Research (IDPAR) in an effort to convince representatives of the business community that they needed to financially support research on the project.

Startup funding was received from Health and Welfare Canada, the National Research Council and the Foundation of The Hospital for Sick Children. It was also expected that each participant organization would contribute funding. The Institute for Health Care Facilities of the Future was launched as an independent organization in December 1986 and rented space from CHA. It was governed by a board of directors composed of representatives from fourteen organizations from the voluntary sector, industry, consumer groups and government.[3] The institute was to identify and explore special research themes, as approved by the board, in addition to its role of fostering debate and producing regular future-oriented environmental scanning reports.

By late 1987, the institute was experiencing serious problems. Two major issues had to be addressed. One was the gradual shift in the focus of the institute from health care facilities to health services of the future. This broadening scope meant that the institute required more human and financial resources than originally planned. The second issue was its already limited budget and the need to find additional funds to support its wider focus on the health care system.

CHA's board approved a proposal requesting that each of the member organizations commit adequate funding to the institute each year for the next three years to maintain it. The board also directed CHA's president to meet with the chair and the executive director of the institute to express the association's serious concerns about the direction that the institute was taking. Because only four member organizations were willing to commit long-term funding, including CHA, CHA had no other alternative but to withdraw its support from the project. The institute officially ceased its operations at the end of June 1990. But, during its short existence, it had published two major reports that looked at current and emerging trends in the system and how these might impact Canada's future health delivery system.

Canadian Institute for Health Information (CIHI)

The Canadian Institute for Health Information (CIHI) is an independent, not-for-profit organization that provides high-quality, objective and reliable information about Canada's health care system. It generates statistics and analysis about the system and its performance, and on the delivery of health care and the health status of Canadians. It is governed by a fifteen-person board, whose members represent both government and nongovernment, including the health sector and regions of Canada, to provide links between the two. The organization is funded through bilateral agreements with the federal health department and the provincial and territorial health ministries, as well as individual health facilities. It also generates revenues from the sale of its products and services (www.cihi.org).

CIHI was founded from a merger of several organizations in Canada that were involved in developing standards, collecting information and analyzing data on the financial performance of Canada's hospitals. The development and reporting of uniform information had been a major goal of the CHA since its founding in 1931.

Technology advancements by the late 1970s had made the fulfillment of this vision entirely possible and CHA and its members were prepared to play the leadership role in every way possible to ensure that this goal was reached.

CHA's Sub-Committee on Hospital Information Systems recommended to the board in late 1977 that it become involved in the development of an integrated information reporting system. A task force was to be set up with membership from the federal and provincial governments, CHA and its member associations, and the task force should seek funding from the National Health Grants Program. The board supported these recommendations and approved the project as a long-term ongoing activity for the organization.

When the project was discussed at the meeting of the CHA and its provincial member CEOs in June 1978, the resulting recommendations were also approved by the board:

> WHEREAS all provincial hospital associations recognize the need to maintain a consistent information system throughout Canada, and
>
> WHEREAS a national hospital information base is essential for the analysis and planning of health care in Canada,
>
> THEREFORE BE IT RESOLVED that the CHA recognize and endorse the need to maintain a system capable of consistency from province to province, and further,
>
> BE IT RESOLVED that Health and Welfare Canada be requested to grant funding to the Canadian Hospital Association for the revision and development of the existing H.I.S. . . ., that failing, the member associations and institutions be requested to support this project, and further,
>
> BE IT RESOLVED that provincial hospital associations make representation to provincial governments to endorse this national hospital information system (CHA 1978, 5).

This was the start of the M.I.S. (management information system) Project. (*See* chapter 16 for a description of the goals and products of the project.) The initial funding to get the project underway came from the federal government, with CHA acting as the banker and secretariat. As a result, CHA and its member organizations had much less control over the project than they originally planned. Initiated by Herm Crewson, the executive director of the Manitoba Health Organizations, Inc., he wrote to all the CEOs of the other provincial member associations urging them to contribute to the project, which they agreed to do with contributions amounting to one-third of the cost of the project in 1985. This enabled the hospitals, through their member organizations, to have a "greater voice in the management of the project" (CHA 1984b, 6).

The members' contributions were channeled through CHA and the association's vice-president of research became the representative on the executive. A CHA board member was appointed to the Steering Committee, which, until then, had only government representatives on it. Up to this point, M.I.S. had been in the testing and product development phase. But as it was about to enter the next stage, disagreement occurred among the members of the Steering Committee as to how the project should be managed. The issues involved two areas: 1) Who was ultimately responsible? and 2) Who owned the information that M.I.S. would collect?

Options were proposed that it be directly under the management of CHA, while others proposed that a corporation—to be name HOSTAT—be set up in which association members would buy shares as a means for obtaining tax credits. However, tax law does not allow not-for-profit, charitable organizations to set up a corporation with shares. Ownership of the M.I.S. Project continued to be vested in the Steering Committee which did not have legal status as a corporation. It reported to the Federal/Provincial Advisory Committee on Institutions and Medical Services and to the CHA and its members.

In late 1985, the M.I.S. director, CHA's president and its member on the Steering Committee met to discuss CHA's further involvement in the project. The project director had prepared a strategic plan to be presented to the Steering Committee in March 1986 and CHA's member associations wanted input into it. In 1987, the issue of a merger between the Hospital Medical Records Institute and the M.I.S. Project was proposed. The institute had been founded by the Ontario Medical Association and the Ontario Hospital Association in 1963 and it had been federally incorporated in 1977. But it was a business organization with assets and a merger would be difficult to arrange between these two very different groups.

Management options for the project were becoming limited and CHA's board was anxious for the project to become operational. CHA had invested, and was still continuing to invest, considerable resources in the project; it had also entered into a leasing arrangement with a partner to acquire additional office space for the M.I.S. Project's expanding staff. The association was carrying considerable debt at the time and its members wanted to see results for their financial investment. In fact, by 1987, two provinces—Quebec and Alberta—had opted out of funding the project for the time being. The M.I.S. Project was also beginning to create tension among the members at the board table.

In November 1987, the M.I.S. Steering Committee sent a letter to the provincial CEOs, which was circulated to CHA's board, advising them that it was looking at an organizational model similar to that of the accreditation council. Many of the guidelines developed by the M.I.S. Project were going to be implemented by April 1988 in a number of provinces and it was now imperative that some kind of organization be in place to direct the project. The proposed merger of the project with HMRI had hit several stumbling blocks and was on hold at this stage.

The CHA representative on the Steering Committee submitted a report to the board expressing his view on the future of the project. He believed strongly that it should not be taken over by government and identified three major issues: 1) how to convince more hospitals to become involved and 2) how to provide practical information on the MIS applications. The third issue involved the reluctance of provincial governments to fund the project.

An action plan was prepared and presented to the provincial association CEOs later that year. The plan envisioned a merger of the M.I.S. Project with Health and Welfare Canada's National Health Productivity Improvement Project (NHPIP) into a separate organization effective 1 January 1989. The merger had already been approved in principle by the federal government's Advisory Committee on Institutions and Medical Services, the MIS Steering Committee and the provincial CEOs.

By March 1989, CHA's Steering Committee representative reported to the board that "the testing phase of the project [was] officially completed, some sites [had] exceeded their objectives and some [were] applying the guidelines to long term care with some success" (CHA 1989a, 9). Provincial governments were now beginning to look at the MIS guidelines as a replacement for the *Canadian Hospital Accounting Manual*, which was now out of print. With the Steering Committee being dissolved, it had recommended to the federal government that a new corporation be set up under a new board. It suggested that this board be composed of a representative from each of the provinces and territories, two representatives from Ontario and Quebec, two from the federal government and one from CHA. The funding should be split with sixty percent coming from the federal and provincial governments and forty percent from the provincial associations. These recommendations were approved by the federal advisory committee in 1989 and a subcommittee had been set up to define the precise composition of the board.

The subcommittee's recommendations were delivered in June 1989 and included: 1) that MIS and the NHPIP be merged under a steering committee composed of five provincial government representatives, five provincial/territorial health association representatives, one representative from Health and Welfare Canada and one from CHA. Funding was already in place.

In June 1990, the new corporation under the name, The MIS Group, was set up and had moved into its new headquarters in office space in the Byward Market in Ottawa, under a new president. By now, provincial government support for the guidelines had reached the point where they were now asking The MIS Group to extend these into the long-term care sector.

As the guidelines continued to gain widespread support across Canada's health system, the CHA representative on the MIS board reported to CHA's board in June 1991 that a largely government-based Task Force on Health Information Systems had invited The MIS Group, the HMRI and Statistics Canada to participate in establishing a Canada-wide health information institute. The MIS Group board was fully supportive of this new institution but cautioned that it should be governed by non-government representatives from the user groups, that is, the health facilities and regions across Canada.

On 10 December 1993, the Canadian Institute for Health Information was officially launched as a not-for-profit corporation. In January 1994, the HMRI and The MIS Group boards voted to dissolve to form the new institute. In February the institute assumed responsibility for the programs, staff and obligations of MIS and HMRI and later integrated the programs and services of Health Canada and Statistics Canada into its operations. CIHI held its first board meeting in April 1994.

The relationship between CIHI and CHA has not always been an easy one. Occasionally, issues have come to the board table from the CHA federation membership around issues of timeliness of data and how the two organizations can cooperate and communicate more effectively, so that the institute is aware of the concerns of CHA's members.

In fact, at the November 2001 CHA board meeting, the chair of the CEO Forum reported that the provincial CEOs were concerned "about the need to provide to and receive from [CIHI] timely and relevant data" (CHA 2001a, n.p.). The forum members asked CHA's president, Sharon Sholzberg-Gray, to meet with the CIHI

CEO to raise a number of issues: 1) the possibility of CHA getting a seat on the institute board and 2) improving performance measurement and reporting on system performance. CHA met with CIHI in December 2001 and, in 2002, the CEO Forum established a Working Group of both CHA and CIHI staff to review ongoing issues and performance measurement.

There will be other areas of concern over the coming years and decades that both organizations will need to resolve in order to ensure that Canada's health system acquires reliable, timely and quality information. Since much of this information comes directly from the health system, which is represented by the CHA and its member organizations, it will be in the best interests of both to work together.

Health Council of Canada

In 1981, CHA submitted a document to the Parliamentary Task Force on Federal/Provincial Fiscal Arrangements in which it proposed that an independent health council be set up to review health policy and provide a foundation for health decision-making in Canada.

The Health Council of Canada, as perceived by CHA, would be modeled on other organizations such as the Economic Council of Canada, the Hudson Institute and the Institute for Research on Public Policy. It would be funded through both public and private sources and its board would comprise distinguished members from the health community, government and the public. CHA's provincial member hospital and health organizations were also committed to the creation of a council of this nature.

By 1982, CHA had received support from the Canadian Nurses Association, the Canadian College of Health Service Executives and was discussing the proposal with the Royal College of Physicians and Surgeons. The Royal College was also proposing an oversight agency, an institute of medicine, which CHA saw as having too narrow a focus.

At the March 1982 meeting between CHA's board and Health Minister Monique Bégin, the association presented its vision of the council. It would be "a neutral body to develop health standards—guidelines for both levels of government to better assess the delivery of health care" (1982, 2). CHA further believed that a health council would determine: 1) what the goal of the health system was, 2) provide indicators such as infant mortality and 3) determine how to measure care delivered in other parts of the health care system. The health minister encouraged CHA to define the practical aspects of the council further but cautioned that there was little support among the provinces for such a body.

In June 1982, CHA's board approved setting up an Ad Hoc Committee to develop a proposal including objectives for the council, its membership and funding sources, as well as to implement the council if it was approved. By late 1982, Bert Ayers, who was chair of the committee, reported to the board that the Royal College was now supportive of the CHA proposal and had offered both office space and services in the amount of $25,000, contingent on equal funding being found from other organizations.

Over the following year, CHA made several presentations to other health organizations about the context and need for a national health council. By mid-1984, it had the support of ten major organizations and an initial exploratory meeting had been held with representatives from these organizations to discuss the feasibility of setting up the council. A small Working Party was formed, which had met with the federal health minister, who once again advised the group that the provincial ministries of health did not support the concept.

At a second meeting in December 1984, representatives from the Royal College were invited to discuss how its proposal for an institute of medicine and the health council concept might be compatible. The group failed to reach an agreement and the Royal College went its separate way to pursue its own proposal. Support for a health council was mounting from organizations such as CMA's Task Force on the Allocation of Health Resources, the parliamentary committee reviewing the proposed Canada Health Act and the Canadian Public Health Association. All of these groups either recommended some form of national health council or supported the CHA proposal outright.

The December 1984 meeting of the Working Party, while failing to win over the Royal College, did establish its own terms of reference and membership, and prepared a formal proposal that identified the general objectives of a health council. The members determined that the council would be a voluntary, nonprofit, independent and multidisciplinary corporate body. Its official name should be the Canadian Health Council and its mission would be to: "identify important issues relating to the maintenance and enhancement of health and health care delivery in Canada through research and analysis. It would seek ways to improve the health of Canadians. It would also provide objective information on the costs and benefits of both existing services and new technologies on the horizon."

The Working Party also outlined duties of the board and its membership, the management and operation of the council, it program activities and how it would be funded. The proposal recommended that the council be implemented in three phases over five years. Under the council's charter, it would have a maximum membership of thirty-five individuals, selected on the basis of their interest, experience or achievement in the health field or in relevant fields. The startup phase would entail identifying these members and the Working Party proposed that the Governor General of Canada be asked to name an appointments committee.

After two more revisions, A Proposal for a Canadian Health Council was approved by the Working Party on 23 May 1986 and officially ratified by the National Ad Hoc Committee on a National Health Council on 3 March 1987. At this same meeting, the Royal College advised that it would not be pursuing the creation of an institute and supported the endorsement by CMA on behalf of physicians. Representatives at the meeting suggested names for the Appointments Committee to be submitted to the Governor General; appointed Jean-Claude Martin, CHA's president, as Interim President of the council; and proposed how the council could be funded. To cover initial funding, each organization would contribute a thousand dollars to launch the council. Although the list of potential candidates for the Appointments Committee was forwarded to the office of the governor general, the request was turned down as the office regarded this as a political request.

Unfortunately, in 1988, Canada was hit by another recession. This made it more difficult for CHA's provincial member associations, health care facilities and health professionals, and both the federal and provincial governments, to provide funding for the health council. As a result, interest in the project declined and, eventually, the council was put on hold in 1989 until a more favorable environment would permit its reactivation. With the priorities of the health system shifting to restructuring and downsizing in the 1990s, CHA did not have an opportunity to bring the health council idea forward again.

Fourteen years later, however, in December 2003, as a result of the 2003 First Ministers Health Accord and recommendations from both the Romanow and Kirby reports, the Health Council of Canada was launched. The federal, provincial and territorial governments appoint representatives to the board of the council. The council's mandate is to monitor and report independently to Canadians on health care renewal progress and system performance, and identify strategies for improvement of the system and for better health for Canadians. Its mandate parallels closely the vision foreseen by CHA more than twenty years before its formation.

Summary

During its history, CHA has supported the establishment of several national health organizations. Three of these—the Canadian Council on Health Services Accreditation, the Canadian College of Health Service Executives and the Canadian Institute for Health Information—have become independent, well-regarded health organizations in their own right. Other organizations that CHA launched on its own or in partnership with others could not be sustained with the financial backing available at the time; they were shut down to protect CHA. One of the association's more visionary organizations eventually was set up in the new century to meet a need in Canada's health system that CHA had identified more than twenty years earlier.

Endnotes

1. The accreditation council did apply for a grant from the federal government which they continued to receive for several years; the government advised that the council could not both implement a fee-for-survey and apply for a grant in 1964.

2. The cosponsoring organizations were the Canadian Association of Hospital Auxiliaries, Canadian Association of Social Workers, Canadian College of Health Service Executives, Canadian Council on Social Development, Canadian Medical Association, Canadian Nurses Association, Catholic Health Association of Canada, Consumers Association of Canada, CHA and the Royal College.

3. These organizations were the Association of Canadian Teaching Hospitals, Canadian Association on Gerontology, Canadian Institute of Child Health, Canadian Medical Association, Canadian Nurses Association, Canadian Public Health Association, Canadian Long Term Care Association, Canadian College of Health Service Executives (voluntary); Canadian Association of Manufacturers of Medical Devices and Pharmaceutical Manufacturers' Association of Canada (private sector); Health and Welfare Canada, Federal/Provincial Advisory Committee on Institutional and Medical Services (government); Medical Research and National Research Councils (research bodies).

Part IV

PROGRAMS AND SERVICES

P art four of the book presents CHA's programs and services as they have evolved over the years. Most associations consist of two streams: 1) their core business of representing, lobbying and advocating on behalf of their members, who pay fees for these activities; and 2) ancillary services such as education, publishing, consulting and conferences, which often complement and support the organization's mandate. CHA's services and programs have added considerable revenues to the organization over its history. In some cases, these revenues enabled the organization to survive and, in later years, to expand its role of working on behalf of its members.

Chapter 11 presents an overview of CHA's oldest service, that of journal publishing. Not only did the revenues from this journal support the hospital council throughout the late 1930s and 1940s, it also was the reason for the council to set itself up as a legally independent wholly incorporated entity in 1936. The chapter describes the journal, its growth and contributions to CHA and how the journal progressed over the years. It outlines the changes in journal publishing, the launch of the trustee journal and the end of journal publishing in 1996. The chapter also describes CHA's directory and book publishing activities, launched much later in its history and still part of CHA's services today.

Chapter 12 presents a chronological description of CHA's distance education programs, which were launched more than fifty years ago. One of its younger services, these courses have contributed considerable revenue to the organization over the years and have graduated more than 25,000 health care personnel. CHA's education programs have always been directed to nonmedical personnel. They have enabled health personnel, already working full-time in health facilities, to improve their knowledge and skills through distance study in a number of areas at the senior and middle management levels, in food service, health records and long-term care management. These programs continue to provide CHA with a steady revenue stream today that has enabled the association to support other activities.

Chapter 13, the last chapter in this section, provides a brief look at CHA conferences. When the council was originally set up, the members decided against forming a national association to avoid competing with the powerful American Hospital Association and its annual convention. But as Canada's health care system expanded, and its particular needs diverged considerably from those of the United States, it seemed appropriate for CHA to enter the conference business. Since its founding, the organization had planned and delivered its three-day general assembly meeting. From there it moved to an annual meeting and conference, and then included single-issue conferences, symposia and seminars. Eventually, as the health care environment changed, CHA partnered with other national health organizations to deliver the successful National Healthcare Leadership Conference, which is its main conference event today.

11

SPREADING THE WORD: PUBLISHING OVER THE YEARS

"The lack of an abundance of good writing is only half of the . . . problem in developing a rich and viable literature for health administration in Canada . . . Unless we financially support the Canadian Publishers of such material, we can readily conceive of a scenario where no Canadian sources exist."

(CHOWN 1984, 4)

From its earliest days, the Canadian Healthcare Association (CHA) has been involved in publishing in one form or another. The first mention of publishing comes, naturally, from Dr. Harvey Agnew in his book on the history of Canadian hospitals. Dr. Agnew noted that, in 1910, "A hospital journal, *Hospital World*, was published in Toronto by Dr. G.A. Young . . . [which] became the official organ of the CHA in 1912" (1974, 61). However, with the outbreak of World War I, publishing activities—in fact all association activities—were suspended. However, the journal appeared again (but not the association) between 1918 and 1920. Dr. Young changed the journal's name to *Hospital, Medical and Nursing World* and it became the official journal of the British Columbia and Alberta provincial associations (Ibid.).

Then, in 1924, The Edwards Publishing Company of Toronto, under the ownership of Charles A. Edwards, launched the journal, *Hospital Buying*, as a private commercial enterprise. Subtitled *A Monthly Journal for Hospital Executives*, it became both quite successful—since there were no other hospital journals in the country— and the voice of hospital administration in Canada. The first issue was dated January 1924, although no copy of this issue exists in the CHA archives today.

The first issue of record is February 1924, which ran to twenty pages and was available by subscription to all hospitals in Canada for one dollar per year. In his introductory column, publisher Charles Edwards wrote:

> May we place in the hands of the superintendents, purchasing agents and other executives of Canadian Hospitals and allied institutions, the first issue of *Hospital Buying*?

> The purpose of [this journal] is to provide monthly, a medium for the discussion of all topics relating to hospital administration and a convenient reference for the buying official ("Introducing" 1924, 7).

The journal included twenty-three advertisers, one being the T. Eaton Company Limited, prominently displayed on the cover, and a classified ad page. Advertising was obviously a mainstay of the journal and, throughout the 1920s, included the Kellogg Company of Canada and Imperial Oil Limited. Often, there were more pages of advertising than editorial in these monthly issues.

In November 1924, eight months after its introduction, *Hospital Buying* changed its name to *The Canadian Hospital*, a title it retained until 1974. The editorial about the name change noted that ". . . we decided to change the name . . . to one that would more fully reflect the purposes and ambitions of our journal in the varied branches of hospital work" ("Change", 11). Despite the

Charles Edwards, owner of *The Canadian Hospital*, 1924 to 1936, and CHA's journal business manager until 1963.

name change, the journal continued to focus on hospital products through its advertising pages and featured hospital equipment and supplies, as well as the latest progress in disease treatment in both Canadian and American hospitals.

The first issues of the journal contained lengthy, medical treatises, briefs to government, many hospital photographs and exhaustive reports of medical, provincial associations and other organizations' meetings. There were articles on hospital waiting times and overcrowding (March 1925), editorials on the need for more money from the provinces to pay hospital costs for indigent care (November 1927), and pages and pages of announcements about hospital construction and openings, the acquisition of new equipment and articles on everything from how to lay out an operating room to how to prevent fires. In the 1920s, a fire meant virtual destruction of a hospital because of its wooden structure, non-fireproof supplies and equipment, and the highly volatile gases used in anesthesia, heating and cooling. (In fact, the journal faithfully recorded every significant event of both the hospital council and the association up to and including the 1960s.)

In May 1926, the first annual directory of hospital equipment and supplies was published. Titled "The Hospital Buyers' Directory," it included companies that manufactured and distributed a range of products from building materials; to general equipment, furnishings and supplies; foods and beverages; and clinical and scientific equipment such as sterilizers and pharmaceutical

Leonard Shaw, Superintendent, Saskatoon City Hospital, and the Canadian Hospital Council's First Editor.

preparations. Running to sixty pages, it was filled with advertisers' material and editorial—although not much of this.

Because the 1920s were a period of rapid hospital expansion, each issue of the journal also provided detailed construction and floor plans, and lengthy descriptions of hospitals either being built, under construction or just opened.[1] There was also considerable emphasis on fundraising, and one woman in particular, Mary Frances Kern—with offices in New York, Chicago and Toronto—ran monthly full-page ads in the journal showcasing her successful fundraising campaigns. It should be remembered that provincial governments did not provide capital to hospitals to expand or replace aging physical plants at this time, and hospitals were dependent on the generosity of the local community and philanthropists for their hospital expansion projects.

Canada was a very different country in the 1920s, with its vast geography stretching from ocean to ocean, sparsely populated except in areas close to the American border. Communication across this huge area between and across provinces was limited to the written word, telegraph, unreliable telephone systems and face-to-face meetings, whenever these could be arranged. This made it difficult for hospital superintendents to acquire and exchange information about hospital activities in Canada. While there were a few journals, these were rare and mostly American-published, as were most books. Mass publishing and communication as we know it today was unheard of when the Canadian Medical Association (CMA) set up the Department of Hospital Service in 1928.

One of the department's several functions was to "maintain a clearing-house for hospital information" through various means (Agnew 1974, 66). This included compiling the very first hospital directory. There were few records about the number and type of hospitals in Canada, where they were located or information on the number and types of beds set up. As Dr. Agnew reported, any records that had been kept were either lost, unreliable or nonexistent (1974, 3).

The Department of Pensions and National Health identified the need for better hospital statistics in 1930, and Dr. Helen MacMurchy, director of the division of child health in the department, asked Dr. Agnew to help her compile data about Canadian hospitals; the federal department would publish the results. This was a difficult task to undertake, since many provinces did not keep accurate information on current hospitals, let alone figures about past hospital activities. It was also a confusing undertaking because many hospitals were double listed in various categories such as tuberculosis (TB) institutions, if a general hospital had TB beds set up. And, as Dr. Agnew wrote, many of these institutions would hardly be called hospitals as we know them today. Nevertheless, with the help of the federal government and, at their request, the council assisted in the compilation and publication of a first hospital directory.

Publishing was one way to exchange information between provincial and regional hospital administrators across Canada. In fact, the greatest contributor to CHA's publishing history was Dr. Agnew. On being awarded the George Findlay Stephens Memorial Award in June 1953, the following was written about his contribution to the council's publishing activities over the years:

> Under his leadership, the D.H.S. [Department of Hospital Service] and later the Council, published a series of booklets and bulletins on a variety of subjects, *e.g.*, hospital planning, legislation, medical staff relations, nursing problems, personnel, principles of hospital insurance, the "units of credit system", and many others. All these were valuable additions to hospital literature ("Stephens" 1953, 41).

Dr. Agnew believed that Canadian hospital personnel should make every effort to talk and write about their accomplishments, successes and failures, and share these whenever possible. He set the example by contributing to the pages of the journal both as its editor and as an independent author in his later years. In fact, most of his best editorial writing was done in the column titled "Obiter Dicta" which was first published in the April 1936 issue of *Canadian Hospital*.

The Early Days in Journal Publishing, 1931 to 1952

At the 1933 biennial meeting, the delegates suggested that the Canadian Hospital Council should have an official journal of its own and appointed a special committee to study the issue. Then, at the 1935 biennial meeting, the committee reported that an arrangement had been made with Charles Edwards, the owner of *Canadian Hospital*, for it to become the official publication of the council, a proposal that was endorsed by the delegates.

On 31 March 1936, an agreement was reached between Mr. Edwards and the council to form The Canadian Hospital Publishing Company. The council would share in the net profits and provide editorial and news direction for the journal. In return, Mr. Edwards became its business manager and the council appointed an editor, who was paid an annual honorarium of $200.[2] This arrangement would also permit the council to take over the journal entirely in 1941 or at some later date. Because of this arrangement, it became necessary for the council to incorporate in order to protect it against any liabilities arising from the arrangement. The council would also set aside a reserve from the net profits during the five years following 1936 to purchase the journal outright. In 1941, Charles Edwards generously donated the publishing rights of the journal to the Canadian Hospital Council and, in January 1946, the journal was transferred outright to the council.

The journal became a major communications vehicle during the war years. It informed Canadian hospitals about government regulations and restrictions that would impact their operations, reported on nursing and food shortages—sometimes so severe that hospitals closed—and contributed to the council's reserve fund throughout the war years. The journal paid for itself through advertising revenues, although rising costs for printing and staffing during the late 1940s raised concerns about the continuing financial stability of the council among the members of both the Executive Committee and the provincial associations. In 1949, *Canadian Hospital* celebrated its silver jubilee. However, it did so knowing that the journal was about to lose its high-profile editor, Dr. Agnew, who had submitted his resignation to the council effective in 1950.

Editorial content in the early 1950s included considerable discussion about federal grants under the national health plan and featured many articles on hospital construction which was booming across Canada during these years of the National Health Program of construction grants. In one of his first editorials, as the new executive director and editor of the journal, Dr. L.O. Bradley commented on the growing shortage of nurses in the country. In October 1950, the journal published its first four-color ad for Eaton's Contract Sales. Periodically, *Canadian Hospital* published articles on trusteeship and theme issues. For the council, the value of the journal was summed up by the Executive Committee as ". . . one of the Council's most important responsibilities and that wherever necessary every possible step should be taken to strengthen the journal and to expand its usefulness" (CHC 1950, 272).

To understand the journal's significance, it was a standing agenda item on every Executive Committee meeting. In fact, in September 1950, there were extensive discussions about its staffing, editorial policies, its value to the council and the members, its circulation, subscription and advertising rates. It was the Executive Committee that directed Dr. Bradley to write an editorial on nursing shortages in 1950. Any possibility of another journal being launched in direct competition raised

Merck & Co. (today's Merck-Frosst Canada and one of this book's sponsors) was an advertiser in *The Canadian Hospital Journal*. Date circa 1936.

considerable alarm among the council executive and assembly delegates. The journal was protected both because of the long, ongoing and amicable relationship with Charles Edwards, who continued to manage advertising, and because of its major contribution to the council's finances over the past decades.

Among the reports to each general assembly was one from the editor and, occasionally, Mr. Edwards, who discussed the financial side of the journal. Reports from the treasurer included extensive explanations of the journal revenues and expenses and the journal's contribution to the council's reserve fund. At the end of 1946, when the executive reviewed the financial statements, contributions from the associations and conference members amounted to just over $13,000. The journal assets, including cash in the bank and bonds, amounted to almost $14,000 and the journal reserve fund was at more than $11,000. The role of the journal in supporting the council through its development years had been critical to ensure its survival.

Publishing under the Canadian Hospital Association, 1953 to 1977

At the 1952 meeting of the board of directors, the council approved the publication of a hospital directory and the January 1953 editorial, written by Dr. A.L. Swanson, the new executive director and editor of the renamed Canadian Hospital Association, announced its upcoming release. Dr. Swanson described the directory as containing "a geographic and alphabetical listing of our hospitals with the names of department heads; a buyers' directory beamed at purchasing agents; information on hospital and allied associations; . . . . It is our earnest wish that the annual spring publication will [render] a real service to Canadian hospitals" (31).

A free copy of the directory was sent to each hospital in Canada, with larger centres receiving two or three copies. Additional copies could also be purchased for $2.50. Dr. Swanson reported to the May 1953 board meeting that the direct costs of producing the directory would be fully recovered through advertising and sales. By September 1960, with printing and mailing costs rising, the cost to purchase the directory had risen to three dollars a copy.

The 1950s were successful years for CHA's journal with a steadily increasing number of advertisers, ongoing increases in the Publications Fund (a reserve), and a subscription campaign to increase controlled and paid circulation. Throughout this time, Mr. Edwards continued to manage the business, that is, the advertising component, for both the journal and the directory. In his report to the CHA Assembly in 1957, he reminded the delegates that there had been a net profit from the journal in every year since 1936. He also reported that there were adequate reserves set aside for the journal and that part of its surpluses paid for secretarial costs for the association.

Circulation of the journal had increased to 4,000 copies a month as the decade ended. But, on a somewhat sombre note, in a 1959 editorial, written by Dr. Douglas Piercey, the executive director, he reported that, for the first time in twenty years, the journal would have a competitor. This publication ". . . purports to serve the hospital field in Canada—but . . . is being distributed for purely commercial purposes" (31). He issued a plea for hospitals to contribute original articles and to occasionally identify to an advertiser that their product had been seen in the journal pages. The last issues of the association's journal at the end of the decade carried extensive coverage of the national health insurance plan, with detailed descriptions of how it was being implemented across each province. More editorial content on subjects related to trusteeship, with a regular feature titled "For Trustees Only," had also been introduced in 1956. There was also a sizeable increase in the amount of material published in French, including original articles.

The board continued to review editorial matters, suggest journal content, approve the publications fund and generally support the journal in every way possible. Minutes from meetings of CHA's executive committees and boards indicate how worrisome the entry of a competitive journal into the hospital field was to both advertising and editorial staff at CHA, as well as to the editorial committee and board members during these years. The January 1960 issue touted the fact that *Canadian Hospital* was the only journal in the hospital field to be audited by the Audit Bureau of Circulation. The board authorized subscription increases from $3.00 to $5.00 per year to become effective in January 1961. And, in January 1962, the board again approved—on the recommendation of the Finance Committee—an increase in *Canadian Hospital's* circulation by 1,000 to 3,675 key hospital people in order to compete with the new journal being circulated to more than 5,000 personnel in Canada's hospitals.

Content in the journal during the 1960s ranged from association news to articles on medical staff, nursing and labor relations. Nursing shortages, the conversion to metric and the coming age of computerization by 1968 began to fill the journal's

Samples of CHA's journal publishing between 1936 and 1996.

pages. There were also articles on aging, the increase in the number of elderly and their impact on health care delivery.

With the appointment of Dr. Brosseau as executive director of the CHA and editor of the journal, French summaries of all articles were published in the January 1966 issue for the first time. Editorials appeared in both languages and most issues included at least one full-length original article in French. The journal now had an editorial staff of four, plus the editor, a design consultant and an advertising staff of three.

Charles Edwards retired from his duties as business manager for the journal and the directory effective 31 December 1963. He had served the association for more than thirty years and, in recognition of his service, he received a retirement allowance of $5,000 per year during his lifetime from CHA. Mr. Edwards died in 1984.[3]

In 1968, the Finance Committee of the board requested a review of CHA's publishing activities, including the historically restrictive editorial policies that the board had placed on the journal. During these years, members of the board not only approved the publishing budget, they also determined what would and would not be considered acceptable for publishing in the journal, particularly its editorial. The review was also to look at all financial aspects, staffing and departmental organization. A change in the journal's mailing classification to become effective in April 1969, with potential mailing increases by as much as 150 percent, plus decreases in advertising revenue, had potentially serious implications for the viability of CHA's publishing program by the late 1960s, as well as for the association's viability. CHA needed to position itself in this area for the future.

As the journal entered the 1970s, *Canadian Hospital* became a much more sophisticated business-oriented publication with lengthy and timely articles. Bold graphics had replaced the traditional photo covers of the past. Colored stock was introduced for the news pages and the entire journal took on a more modern appearance. In 1971, the first completely bilingual issue of the journal was published, with each article appearing in both languages in an effort to attract more readers in Quebec. The journal also included special articles written by experts in law and nursing.

In January 1974, the name of the journal was changed to *Dimensions in Health Service* to cover a more diversified readership. This change also coincided with the fiftieth anniversary of the publication of the journal and reflected CHA's position

". . . with respect to the implementation of an integrated health care system in Canada with hospitals to be regarded as only one large component of the system" (Hughes 1974, 6). When *The Canadian Hospital* was first launched, it was targeted to the hospitals and their personnel who needed information on construction, equipment, purchasing, setting up departments, managing staff and numerous other areas in order to operate hospitals. Over the years, the journal included coverage on funding the system, tariffs, new and more technologies and the need for standards and quality care. As the health system evolved in the 1970s, the target audience of the publication needed to broaden to encompass not just the hospital but the health system itself.

The Publications Committee, established by the board of directors at the end of 1974, was asked to look at the considerable deficit in the journal and to consider including more trustee-oriented material. By this time, part of the executive director's salary, occupancy costs and a portion of staff salaries were also being allocated to the journal costs.

By 1975, there was serious competition for advertising revenue and paid circulation between CHA's journal and the commercial journal published by Southam Publishing in Toronto. The Publications Department deficit had continued to increase, mainly due to lost advertising revenues in *Dimensions*. By 1976, Southam was also experiencing serious losses, so much so, that they approached CHA with a proposal to take over the association's publishing operations (e.g., the journal, directory and its newsletter *Product Alert*), a proposal which was roundly rejected by the board at the urging of Dr. Brosseau, who believed that ". . . the membership of CHA would be deprived of an excellent publication . . ." if the board accepted the offer (CHA 1976b, 4).

By 1976, the lack of a voice for the trustees of Canada in publishing, as well as no French-language journal, continued to be serious issues at CHA board meetings. The board asked Dr. Brosseau to investigate the possibility of buying the journal *Administration hospitalière et sociale* which was published and distributed by a private firm in Montreal. Dr. Brosseau was also asked to apply to the Kellogg Foundation for a five-year grant to launch a trustee magazine. In March 1977, CHA received approval for a four-year grant of $155,000 to develop, publish and distribute a trustee magazine across Canada, including a French edition. The first issue of *Hospital Trustee* was launched in July 1977 with paid circulation of over 4,600 copies, reflecting the interest of Canada's hospitals in providing more information to their trustees and their willingness to do so through paid subscriptions.

The *Canadian Hospital Directory* had experienced its own ups and downs through the 1950s as it struggled to prove itself as value-added to the association and its members. In 1972, all copies had sold out and it had set record sales of 3,700 copies by 1973. By 1977, 5,800 copies of the directory were being published annually. Each hospital in Canada, which completed an information survey, received a free copy of the directory. (By this time, there were more than 1,200 hospitals in the country.) The major issue for the board regarding the directory was to computerize the information for easier and faster updating and output. The board approved a recommendation from the Publications Committee for a contract to be signed with a Toronto service bureau to begin computerization of the directory's contents in 1977.

The 1977 board decision to move CHA headquarters to Ottawa had potentially serious consequences for CHA publishing activities. None of the department's staff would be moving and the advertising sales team would remain in Toronto for the time being. The loss of many years' of editorial and circulation experience was a major setback for CHA's Publishing Department. As CHA prepared to pack up, the journal deficit continued to climb due to falling circulation, declining advertising revenues and a serious lack of marketing expertise within the department.

Over the years, CHA had dabbled in book publishing. It released the first edition of the *Canadian Hospital Accounting Manual* in 1952 with a third edition published in 1968. The association had also worked with the Department of National Health and Welfare to publish *Canadian Hospital Terminology and Definitions*, which was released in 1972 in both official languages. The book had been endorsed by the Federal-Provincial Advisory Committee on Hospital Insurance and Diagnostic Services, with assurance from the working group that it would be reviewed and updated periodically to ensure that it remained "current with changes occurring in the hospital field" (Working Party 1972, 4e). CHA had also published *Canadian Hospital Law: A Guidebook* in 1974, with all hospitals receiving a free copy. And, in 1977, CHA had contracted with a former CHA employee to revise *Canadian Hospital Statistical Review*.

In one of the last meetings to be held in Toronto in February 1977, the Publishing Committee expressed concerns about the increasing shortfalls in advertising for both the journals and the directory. They did draw to the board's attention the success of the newsletter *News and Careers*, which had been launched in 1976 and which consistently sold all its ad space. The committee also recommended that CHA's circulation lists be computerized to cut down on maintenance costs. Committee members were also supportive of the request from staff that CHA's Publishing Department remain in Toronto, along with its advertising and sales team. The committee strongly recommended that the department remain in Toronto and, at one point, the Headquarters Committee agreed. Eventually, a compromise was reached whereby new editorial staff would be hired well in advance to enable them to be trained thoroughly in their editorial duties before the move to Ottawa.

Publishing in the Nation's Capital, 1978 to the Present

With the move to Ottawa in January 1978, CHA's publishing activities were now being handled by entirely new editorial and circulation staff. Many of them had barely had two months of training with their counterparts in Toronto before they reported to their respective jobs at CHA's Ottawa offices on Laurier Street.

In the newly reorganized CHA, under Jean-Claude Martin as executive director, CHA's publications would now have to absorb organizational service costs in a new budget format. These costs amounted to twenty-two percent of the administrative costs shared by all departments in the CHA budget. With advertising revenues in decline and paid circulation for both journals at a standstill, the future outlook for one of the association's oldest activities did not look healthy for the coming decade. Furthermore, member associations wanted reassurances, which they received, that their fees were not being used to support any CHA services.

CHA was also aware that the former managing editor of the directory was compiling information for a long-term care directory and was struggling financially to complete the work. She had approached CHA for assistance and negotiations were ongoing in late 1978 to acquire the rights for the project. By the fall, a new advertising manager had been hired (a former CHA managing editor with considerable knowledge about the association's publishing activities) and the department's staff were beginning to build a more cohesive publishing team. As requested by the board, the department released the first issue of *Administrateur hospitalier* and published updates of both *Canadian Hospital Statistical Review* and the *Canadian Hospital Law Manual*. To keep costs down, the department had also purchased its own typesetting equipment and hired a typesetter.

In 1979, a new circulation supervisor had been hired to clean up CHA's subscriptions lists and an agreement was in place to purchase the copyright for the long-term care directory. The CEOs of Canada's hospitals had also asked that data collection for updating the hospital directory coincide with their fiscal year end. The directory would now be released annually in early fall, which was considered a better time to generate sales and to conform with the request to collect information after the end of the hospital fiscal year. Once again, the board expressed concerns about the lack of marketing expertise in the Publishing Department, a skill essential to the promotion and sale of its products.

With the new decade, the publishing deficit continued to grow. By 1981, the department had a new senior manager with a mandate to cut the losses in advertising revenue and any other money-losing projects. The French journal *Administrateur hospitalier* was the first title to cease publication. The department also began to focus more and more on book publishing as a way to shore up its advertising shortfalls in other areas. The department published the first *Policy and Procedures Manual* in 1981 and a second edition of *Health Care Institutions: Terminology and Definitions.*

Between 1982 and 1986, the Publishing Department released over fifteen new book titles including a four-volume history series about Canada's health system and a brief titled *Privatize Hospitals?* the rights for which were sold to the Australian Hospital Association in 1986. This document had been prepared by CHA's Research and Development Department to address the issue of privatization in Canada's hospitals. The editorial staff also published a textbook in both English and French for the joint CHA-CNA Nursing Unit Administration Program, working closely with both the director of the program and CHA's French translator.

With the hiring of the new vice-president in 1981, the Publishing Department had finally acquired some marketing expertise. The vice-president focused on marketing and promoting every product line in the department, as well as selling staff expertise in editorial, sales, circulation, printing and design. The department developed newsletters for other health organizations, redesigned journals and launched a catalogue of products in 1986. It also became the distribution centre for the Education Department's textbooks and for the resources created by CHA's Research and Development Department, thus consolidating all customer service activities under one department.

Samples of CHA's directory and guide publishing between 1953 and 2006.

Directory of
Long Term Care Centres
in Canada

Répertoire des
Centres de services de santé à long terme
au Cana...

FIRST EDITION PREMIÈRE
1980

1953

Volume 14 2006-2007

...ORY

...utions
...ersonnel
...izations
...d supplies

...TAL COUNCIL

GUIDE
to CANADIAN HEALTHCARE FACILITIES
des ÉTABLISSEMENTS DE SOINS DE SANTÉ DU CANADA

DES ÉTABLISSEMENTS DE SOINS... SANTÉ DU CANADA
TO CANADIAN HEAL... FACILITIES

Canadian Healthcare Association
Association canadienne des soins de santé
75 years of service / 75 années de service

New regulations from the Canadian Circulation Audit Board (CCAB), to be in place by 1984, would adversely affect CHA's journals and add further costs to their production, particularly *Dimensions*, which had a circulation of 17,000 health personnel by this time. To maintain audit status, every publisher had to verify the name of each person and organization that received a copy of its publication. The amount of work and cost to an organization such as CHA, with only one staff in its circulation division, would be particularly burdensome. To cut costs further, CHA closed its advertising office in Toronto in 1985 and outsourced these services.

As advertising revenues in both the *Canadian Hospital Directory* and the journals continued to decline, management staff in CHA's Publications Department (as it was now called) began to assess the viability of launching a book publishing unit. An analysis of departmental revenue, presented to the Publishing Committee in early 1986, indicated that revenue increases were mainly being produced through book sales. The senior management of the reorganized department developed a business plan to set up a for-profit corporation, wholly owned by CHA and named Canadian Health Publishing Limited. It would be required to raise at least $250,000 in initial investment capital.

CHA had several advantages to support the move into book publishing. First, it had access to Canada's health care market through the information collected and maintained in the hospital and long-term care directories. This could be used to build a customer base. Second, departmental staff had a total of more than forty year's experience in journal, directory and book publishing. Third, CHA had already developed an author list through its journals, which could be tapped into as a resource to create books. Fourth, the department had its own in-house printshop and typesetting unit, which could support production and keep costs down. Fifth, it provided inventory, distribution and circulation management for both the directory and the journals, as well as the Education Department for its student textbooks. Finally, CHA had been publishing books ad hoc since the early 1950s, so the move into book publishing was not a new one but rather the expansion of past projects, which had been relatively successful.

The senior management of the department believed it was only a matter of time before one of the medical publishers in Toronto ventured into health administration publishing and, given that many of these were American-owned, a Canadian perspective on managing health facilities in the country would be lost. The market was wide open for someone—preferably a national health organization such as CHA that knew the needs of Canada's health facilities and the issues—to step in.

John Huenefeld, a publishing consultant, was hired in August 1986 to provide an outside objective review of CHA's publishing operations and to assess the financial, human and technical resources of the department. He was to deliver a report on the feasibility of setting up and focusing resources on book publishing at CHA. His major criticism, which had also been a concern of various board committees over the years, was the lack of full-time marketing expertise in the department. For the most part, his recommendations were positive. Based on this, the vice-president of the department sought approval for the proposal from the Education and Publishing Committee of the board. In 1986, the board of directors approved the launch of the book unit in January 1987 but not the corporation.

The department was reorganized late in 1986 to reflect the organizational structure of a publishing house. It included new positions such as a business manager, circulation manager, editor-in-chief and an associate publisher, with the vice-president becoming the publisher. All units within the department were reorganized and reported to one of these new management positions. The publishing team met weekly to develop a frontlist of new titles for the next three-year period, as well as marketing plans to promote books and to create a catalogue of publications.

In the first year of its launch, the book unit, as it was known, published five books and three titles in a new Executive Brief Series. The focus was on textbooks to support CHA's students in the distance education courses, trustee titles and books for the management of the health care facility in areas such as quality control, risk management and disaster planning. Many of these titles have been revised and updated several times over the past twenty years and several have been issued in third and fourth editions. (*See* appendix 4 for a list of some of these CHA Press books.)

In late 1989, incoming president Carol Clemenhagen separated the book unit from the Services Department into a new entity called CHA Press, a name it retains today. CHA incorporated CHA Press in 1993, although the corporation is inactive. The expectation was that CHA Press would be eligible for book publishing grants from both the federal and provincial governments under the corporation. However, after considerable time and consultation, CHA was advised shortly after incorporation that, because book publishing was part of a registered, charitable, not-for-profit organization, it would not qualify for these grants.

The major competitor for CHA Press in Canada at the time was the American Hospital Association (AHA), which marketed its titles directly to Canadian hospital managers. To lessen the impact of and to control American books being sold in Canada, CHA renegotiated its distribution arrangement with AHA to purchase, promote and market several of their titles each year to the Canadian health care market. This agreement was maintained for many years and was relatively successful from CHA's perspective. CHA Press purchased fewer and fewer AHA books throughout the 1990s, as it published Canadian-authored titles and as the declining Canadian dollar made these books exorbitantly expensive to import and sell. CHA Press also became a major book distributor of titles from other North American and British publishers, as well as purchasing rights to publish Canadian editions of books.[4]

In the 1990s, CHA Press negotiated distribution arrangements with some of its member organizations. They would be eligible to purchase bulk quantities of books at discounts for sale to their members. The Ontario Hospital Association became a large purchaser of textbooks, particularly *Risk Management for Canadian Health Care Facilities*, which it used in one of its courses. CHA Press also purchased the rights to publish *The ABC of Drug Utilization Review* from the Association des hôpitaux du Québec in 1993, assumed all English translation costs and shared in revenues with AHQ.

CHA Press entered into joint publishing arrangements with the Canadian Medical Association and the Canadian Nurses Association in 1991 to publish an overview of all the provincial and federal task forces and commissions that had been set up through the late 1980s and early 1990s to review Canada's health system. CHA Press also launched the Medical Devices Guidelines Series, in both official languages, for Health and Welfare Canada's Bureau of Radiation and Medical Devices. It also published a colloquium for several years for the University of Montreal. In March 1993, when the membership approved the release of the final document of CHA's National Health Policy Reform Project, more commonly referred to as the Vision Project, CHA Press managed to publish the document just in time for its release in June 1993.

In what may well have been its best year, CHA Press published seventeen titles in 1994 with only two full-time staff. The management of the renamed *Guide to Canadian Healthcare Facilities* was moved into the division and CHA successfully negotiated an agreement with the Canadian Medical Association to become its fulfillment house, which included maintaining inventory and handling all processing of book orders. Hundreds of CMA titles were moved in-house; the entire operation was moved to CHA Press management in March 1996.

CHA's journal publishing activities in the 1990s encountered difficult times. Regionalization of the health system in every province, except Ontario, had radically reduced the market for journal subscriptions, books and guides as health facilities were merged or closed. With fewer facilities, fewer copies of CHA's two journals were needed. Declining circulation meant declining advertising as few companies wanted to pay increased advertising rates for smaller circulation. In 1990, CHA's two journals were merged in an effort to cut costs. The new journal was named *Leadership in Health Services*. Part of the membership fees was used to support it in the repositioning of CHA services by president Carol Clemenhagen, who had been directed by the board to find savings and cut costs.

CHA also dropped its advertising contract with its supplier and contracted with a new service in an effort to attract more advertisers to the journal. Unfortunately, the new firm was not able to make much headway in attracting additional advertising revenue. The newly named journal was less focused on one target audience, and with the inclusion of editorial for trustees, who were not seen as health facility buyers, the same old problem emerged. Declining advertising revenues, decreased paid subscriptions, higher salaries and postal rates, and increased printing costs forced CHA to look at its journal publishing activities once again.

By the end of the 1980s and during the early 1990s, CHA's publishing included both the *Canadian Hospital Directory* and the *Directory of Long-Term Care Centres in Canada*. (In 1980, editorial operations for the long-term care directory moved to CHA from Toronto.) Regionalization was shifting the health facility landscape in major ways throughout the late 1980s and early 1990s, and these shifts meant major changes in the way that information was collected, maintained and produced on Canada's health facilities. In 1993, the two directories were merged to become the *Guide to Canadian Healthcare Facilities*.

As with the journal, sales of the directory in the health care market began to decline from highs of more than 5,000 copies sold in the late 1980s to fewer than 1,100 copies by 1994. To offset losses in print sales that year, CHA developed and sold the healthcare database information in electronic format in a new product called the *Abridged Guide on Disk*.[5] In 1995, editorial staff in CHA Press undertook an extensive revision of the healthcare database in order to set up regionalized listings, along with the facility listings ". . . to reflect the significant restructuring in healthcare that [was] occurring across Canada" (*CHA News* 1995, 2).

In March 1996, with the resignation of president Carol Clemenhagen and the appointment of Tim Julien as acting president, the board of directors was asked by the CHA membership to review all CHA services and assess their value in light of the changes happening across provincial health systems. Discussions among the member CEOs and the board continued throughout 1996 about the service side of the organization and which of these services would be considered as core services in CHA.

In September 1996, the board decided to cease further publishing operations in CHA Press and directed CHA management to find another home for CHA's book publishing activities, including the guide. The board also approved the sale of the journal and its circulation list to MCB University Press in Great Britain. By the end of 1996, CHA was no longer in the journal publishing business for the first time since 1936.

At the December 1996 meeting, the board rejected an offer of purchase from a national health organization for the guide and its products but continued to support it as a core service. However, it would be offered as part of any sale of the publishing operations that might occur in the coming months. The board also directed all publishing activities at CHA—except the guide—to cease by the end of 1997, if a buyer was not found for CHA Press, as a reorganized CHA was being set up for the future.

At the beginning of 1997, under Interim President Joyce Bailey, editorial staff in CHA Press were notified by the National Forum on Health, the commission set up by then Prime Minister Jean Chrétien, that CHA Press was on a list of several Canadian publishers to submit a Request For Proposal (RFP) to publish the several volumes of papers that would result from this major review of Canada's health system. With this unexpected development, CHA's publishing activities were resurrected in order to respond to this publishing request. The guide continued to collect information on the health system and CHA Press informed its authors that some publishing activities would begin again in 1997.

CHA's Policy and Development Department launched a new series in 1998—the Policy Brief Series to be published by CHA Press—to support the policy positions being developed on behalf of CHA's members. The Publishing Department, which had been restructured in March 1996, now included book and guide publishing, customer service and mailroom support, and the management of CHA's property at 17 York Street. Although its focus was to be publishing, with only part-time staff in

CHA Press, the book division was unable to publish books of the type and in the numbers it did in the 1980s and 1990s. However, the decline in book publishing at CHA was also a reflection of the serious state of the publishing industry across North America by the beginning of the twenty-first century.

In 2001, the federal government identified CHA's healthcare database as one of six critical databases in existence in Canada that would be essential in the event of a major disaster in the country.[6] For many years, CHA's guide has served as a reference source for the Canadian Council on Health Facilities Accreditation to verify facilities for accreditation surveys and by Revenue Canada personnel for GST rebates. In 2003, the *Guide to Canadian Healthcare Facilities* celebrated fifty years of publishing information about Canada's health system.

Publishing in and for a country as large as Canada is not easy—and for most specialty publishers in Canada—rarely a financial success. With Canada's health care system considerably reduced in 2006 to less than 970 health facilities from a high of 1,200 hospitals in the mid-1980s, the demand for Canadian-authored titles began to shift from the acute care sector to the long-term care sector. In an integrated health system, CHA has continually needed to reassess and refocus its activities to meet the needs of its members, and this has been the case for the publishing activities throughout the course of CHA's history.

Summary

Very early in its history, CHA committed to publishing activities to support its members' needs, and more particularly, its own finances. In 1935, the adoption of the journal, *Canadian Hospital*, provided the Canadian Hospital Council with a mechanism to report on its activities, committee studies, assembly meetings, federal legislation, provincial issues and problems to its members and Canada's hospitals. The journal was a vital tool for keeping the hospitals of Canada informed about issues of national interest throughout the depression and war years, and through the establishment years of hospital and medical insurance.

Over the years, CHA members' needs for more information about what was happening on the national scene changed. As they did, CHA developed various information tools from a directory to books, to a trustee journal and newsletters in an effort to keep its membership informed.

As faster communication tools have evolved at the turn of the twenty-first century, it is difficult to predict where publishing at CHA may be headed. It is possible that electronic communication will supplant print media so much so that book and guide publishing will cease. Or new markets such as those in long-term care and home care may provide new opportunities for CHA's oldest existing service—that of publishing—to continue to contribute to the organization in the future.

Endnotes

1. These journals contain pages and pages of information about hospitals across Canada and provide one of the more complete historical records about the expansion of hospitals in both the 1920s and 1950s.

2. The first editor of the journal was Leonard Shaw, the superintendent of Saskatoon City Hospital.

3. Over the course of his retirement years, CHA paid out $105,000 for the next 21 years.

4. Some of these publishing houses included Jossey-Bass, Health Administration Press, the King's Fund in London, England, Key Porter, McLellan and Stewart, University of Toronto Press and several other Canadian publishers.

5. In an effort to cut production costs and to control access to the information in the directory, CHA had developed an in-house database for facility listings, which enabled CHA staff to maintain the information on-site.

6. The other critical databases that would be required for access in the event of a national disaster (or terrorist attack), as identified by National Defence Canada, are those maintained by the RCMP, Transport Canada, the Canadian Coast Guard, National Defence and the Department of Fisheries and Oceans.

12

HELPING HEALTH CARE PROFESSIONALS DO A BETTER JOB

The desire for more knowledge has brought a demand in the hospital field for organized plans of study through which [hospital personnel are] privileged to benefit from short, intensive courses . . .

(MacEachern 1937, 15)

In the 1920s, a hospital superintendent did not require any special training to hold this position. In fact, there were no formal training courses. Superintendents were either businessmen, former army officers, retired doctors and, often, nurses with some supervisory experience (Agnew 1974, 126). A few Canadian hospital superintendents were members of the American Hospital Association (AHA). They had access to the AHA library and subscribed to American hospital journals. Many Canadian superintendents also attended the annual convention of the AHA, which provided a varied program of hospital topics.

At the 1924 annual meeting of the AHA, members discussed the urgency to train hospital executives because there were no formal training courses available for administrators. Hospital administration needed to be put on the same educational and professional basis as physicians, lawyers, school superintendents and other professionals (Committee 1925, 28*)*.

The first graduate course in hospital administration was established at Marquette University in Chicago in 1928. The program was discontinued a year later due to poor enrolment. Other universities in the United States also established similar programs in the 1930s and 1940s to train hospital superintendents. Canadians wishing to pursue further education enroled in these American programs. Then, in 1933, the American College of Hospital Administrators (ACHA) was set up as a professional body to educate and credential hospital administrators.

The Canadian Hospital Council, 1931 to 1952

Through his work with the standardization committee of the American College of Surgeons, Dr. Malcolm T. MacEachern, a Canadian physician and former superintendent of the Vancouver General Hospital, was instrumental in creating the American College of Hospital Administrators. He addressed the first convention of the newly formed ACHA in 1934 and urged universities to ". . . establish a four year course providing special professional training . . . for hospital superintendents" ("American" 1934, 24). Ten Canadians were granted charter membership in the college that same year.

While neither the Department of Hospital Service of the CMA nor the Canadian Hospital Council were formally involved in educating hospital personnel, they did provide some informal services to keep hospital superintendents up to date about issues of importance to their field. For example, the CMA provided a library service, which was available to hospital superintendents, and the council published reports from its standing committees which it placed in the CMA library for reference.

These various standing committees reported to the members on hospital activities such as administration, finance, legislation, public relations, medical relations, nursing and small hospitals. On approval by the Executive Committee of the council, these study reports were published in booklets and copies were sent free of charge to all public hospitals and libraries in Canada. These proved to be a tremendous asset as educational resources for Canadian hospital personnel.

As early as 1941, the Executive Committee expressed concern that some hospital boards were appointing administrators who lacked the necessary experience and training in hospital administration. The council supported a new, two-year graduate course in hospital administration to be inaugurated by the University of Toronto in 1947. At the same time, the council recognized that working hospital administrators would not be able to attend this university program.

For many years, institutes were held in both Canada and the United States which were designed for those currently working in hospital administration. They were usually twelve-day-long sessions that offered learning opportunities for those with different levels of experience and who were from both large and small hospitals. But these institutes were difficult to plan. And, in 1947, Dr. Agnew proposed to council delegates shorter, more intensive three- to four-month courses might be considered as an option to these institutes and graduate courses. But no resolutions were approved by the council at the time.

In 1948, the Executive Committee discussed the possibility of an educational program in hospital administration that would be designed to help those already employed in administration, particularly in smaller Canadian hospitals. The committee recommended that a small committee of the council be set up to look into the situation. At the 1949 biennial meeting, the delegates approved a resolution requesting the executive of the council "to consider ways and means for the expansion of the educative work of the Council" (CHC 1949a, 127).

Both Dr. Agnew, who resigned as executive secretary of the council in 1950, and his successor, Dr. L.O. Bradley, were both strong supporters of educational programs for Canadian hospital administrators. In fact, Dr. Bradley had written to the council to encourage it to develop some kind of educational program before he became executive secretary in 1950. And Dr. Agnew had already been investigating the possibility of obtaining financial assistance to develop educational programs at the time of his retirement from the council.

In 1950, the council appointed an education committee to provide guidance in delivering broad, educational programs for nonmedical personnel in health care. These management programs would be geared to senior personnel such as administrators, assistant administrators, nurses and middle management department heads, whether or not university graduates. The programs would enable hospital personnel to better equip themselves for their current work and prepare for advancement to more responsible positions in hospitals. Two technical programs were also set up: one for medical record personnel and another for those working in the food service department. The essential criteria for all these programs was that applicants had to be working in their specific field in a hospital.

Dr. Agnew had been persuaded to accept the position of chairman of the council's Committee on Education in 1950 on his resignation as executive secretary. The council also appointed a representative from each of the member associations, or an alternate, to ensure that input was received from across the country in the development of the course. He agreed to prepare a draft of an in-service training program in hospital administration for the members of the committee to review at its first meeting in Ottawa on 27 May 1951.

Hospital Organization and Management (HOM) Program

The first program proposed by the Education Committee was Hospital Organization and Management (HOM). The course would be two years long, involve two winter sessions conducted by correspondence (home-study), to be followed by an intensive four-week summer session (intramural) of lectures and demonstrations at one or more universities across Canada. Initial enrolment would be limited to forty students with a quota from each province. In establishing entrance requirements, educational background would be secondary to experience in the hospital field, demonstrated ability and interest. Readers of *The Canadian Hospital* were invited to write to the council expressing their views on the need for such a course and, in particular, whether they would be interested in enroling in it. The response was positive.

In January 1951, the council requested funding from the W.K. Kellogg Foundation for a course in hospital organization and management. The proposal was approved in 1951 and the council received a grant of $110,000 for five years. Donald M. MacIntyre joined the council staff as assistant secretary to set up and direct this education program. By the end of the year, it was apparent that more than one person would be needed to deliver the course. The council again sought additional funding from the Kellogg Foundation, which was approved in late 1951, to hire a research assistant. This position was staffed in early 1952.

A course outline was developed and individuals were selected from various professional organizations to assist in putting twenty-eight lessons together. Faculty members from the Department of Hospital Administration, University of Toronto, were very involved in developing the curriculum. Both Donald MacIntyre and Dr. A.L. Swanson, the executive director of the Canadian Hospital Association (CHA) as it was called in 1953, were members of the university faculty under the direction of Dr. Agnew.

Thirty-three students graduated from the program in 1953. Two summer sessions were held in the first year, one in the east (in Kingston) and one in the west (in Regina). The following year all the second-year students met at Macdonald College in Ste. Anne de Bellevue, Quebec. Two sessions were also held for first-year students. In 1954, the Education Committee decided to hold only one session, thus bringing students from both eastern and western Canada together at one university site in London, Ontario. From 1969 to 1978, with one exception, the intramural session was held at the University of Manitoba in Winnipeg.

Figure 2: Sample of the original certificate awarded to students on completion of the Hospital Organization and Management program.

In 1969, the CHA launched the Executive Skills Seminars Hospital Administrators Development Program, a week-long program on management techniques, which had been requested by HOM graduates. This program was to continue at CHA until the proposed Hospital Administrators Council of Canada (later the Canadian College of Health Service Executives) could take it over. The HOM course attracted individuals from various sectors of the health field, including government, the armed forces and educational institutions. To reflect current trends and changes in the health system, the program was renamed Health Care Organization and Management (HCOM) in 1975.

In 1976, a continuing education program called Change Can Be Managed was held in conjunction with the summer session of HOM. This program was intended for HOM graduates. Second-year students were able to choose from several electives, which enriched their program. It proved to be very successful and continued for the next four years.

In 1977, CHA moved its headquarters from Toronto to Ottawa. Only two members of the Education Department stayed with the association: the director and assistant director of education. Despite this, there was little disruption to the students in maintaining and delivering the association's distance education programs. In 1978, the intramural session was reduced to two weeks and moved from the University of Manitoba to the University of Ottawa.

In 1978, the HCOM program celebrated its twenty-fifth year in continuing education. To celebrate this achievement, the intramural was held at the University of Manitoba. Not only did previous graduates attend but also many of those who had assisted in developing the program over the years. Dr. Leo Bradley, who had been the executive secretary of the council when the program started, noted at the anniversary celebration that "there can be no question that H.O.M. [now HCOM] had a very early impact on the quality of administration from coast to coast, and of particular satisfaction to me was that it extended steadily to the smaller hospital units" ("A Quarter," n.p.). He added: "Perhaps one of the greatest satisfactions, however, has been the stimulus given by H.O.M. to the development of additional extension programs under the auspices of the Canadian Hospital Association" (Ibid.).

With the assistance of a three-year W.K. Kellogg Foundation grant, this program was revised in 1983 to respond to a dynamic health care system and the need for more sophisticated management skills and knowledge. More middle managers were now enroled in the course, and a new feature—university credit courses in organizational theory—was added. A network of courses at twenty-five universities across Canada was established to accommodate the university component. The program was renamed Health Services Management (HSM); it provided a starting point for those wishing to proceed to degree studies with some advanced standing. The program was also offered in collaboration with the Canadian College of Health Service Executives.

Ongoing discussions took place with several universities to ascertain what needed to be done to make HSM acceptable to most of them. CHA and Athabasca University in Alberta reached an agreement in 2000, in which HSM and the Long Term Care Senior Management program could receive advanced standing toward a bachelor of administration degree.

Graduating Class at the University of Ottawa. (Front row far left) Dr. Erwin Waschnig, Director, Education, and (fifth from him) Marion Stephenson, Program Director, LTCOM

Over the years, CHA has reviewed and assessed its programs and the intramural session, which ceased to be held at the University of Ottawa. The session was reduced to one week for all management programs to eliminate the cost barrier and the length of time that students were required to be away from their jobs. In 2002, second-year students in the HSM and LTCSM programs were no longer required to attend the intramural session. However, it has been retained for first-year students enroled in these two programs. An extra study unit has also been added to the second year for both groups in order to maintain the number of hours and the level of effort required to obtain credits from Athabasca University.

The Canadian Hospital Association, 1953 to 1977

Hospital Management

At the recommendation of Dr. Bradley, who was the chairman of the Education and Research Committee, the CHA board approved a motion in 1963 to use the annual grant from the Sun Life Assurance Company of Canada to finance the development of a departmental management program. The program—hospital management—was started in the fall of 1965 to introduce the basic principles of management and supervision. It was offered to those employed at the middle management or department head level in Canadian hospitals, and related health care institutions and agencies. The goal was to improve the quality of departmental management and provide a recognized yardstick by which an individual's training could be assessed and evaluated.

A group of advisors, who were experts in their field, assisted CHA in developing lesson material. The program covered the principles of management and communication, personnel management and supervision, business management, labor relations, legal issues and public relations. The program was launched in 1965 with an enrolment of 240 students. In 1966, the Education Committee of the CHA Board of Directors recommended that an intramural session would be a valuable addition to this program. The committee suggested this could be done on a regional basis and, in 1968, sessions were arranged in five locations across Canada on completion of home-study lessons.

In 1982, the program was renamed the Extension Course in Departmental Management and had an annual enrolment of more than 350 students. Successful completion of this program would prepare a candidate for transition into the HOM program.

This extension course for middle managers was completely redeveloped in the early 1990s to reflect the continuum of care and the ongoing changes in the health system across Canada, particularly regionalization. To reflect these changes, the name of the program was changed again to Modern Management. Graduates of CHA Learning (formerly the Education) Department's management programs and this newly revamped program could receive advanced standing toward Athabasca University's bachelor of administration degree.

Medical Record Librarians

The startup of the HOM program in 1953 stimulated the development of new distance education programs by CHA. The first course was for medical record librarians. By the early 1950s, both the council and the Canadian Association of Medical Record Librarians (CAMRL) were concerned that the six Canadian schools for medical record librarians were not graduating significant numbers of trained professionals. Again, with the support of the Kellogg Foundation, the two organizations initiated the Extension Course in Medical Records to commence in the fall of 1953. It was modeled after HOM, with a home-study component and an intramural session, and was open to candidates already employed in medical records. The intramural session consisted of one month of training in a medical record department in a hospital that was approved for this type of instruction. The curriculum was developed in consultation with the School for Medical Record Librarians at St. Michael's Hospital in Toronto.

The response was excellent and thirty students completed year one of the course in 1954. At the end of the second year, students were entitled to a certificate of achievement. If they met all the registration requirements of the CAMRL and had at least three years of experience in a medical record department, they could apply to write the CAMRL examinations, which would lead to registration.

In 1961, CAMRL advised CHA that, since other schools for medical record librarians had been established, there was no longer a need for the CHA program. However, CAMRL stressed that support staff in hospital medical record departments required training. Approved by CAMRL and supported by the Canadian Council on Hospital Accreditation, a course for this level of personnel was developed.

The lesson content used in the medical record librarian course was revised and consolidated into a one-year course to train medical record personnel. It was offered in two stages: a home-study session over eight and a half months, followed by an examination. If successful, the student received a diploma as a medical record clerk from CHA. For students, who had graduated from high school, the second stage consisted of lesson material, an intramural session in a hospital approved for this purpose, plus an examination. If the student passed, he or she received a diploma as a medical record technician. In 1953, there were forty-two students enroled from every province in Canada.

CHA received many requests to offer this program in the French language. In 1967, the Association des Hôpitaux de la Province du Québec gave their support to CHA to conduct this program in French and thirty students enroled in the first year. The French version of this program was delivered over the next five years until 1971. It was discontinued when similar programs were offered in the collèges d'enseignement générale et professionnel (CEGEPS) in Quebec.

In 1973, the Extension Course in Medical Records was renamed the Extension Course for Training Health Record Technicians. In conjunction with this, the entrance requirements were expanded to place more emphasis on the experience of the applicant, in addition to their educational standing. These concepts of experience and educational standing were more in keeping with the trends, as well as the ultimate classification, within the newly formed Canadian College of Health Record Administrators (CCHRA), the standard setting and professional certification body.[1] These changes were approved by CAMRL.

CCHRA developed a new curriculum for all health record technician programs across Canada. At the same time, this body accredited all health record technician programs. Attaining accreditation was a requirement for CHA graduates in order to continue to be eligible to join the professional organization (CHRA/CCHRA). CHA revised its program to encompass the new national curriculum. The cosponsorship of the CHA program was phased out, as CHA intended to apply for formal accreditation from CHRA/CCHRA. In 1985, CHA was awarded its first two-year accreditation and, in 1988, was granted full accreditation for the program.

Throughout the 1990s, several major innovations were made to this program, including revisions to expand to a two-year program, now known as the Health Information Services (HIS) program. The CHRA/CCHRA informed CHA that it would set a single certification examination for health record practitioners beginning in 2001. In the past, there had been two examinations, one for health record administrators and another for health record technicians. All health information programs in Canada had to apply for recognition by the CHRA/CCHRA in order to have their graduates sit for the new examination.

CHA's revised two-year HIS program was approved in 2001 by CHRA/CCHRA as meeting the criteria that would lead to certification as a health record practitioner. Graduates certified by CHRA/CCHRA were now able to enter directly into a post-diploma bachelor of health administration degree program to be offered by Ryerson Polytechnic University in 2002-2003. As of 2005, any graduates of CHA's HIS program were awarded a number of credits toward the health administration degree program at Athabasca University. It is apparent that health information education programs may continue as a major growth area as the demand for coding/classification experts in areas such as ambulatory care and home care increases.

Nursing Unit Administration Program

The Nursing Unit Administration (NUA) Program was set up jointly by CHA and the Canadian Nurses Association (CNA) in a partnership arrangement. It was directed independently through a joint committee of both organizations. (*See* chapter 10 for details on its establishment.)

The program included home-study lessons with practical assignments. Five-day workshops were held at the beginning and the end of the program in several provinces. While the program was under joint sponsorship, the operation of the

Graduates from the Long Term Care Organization and Management Program, 1984, University of Ottawa.

program were carried out by CHA. The program was first offered in 1961, and, by 1965, 1,500 nurses had graduated. For more than thirty years, the NUA Program enjoyed both financial success and considerable recognition for the two national associations for planning, implementing and delivering an education course that enabled nurses to enhance their management skills.

Hospital Food Service Supervision Program

The Ontario Hospital Association (OHA) had been operating the Hospital Food Service Supervision (FSS) program since 1963. By the early 1960s, there was considerable interest in enroling in the program from hospital staff in other provinces. In 1968, OHA advised it would transfer the program to the CHA, which would offer it on a national basis. OHA's main conditions under the transfer were that 1) the standards and quality of the program were to be maintained and 2) the program was to continue to be available to Ontario applicants.

CHA agreed to manage the program in conjunction with the Canadian Dietetic Association (CDA). In turn, the dietetic association would provide professional input through an advisory committee and assist in selecting student advisors. The program content and organization were changed to a large extent, with the program oriented to health care institutions rather than hospitals specifically.

Although the program was to be provided in both English and French, it was, in fact, only available in English. Program materials had been translated at the time but were not acceptable to Quebec dietitians. This caused some concern for both CHA and

CDA because of their commitment to bilingualism. However, funding to translate the program properly was not available and, because of the small number of students involved, the best that could be done was to offer assistance to Quebec students.

The program consisted of home study, plus a two-week intramural session to be held in Toronto and, later, in Guelph, Ontario. All hospital food supervisors in Canada were eligible for enrolment. In its first year, 130 students graduated from the program. The CHA/CDA Advisory Committee recommended that the name of the course be changed to the Extension Course in Food Service Supervision in 1974.

In 1988, a recommendation was made by the advisory committee to the CHA board to discontinue the program after the 1988-1989 students had graduated. Because of the growing demand for food service personnel to have broader knowledge and higher-competency levels, the OHA and the CDA advisory board recommended that a two-year program be developed. Year one of the program included home study on administrative functions and management theory, plus an examination under the supervision of an education consultant with a two-week practicum in a facility other than their own. Year two covered clinical nutrition sources and included a two-week intramural session and a final examination. The revised program was offered in 1990.

CDA withdrew from cosponsorship of the program in 1990 because of possible conflict (they set the national standards). In cooperation with the Canadian Food Service Supervisors Association, CDA assumed the task of developing national standards for FSS educational programs.[2]

In 1999, CHA received full accreditation from the Canadian Society of Nutrition Management for its Food Service and Nutrition Management program. (The name of the program had been changed to reflect the revised material.) In 2003, CHA contracted with Kemptville College to manage and deliver the program to students. This affiliation has worked well for both CHA and the students enroled in the program.

Long Term Care Organization and Management Program

The Ontario Nursing Home Association approached CHA in 1968 about developing a program for nursing home administrators. Changing concepts in health care administration, together with the growing complexity of caring for the aged and chronically handicapped, had created a demand for an education program for senior management staff in nursing homes and related facilities in Canada.

In 1972, CHA was awarded a federal grant of $29,400 for the development of such a program. An advisory committee, consisting of representatives from the Ontario Nursing Home Association, the Ontario Hospital Association and the Ontario Ministry of Health, as well as representatives from most of the provinces, developed the program outline.

The Extension Course in Extended Care Organization and Management (ECOM) was launched in 1973. This was a one-year, home-study program with two one-week intramural sessions held in three locations—Halifax, Toronto and Calgary—at the beginning and at the end of the academic year. In 1974, 141 students graduated from the program.

Feedback from graduates and practitioners in the field was used to evaluate the program over the next four years. The evaluations indicated that, while the program was very successful, there was a need for more extensive coverage of some areas, particularly gerontology; this would only be possible by redesigning and expanding the program to two years.

In 1974, the CHA board approved the delivery of the program to French-language hospitals. Seven candidates participated in the program which was held at the Montreal Extended Care Centre in September 1976. Several representatives from the Quebec Department of Social Affairs attended as observers. Unfortunately, the program was discontinued after one year due to cost cutting in hospitals.

In 1977, CHA met with several organizations involved in long-term care. The organizations included the Ontario Nursing Home Association, the Ontario Association of Homes for the Aged, the Canadian Institute of Religion and Gerontology, the Psycho-Geriatric Association, the Canadian Council on Hospital Accreditation and the Ontario Ministry of Community and Social Services. The group endorsed a proposal for the revision and expansion of the program. They also advised that the possibility should be explored for obtaining a university credit for this program at a future date.

The program was developed by a number of long-term care administrators, academics and others across the country. The course outline was designed by a national advisory committee, with representation from provincial long-term care associations. A task force, consisting of experts in certain content areas, wrote and reviewed the home-study material. Partial funding to develop the program was provided by a grant from the Manpower Consultation Service of Employment and Immigration Canada.

The new program, called the Extension Course in Long Term Care Organization and Management (LTCOM), was offered in 1978. It required nine months of home study, followed by a two-week intramural session each year. The session was held concurrently with that of CHA's HCOM intramural to allow for some joint sessions and to use university faculty in both programs.

Shortly after the commencement of this new, two-year LTCOM program, graduates from the one-year ECOM program asked CHA to offer a continuing education program in long-term administration to permit them to qualify for the LTCOM certificate. This request was approved and a professional update program was designed to focus on those subjects that were offered in LTCOM but not well covered in the ECOM program. This update program was offered in 1980 and 1981.

Over the next six years, the role of long-term care in the health system gained increasing recognition. New concepts in the organization of services emerged, which merited inclusion in a new curriculum. In 1984–1985, the program was completely revised to promote long-term care as a dynamic and increasingly important part of Canada's health care system, not merely an isolated entity.

Although LTCOM was widely recognized for its contribution to the improvement of the management of long-term care facilities and the quality of care for residents in these facilities, many applicants to the program were not eligible for admission because they lacked senior management experience. In order to assist them, CHA introduced a new, three-level management program in 1990 for students with middle and senior management backgrounds. Following a new, generic year one component, which focused on long-term care theory, students were then streamed into one of two levels: middle managers were directed to the Departmental Management program in long-term care, while level two and senior managers were placed in the Long Term Care Senior Management program. In 2000, the level one DM program was discontinued. LTCOM continues today to provide opportunities for health facility and other health agency staff to increase their knowledge and understanding of long-term care management.

Nutrition and Diet Therapy Refresher Course

This refresher course originally started in 1953. It consists of five study units and is designed for food service supervisors and health professionals who have basic postsecondary training in nutrition and who want to expand their knowledge. Students may enter the program on three specific dates during the year but must complete the five units within one calendar year.

The Canadian Healthcare Association, 1978 to 2006

As CHA settled in the nation's capital, it had to reestablish a new education department, as only two education staff had been able to move to Ottawa, when CHA relocated. By this time, CHA had been involved in developing education programs for almost twenty-five years. Many of them had added considerable revenue to the association and continued to do so over the next twenty-five years.

CHA Education Department staff and the various advisory committees reviewed the programs each year for their continued relevancy to those working in the field. Committee members also questioned whether new areas should be explored and offered to students. Suggestions and recommendations for new programs were also received from other health-related organizations and individuals. As well, new programs would be designed and introduced to meet education needs about new practice requirements or to provide knowledge on new theories in such areas as quality and risk management in the coming years.

Total Quality Management

In 1993, the association recognized the need for a new program on total quality management. This program, now known as continuous quality improvement (CQI), was designed for managers and staff in health services who wish to expand their knowledge of CQI and techniques, and to integrate them with their department's programs or organization's operations. The program includes seven study units, a research paper, a one-week intramural session, which is held in Ottawa in conjunction with the other management programs, and a final examination. To date, this program has graduated 147 students.

Risk Management and Safety in Health Services

The Risk Management and Safety course provides a thorough introduction to health risk management. The program was introduced in 2004. It is intended for executives, direct care providers, staff supervisors and managers, patient representatives, quality control and risk managers and patient safety officers. It includes seven study units, a five-day intramural session in Ottawa and a final examination. Since its introduction, thirteen students have graduated.

Medical Terminology Short Course

This short course, consisting of six study units, which must be completed within six months, provides an introduction to the principles and language of medical terminology. It is designed for unit secretaries, community care access centre team assistants, home support staff and other health service providers.

CHA Distance Learning in Transition

As restructuring and regionalization occurred throughout Canada's health system during the early 1990s, the impact was also felt by CHA. Provincial member organizations, uncertain whether they would continue to exist, or if so in what form and under what financial circumstances, began to question whether CHA should continue to deliver distance education courses.

During the pivotal transition year of 1996, CHA's highly successful distance learning programs came under scrutiny at the board table and in consultation with provincial member CEOs. Although there was never any question about the quality of the programs, the issue was whether this should be one of CHA's core activities. At the September 1996 meeting, the board directed CHA senior management to seek an outside partner for the distance education programs over the coming year. If CHA was not successful in placing these programs in a partnership elsewhere, the board proposed that CHA cease to deliver these programs by August 1998.

Students Writing Examinations at the Chateau Laurier, circa 2000.

As the association's finances stabilized over the next two years, the distance education courses continued to be delivered. By the turn of the twenty-first century, although enrolment never returned to the high levels of the 1960s and 1970s, nevertheless, these programs continued to contribute to CHA's revenues and, in some cases, to support core activities.

CHA's Library

A valuable tool for any student in advancing their studies is access to a quality library. At one time, CHA housed one of the finest collections of information on hospital administration available in Canada.

Naturally, the first reference to a library is made by Dr. Harvey Agnew in his history of hospitals in which he notes that one of the functions of the CMA Department of Hospital Service was to establish a library service to hospital administrators. It would be one way in which the department could act as a clearing house of hospital information (1974, 66).

Major support for the library was provided by Dr. A.D. Blackader, editor of the *Canadian Medical Association Journal*, when he set up the Blackader Library at CMA as a memorial to his son, Captain Gordon H. Blackader who was killed in World War I. The memorial included a fund to support the collection, which was maintained by the CMA until 1945. On separation of the council as an independent organization, CMA transferred the entire Blackader Library collection and Blackader Fund on permanent loan to the council.[3]

As the growth of educational institutes developed in Canada to provide learning opportunities for hospital administrators, and with the launch of the University of Toronto hospital administration course in 1947, the council library resources became more important as information sources to support students' work. As the council's member associations began to set up more permanent offices of their own, it was agreed that the library service was best handled by the national office (CHC 1949b, 255). When the council itself began to explore options for developing its own course for hospital administrators, the availability of a library to develop a curriculum was an added bonus. Students in the course would have access to library materials as well.

Dr. Arnold Swanson reported to the delegates at the council's 12th Biennial Meeting that the library service provided support to both the staff and students of the University of Toronto hospital administration course. Since the council offices were in Toronto, it was not too difficult for these groups to access the material in the library. In 1947, the council had also introduced a "package library service" which was available to anyone in Canada's hospital field. Dr. Swanson noted that: "By requesting information on a specific topic, a comprehensive file (or package) of pertinent information may be obtained through the mail on loan from our library" (1953, 42). This service was being used extensively by hospital staff all across the country, materials were loaned for a three-week period, and the cost to the hospital was return postage.

CHA's library was moved from Toronto in 1977 to CHA's rental offices on Laurier Avenue in Ottawa. It continued to offer a loan service to hospital personnel and, by the time of CHA's next move in 1983 into its permanent headquarters, the library took up considerable floor space in the organization. It was staffed by two part-time librarians, who split their hours to ensure full-time staff were available to answer questions, research material and loan books and cassettes to Canadian hospital staff. Unfortunately, because CHA did not have the financial resources to continue staffing the library on a full-time basis, senior management decided that the library would have to be cut down considerably before the move to CHA's permanent headquarters in 1983. Much of the hospital administration collection was dismantled and a much smaller version set up at 17 York Street.

CHA's library was only staffed part-time over the next few years. It no longer purchased new material or loaned any material outside the CHA. It was available to CHA staff and most of the new titles added to it between 1986 and 1996 were given to the library by CHA Press, which was eligible to receive complimentary copies of books for review as part of its publishing mandate. In the major staffing cutbacks of 1996, the part-time librarian position was also cut.

Finally, in 1998, the last remaining part of CHA's library was dismantled in order to consolidate all services and departments on one floor and to free up this space for leasing. Most of the titles were either given away, moved to the small reference library maintained by CHA Press or thrown out because of their age. However, all CHA archival records including board documents, bound copies of minutes and all the Blackader bound issues of journals were kept for historical purposes in order to leave a record about CHA's history for posterity.

Summary

Over the years, CHA has continually questioned what its role in the education of health care personnel should be. In a July 1969 editorial, Dr. B.L.P. Brosseau, the executive director of CHA, wrote that CHA had moved into this field to meet a very urgent and widespread need in education. He pointed out: "The CHA has no vested interests; it does not wish nor want to continue programs, which can better be provided by other agencies. . . . but it must ensure that all categories of hospital and health personnel are prepared, both in quality and quantity, to meet the requirements of all categories of hospitals to provide quality patient care" (Editorial 1969, 8).

The CHA has long been active in the education of health personnel, beginning with the Hospital Organization and Management program, first introduced in 1952, to the newer and shorter courses which have been added since 1993. Over this more than fifty-year span, CHA has graduated more than 25,775 students across Canada.

At the CHA board meeting in June 2003, the future of CHA Learning was discussed in some detail. The board was advised that, for the most part, CHA's distance learning programs have been and continue to be successful. They respond to an important need, they fill a unique niche and they have a high enrolment. Sharon Sholzberg-Gray, president and CEO, noted that CHA Learning must review all its distance learning programs, so that it can alter course content, invest in state-of-the-art technology and form partnerships that will move the programs forward on all fronts. This will continue to be necessary to meet the changing needs of the professionals who work in all areas of Canada's health care system now and in the future.

Endnotes

1. As of 2003, the CHRA became the Canadian Health Information Management Association. The name of the certifying body is still the CCHRA.
2. The Canadian Food Service Supervisors Association was originally formed in 1965 to ensure high standards of training for its members and quality food service to the public. It is now known as the Canadian Society of Nutrition Management.
3. Part of this collection, albeit a very small part, remains in CHA's archives at 17 York Street. This collection includes the bound copies of *Canadian Hospital* from 1924–1925 to 1974. Without access to some of this information this book would have been extremely difficult to write.

13

PROVIDING A NATIONAL FORUM

"The goal of the [CHA Annual] conference is to provide a forum for current thought and practice in health care from a national and international perspective . . . and to provide an opportunity for the exchange of ideas on both a formal and informal basis."

(CANADIAN HOSPITAL ASSOCIATION 1986a)

The objectives of the Canadian Hospital Council did not originally include organizing and holding conferences. But the council's biennial general assemblies did provide an educational component. In fact, member associations asked the council to consider allowing other hospital personnel, as well as delegates, to attend these sessions. Eventually, the means of transportation across Canada improved. This permitted people to travel greater distances more frequently and gather together more often in various types of organized meetings such as assemblies, conferences, conventions and seminars. It was only a matter of time before Canada's hospital association would become involved in providing a forum where the hospital field could come together to consider issues of common interest.

The Early Association Meetings, 1900 to 1930

In describing the early meetings of the first Canadian Hospital Association between 1907 and 1913, Dr. Agnew writes that one of the main purposes of this early organization was mainly ". . . to arrange to have annual meetings" (1974, 61). The minutes of these first meetings also note that various papers were solicited from physicians and hospital superintendents on subjects such as public health measures, the future of nursing and sanitary precautions in hospitals. Clearly, the intent of the first CHA was to educate and inform hospital superintendents and provide an exchange of information that would eventually extend across Canada in a true national forum.

Council Meetings, 1931 to 1952

When the Canadian Hospital Council was established in 1931, the founding members decided that it would adopt the less formal name of council, so that meetings could be called "without the attendant trappings of a national convention" (Agnew 1974, 68). The council met at two-year intervals, although the question of an annual convention was discussed several times but not deemed to be feasible (Ibid., 70).

There were several reasons for not calling annual meetings. First, the sheer geographic size of Canada made travel across the country difficult, impractical and slow. Second, many of the council's members already held annual conventions and a national meeting of this type could be seen as a potential competitor. Third, many Canadian hospital superintendents were members of the American Hospital Association (AHA) with its large established and successful annual convention. The council would have had difficulty competing with AHA in these early years.

The council's early mandate was to act as a national forum to enable the hospitals of Canada, through their provincial and regional associations and conferences, to discuss matters of national or interprovincial interest and concern. By 1931, the council's executive had identified the federal customs tariff, disparities among the various provincial hospital acts and the reciprocal recognition of indigent claims by the provinces as key issues for discussion by the membership. To enable discussions, the council set up several committees, all of which were required to study a particular subject or area and compile a report for review and approval by the Executive Committee. The chair of the committee would then present the report at the next biennial meeting of the membership.[1]

The second biennial meeting of the council, held in Winnipeg in September 1933, had adopted a three-day format in order to accommodate both the business meeting and a full educational session. The agenda included reports on provincial hospital legislation, construction and equipment, public relations, the problems of small hospitals, administration and statistics, and relations between the medical profession and hospitals. In addition to the discussions that resulted from the various

Delegates at the 7th Biennial Meeting of the Caandian Hospital Council at the Chateau Laurier, Ottawa, 9-10 September 1943.

reports, the assembly delegates also reviewed the governance of the hospital council. They elected officers for the next two years to carry out council business based on resolutions that they had approved. Guest speakers, representing hospital administration, medicine, government and governance, were also invited to these biennial meetings.

By 1937, when Dr. Harvey Agnew was elected as the incoming president of the AHA, plans were well underway for a conjoint meeting of the Canadian Hospital Council, the International Hospital Association (IHA) and the AHA to meet in Toronto in 1939. This would have been the second time that the AHA had held its annual conference in Canada and the first time for an IHA meeting. This was to have been a banner year for both the hospital council and Canada.[2] More than forty-one study committees had submitted reports, all of which had been translated into five languages. Considerable money had been spent by both the council and the Ontario Hospital Association to organize the opening and closing ceremonies.

But the outbreak of World War II forced the IHA to cancel its plans to attend this conference. However, both the council and OHA did proceed to host the AHA and its allied organizations. And to celebrate this joint meeting, the council presented to the AHA a gavel made from silver and Canadian hardwood, which had been taken from the Hôtel-Dieu du Québec, the oldest hospital in North America ("Report" 1939, 17).

By 1939, from the more than 40 delegates who had attended the founding meeting in 1931, attendance had grown to approximately 150 delegates at this biennial meeting. The records of these assembly meetings show that hospital problems continued to grow throughout the war years, especially as resources and personnel for the hospital field decreased. By the end of the war, attendance had increased again as federal representatives began to return to council assembly meetings.

In between council assembly meetings, each of the provincial member associations and Catholic conferences held their own annual meetings. There were several opportunities for hospital administrators to meet locally and provincially to exchange information and to discuss hospital matters. It would not be long before the hospital field in Canada would suggest that the council develop a national education conference or convention of its own similar to that of the AHA.

Throughout the 1930s and 1940s, the agenda, the list of guest speakers, the approval of committee reports, the subject matter, the dates and the city where the next biennial meeting would be held were decided by the Executive Committee. These three-day meetings were then organized by Dr. Agnew and his small, mostly part-time staff.

The Canadian Hospital Association and National Conventions, 1953 to 1977

In May 1953, the delegates at the Canadian Hospital Association (CHA)'s biennial meeting asked the board to consider whether annual meetings should be held between biennial meetings. These annual meetings would be attended only by the presidents and secretaries of the constituent members (CHA 1953b). CHA's board discussed this issue again in both 1955 and 1957. The problem was always one of money as the active members would have to pick up the costs of annual meetings and most of them declined to do so. In fact, the assembly delegates defeated a motion for annual meetings in 1955.

While the council held its meetings in various cities—usually no further west than

2000 Delegates Attend CHA's 3rd National Convention at the Jubilee Auditorium in Edmonton, June 1970.

Winnipeg or east than Quebec City—the CHA assembly delegates agreed in 1955 to hold the next convention jointly with the Western Canada Institute for Hospital Administrators and Trustees in Saskatoon in May 1957. This was the first-time that a CHA meeting had ever taken place farther west than Winnipeg and the first joint meeting with another organization.

Much of the organizational work for this week-long meeting was arranged by the Saskatchewan Hospital Association, with additional support provided by CHA's executive director, Dr. Douglas Piercey, and by the institute's programming committee chair, Dr. Arnold Swanson. The event attracted more than 1,200 delegates and set a precedent for CHA to work more closely with its provincial members to arrange joint meetings in the future.

But the issue of CHA annual meetings did not go away. Finally, at the May 1959 assembly meeting, the CHA board agreed to move to annual meetings. The recommendation was ratified by the members at the General Assembly and CHA received an invitation from the British Columbia Hospitals Association to hold its first annual convention in Vancouver. The board declined the invitation and opted for Toronto instead in May 1960 as CHA was officially opening its new building at 25

Imperial Street. But the board did agree to consider invitations from the members for conjoint meetings in future. And, for the first time, the board also authorized staff to consider alternate sites between the west and the east for future assemblies.

In 1962, the board officially approved a conjoint meeting of the General Assembly and a provincial association meeting. The executive director, Dr. Piercey, was directed to work with his provincial colleague from the Associated Hospitals of Alberta to develop a program, work out the financial arrangements and plan the meetings, exhibits and all the other necessary steps for this first joint effort. Then, on a recommendation of the CHA Aims and Objectives Committee in 1968, the general assembly meeting was changed to a full-fledged annual convention with commercial exhibits. The committee also suggested that CHA should find a way to include programming that was suitable for other national health organizations, so they could participate in the convention. This would broaden the potential attendance.

The first CHA Convention was held in Vancouver in May 1968. As directed by the board through its Convention Program Committee, it was a combined business and educational meeting, with commercial exhibits, under the theme "Your Health . . . Your Hospital . . . Your Responsibility." More than 1,600 delegates, exhibitors and visitors attended the convention, exceeding by far expected numbers. For a first attempt, the convention was considered to have been remarkably successful (CHA 1968a). The board meeting was held on the final day of the convention and members discussed finding ways to preregister delegates, to add more floor space for exhibits and how to implement a trustee section in the program. This pattern of an annual conference, along with the business meeting, remained unchanged until 1976, when the membership decided to drop the commercial exhibition. CHA's exhibition was competing with those of its provincial member associations.

In conjunction with the Canadian Medical and Canadian Nurses' Associations, CHA was largely instrumental in organizing the First National Conference on Hospital-Medical Staff Relations in 1967 in Montebello, Quebec. The conference's main purpose was "to provide a forum for the exchange of views between medical staff representatives, hospital trustees and administrators, and the directors of nursing service. A secondary purpose [was] to improve communications between these groups" ("First" 1967, 28–D). This educational conference was restricted to hospitals with more than one hundred beds and each hospital that registered had to send a team of no less than three delegates from the medical staff, the nursing service, the administrator or a trustee. The format included formal presentations, panel discussions and workshops. Because it was successful, a second conference took place in February 1969 in Quebec City.

CHA's second national convention was held in Ottawa in May 1969 and focused on looking at the hospital of the future. The educational component included presentations on the moral and legal aspects of organ transplants, computerized hospitals and hospital design in the year 2000. Sessions were added for trustees, small hospitals and extended care facilities and were held on trends in research and teaching hospitals. By this time, a number of "stars," that is, experts had emerged in the hospital field to become regular attendees and presenters on both the national and provincial conference scene.

By the early 1970s, CHA was playing a leading role in organizing single-issue conferences and symposia. At the time, the health care system in Canada was experiencing a rapid growth in the areas of technology, communications and computerization. In fact, the federal minister of health, his provincial counterparts and many health care professionals were beginning to express their concerns about how computer applications were being used in the health field. The report of the federal Task Force on the Costs of Health Services in Canada had also made several references to this new technology in its report of 1969.

To respond to questions about the new computer technology, the Department of National Health and Welfare awarded a $9,000 grant to CHA to set up the National Symposium on Computer Applications in the Health Care Field. The conference was held in Ottawa in March 1970. It was aimed at some two hundred carefully selected federal and provincial health officials, representatives of professional and hospital associations, educational institutions and computer specialists ("National" 1969, 26). There were formal presentations and workshops, and lecturers included experts from Canada, the United States, Europe and Puerto Rico.

CHA's third national convention (and twenty-seventh assembly), which was held in Edmonton in June 1970, was notable for several reasons. First, attendance at this meeting was close to two thousand delegates. Second, the CHA film titled *A Hospital Is . . .*, sponsored by Johnson & Johnson Companies, was premiered to publicize to the public the complexity of the hospital and to encourage hospital careers. And, third, the organizational meeting of the Hospital Administrators' Council of Canada—now known as the Canadian College of Health Service Executives (CCHSE)—was held with more than three hundred hospital administrators attending the founding meeting. As a result, the college held its own annual meeting at the same time and in the same city as CHA for the next thirty-six years.

In response to what was seen at the time as an enormous use of illegal drugs—mainly by young people—the effects of these drugs and the difficulties that hospitals were experiencing in treating drug users, CHA organized another single-issue conference. The National Symposium on Hospital Responsibility towards Drug Users was held in Montreal in February 1971. CHA was fortunate once again to receive financial support through a grant from the Department of National Health and Welfare. The original symposium plan called for three hundred invitees. But the demand to participate raised registration higher and, in fact, over five hundred people attended—many unregistered. Over 150 hospitals sent delegates from every province, including 20 psychiatric hospitals, four police departments and 25 youth.

The association also delivered the National Purchasing Symposium in the Health Care Field in Saskatoon in March 1972, which was considered an overwhelming success. The Department of National Health and Welfare provided a grant, as did the more than fifty manufacturers and suppliers of health products, who made sizeable financial contributions to participate. More than three hundred delegates registered to debate the merits of group purchasing for the health care field. The twenty-two papers that had been presented during the symposium were published in CHA's journal.

The International Hospital Federation (IHF), which had originally scheduled its first meeting in Canada in Toronto in 1939, had been forced to cancel the event because of the outbreak of World War II. This first-time IHF meeting was held in Montreal in 1973 jointly with CHA. More than two thousand delegates from fifty countries attended the meeting. To deliver an event of this size, CHA's staff and finances were stretched to the limit. Dr. Brosseau, who was on the IHF executive and planning committee, played a major role in setting up the event. This major international conference included 160 exhibitors, 42 architectural exhibits and delegates had an opportunity to visit 42 health care facilities in the Montreal area.

In September 1975, in cooperation with the Canadian Bar Association (CBA), the Law Reform Commission of Canada, the CMA, the CNA and the Canadian Public Health Association (CPHA), CHA offered the first National Conference on Health and the Law. This three-day conference was supported by a grant from National Health and Welfare and took place in Ottawa. It included a wide range of speakers from Canada, England, France and the United States—lawyers, doctors, nurses and government representatives—who discussed issues such as consent to treatment, malpractice and the role of ethics committees and hospital lawyers. The delegates approved a resolution urging the CBA and the CMA to collaborate on draft legislation to reduce uncertainties surrounding consent to treatment for the mentally disabled, minors and others unable to consent. This conference was so successful that a second one was held in 1979 and a third in 1985.

CHA's 1976 convention, while a success, had suffered from reduced attendance and had not met revenue predictions. By the mid-1970s, severe budgetary constraints had been imposed on Canada's hospitals and the country was feeling the impact of the federal government's anti-inflation legislation. Two of CHA's active members were also preparing for major labor disruptions in their health sectors. The Executive Committee was beginning to express concerns about CHA's financial control over its annual convention and how it was currently administered. CHA also needed to deal with the fact that both it and the Canadian College of Health Service Executives held their annual meetings and conventions at the same time in the same city. Both organizations were trying to attract the same audience. With the economic situation in the health field not expected to improve any time soon, these issues would have to be dealt with in the future if CHA was to remain in the conference field.

In June 1976, CHA's board set up a Study Committee on Conventions. The committee was to report back to the board on whether the association should continue to hold conventions in the future. Reporting in late 1977, the committee supported a CHA annual convention. It recommended that the format continue to include an educational program, the business meeting and a social program but discontinue commercial exhibitions. The committee also recommended that CHA study the feasibility of organizing a national health products trade show to replace exhibits at the convention. CHA also needed to find a way to generate membership interest in the annual meeting; membership attendance had been steadily declining over the years. The board agreed to the recommendations to continue holding a convention and the suggested format but deferred the suggestion for a trade show.

The CHA board Convention Committee delivered its report in March 1977 regarding that year's plans for the convention. Along with board members, both Dr. Brosseau and the incoming executive director, Jean-Claude Martin, sat on the committee. So did the executive director of the Canadian College of Health Service Executives. The college's president was also a member of CHA's board at the time and, as directed by the college, he raised the issue about the conflicting dates of both organizations' annual conventions. The college was so concerned that it was considering planning a separate event entirely. Since the audience for both organizations was the same, this could be detrimental to one or both organizations in future convention planning.

Dr. Brosseau reminded the board that the college was represented on CHA's Planning Committee for its annual convention. However, the reverse was not the case. He believed program planning would have gone much better if CHA had been represented on the college planning committee for its annual meeting. The board urged that members of the various committees, including CHA's Study Committee on Conventions, find resolutions to these conflicts around programming and scheduling. This would not be the last time that the association and the college ran into difficulties about conference planning.

Conferences in the Capital, 1978 to 2006

CHA was now established in Ottawa along with most of the other major Canadian health organizations. This would present considerably more opportunities for the association to collaborate with others on joint conferences. The association also strengthened its conference activities by establishing a standing board committee in 1979 to oversee conference planning. In July 1979, William Kilpatrick, chair of the Special Committee on CHA Conventions, recommended to the board that its annual convention be changed to the annual conference and that the committee be renamed the Annual Conference Committee. It would oversee the organization and planning of future conferences for CHA.

Early in 1979, CHA learned that the AHA was considering holding its huge annual convention in either Toronto or Montreal. Because it held the largest health trade show in North America at the time, a move by AHA to a Canadian city would have considerable impact on the trade shows of CHA's members in Ontario and Quebec. Lengthy consultations took place between CHA and AHA, and the Quebec and Ontario Hospital Associations. AHA agreed to pay both provincial associations a specified sum of money not to hold a trade exhibition in 1980. CHA would also be guaranteed a profit, based on its past ten years' experience, and would benefit by providing certain specific services. Formal agreements with the three associations were signed, and planning began for a first joint AHA/CHA convention in Montreal from 28 to 31 July 1980.

For those CHA staff involved in the preparations, the experience in both planning and holding a joint conference of this size was somewhat akin to a minnow being swallowed by a whale. The AHA machine moved into Montreal, occupying every hotel room, university residence room and virtually taking over the bus transit system in order to move the seven thousand delegates from education sessions to the exhibit hall to banquet facilities. Although the scope of preparations was overwhelming, CHA was involved from the beginning in planning program content and arranging for many major Canadian speakers to be part of the program. Of the more than 7,000 delegates, over 2,400 were Canadian.[3]

The Annual Conference Committee continued to report to the CHA board on its conference planning. It recommended future sites for the event, approved the program and worked closely with CHA staff to monitor conference expenses and revenues. Over the years, delegates indicated that they wanted a greater variety of sessions on current issues, more concurrent sessions and a broader educational program.

To accommodate these requests, the committee recommended that CHA establish a conference division in 1980 to manage the annual event, other national conferences and single-issue symposia, as well as provide additional forums to discuss emerging subjects in the health system. A full-time conference director was hired and CHA's annual conference acquired a more professional look and format for its educational sessions.

In late 1980, CHA met with the college to discuss arrangements for future CHA and college annual conferences. Both the college and CHA were scheduled to hold their annual conferences in Winnipeg in 1981 with the college event scheduled immediately prior to CHA's meeting. This meant that both organizations were competing for hotel meeting space and accommodations, not to mention the same audience. In fact, both organizations had actually booked the same hotel in Winnipeg for their headquarters. Although this practice had been established since 1970, the hospital sector was under severe financial strain. It could support only so many conferences.

In 1982, CHA's board continued to urge staff to work out an arrangement, not just with the college, but with other organizations as well to deliver conferences. The board insisted that, while the association must deliver its own annual conference, it could collaborate with its provincial members and others to cohost such events.

The board also agreed that CHA should be allowed to work out revenue-sharing arrangements with any partners as needed. CHA was also directed to set aside a half day of its annual conference program to provide educational sessions for its associate and affiliate member organizations.

By the mid-1980s, Canada's health system was under serious financial constraints and the impact was being felt with falling attendance at national conferences. The field was crowded with several organizations providing numerous events. The college offered evaluation seminars jointly with their local chapters, the Canadian Council on Hospital Accreditation began planning conferences and CHA's members continued to put on their own annual conventions. In 1983, CHA undertook an internal review of its conference division. Once again, the board asked it to give serious consideration to cooperating with other organizations to put on its annual conference.

As a result of the review, the conference division was to provide support to CHA's other departments in the future, as well as to offer conference management services on a contract basis to other national health organizations. It would also coordinate CHA's public relations activities such as Canada Health Day, the CHA brochure and the booth. The review also recommended that CHA's annual general meeting be held at a time other than that of the annual conference in future.[4]

CHA held its first invitational conference in Toronto in April 1982. This conference was organized along the lines of those developed and held annually by the Conference Board of Canada. The format was based on selecting twenty to twenty-five participants, who were asked to speak extemporaneously and share their views on a health care subject of their choice. There was a twenty-minute time limit to speak and respond to questions from other participants.

The sessions were presided over by a moderator who ensured speakers kept to the time limit. One of the invitees was preselected to summarize the discussions and, more specifically, to identify common issues raised by the participants. All presentations and discussions were confidential and no written record was kept of the event. The invitational session was held for the next eight years in various cities across Canada. Eventually, it was dropped because of lack of interest and funding.

The CHA Long Range Planning Committee, which had been set up by the board to look at current activities and determine future planning for the association, provided some feedback on the conference division in its report of 1983. First, the committee members reminded the board that this division was still very new and struggling to survive. The report stated: "The Committee recognizes that conferences and seminars are risky business—costs are largely fixed, while revenues can fluctuate greatly" (CHA 1983b, 12). Committee members, nevertheless, believed that there was considerable potential for the conference division to meet membership needs and to enhance CHA's image. It recommended that this area be strengthened, marketing

Dr. Gustave Gingras, Past President, Installs CHA's New Board Chair, Ted Bartman, at the Ottawa Congress Centre, during the 16th Annual Conference, 11-14 June 1985.

efforts be improved and that, before any collaboration be undertaken with others, joint projects should be carefully studied.

In 1984, CHA experimented with teleconferencing for the first time. The Health Institutions in the Future Conference was held in Ottawa in February with 180 participants registered. The program was teleconferenced to Newfoundland, in cooperation with the Newfoundland Hospital Association, where more than 250 people tuned in to the conference proceedings. A second conference was held in Toronto in 1985; both conferences were set up to inform the hospital sector on how the Hospital of the Future Project was progressing. (*See* chapter 16 for details.) CHA had hoped to attract and stimulate more interest in this project.

During the 1980s, CHA's conference activity expanded to meet the needs of both its member organizations and to provide an opportunity for the providers in the health system to meet and discuss the complex issues around delivering health care. In 1985, CHA successfully delivered the Third National Conference on Health and the Law in Ottawa. This particular conference was organized to provide the health sector with information on hospital liability issues, an area that was receiving considerable attention at the time.

CHA held the first national Conference on Mental Health Services in Vancouver in August 1987. As the AIDS epidemic began to dominate Canada's health agenda, the association delivered a national conference on the Implications of AIDS. Held in

Delegates, Including Those on the International Hospital Study Tour, at the CHA Annual Conference in Edmonton, June 1986.

Toronto in 1988, it was organized to enable key hospital personnel to share their knowledge and experience with each other.

In order to position itself and to meet the ongoing challenges in the conference field, in 1985, CHA set up a separate Conference Department. In future, CHA would provide an exhibition open to non-commercial exhibitors such as its members and other not-for-profit health organizations. The department's vice-president would report to the Education and Conference Committee of the board. The conference staff would plan the annual conference, offer smaller specialty conferences such as the Third Health and the Law Conference in 1985 and support the upcoming IHF study tour.

CHA played a major role in the 1986 IHF Canadian Study Tour. These tours of health care facilities were offered by the IHF every two years in a selected country. Canada was chosen because the World Exposition was being held in Vancouver. In cooperation with the Alberta Hospital Association and the British Columbia Health Association, CHA helped to plan for 150 international delegates to tour health facilities in Edmonton, Calgary and Vancouver in June 1986 in concert with CHA's annual conference, which was held in Edmonton.

In the same year, CHA also negotiated a letter of agreement with the college to organize a joint national conference. It would be managed alternately by both CHA and the college and a draft letter was prepared for both organization's boards to approve. These joint conferences took place at the same time and in the same city. But delegates attended the educational component of the organization of their choice. In effect, they were separate joint conferences. Competition for conference delegates continued to increase and both CHA and the college began to experience declining attendance at their conferences throughout the late 1980s and early 1990s.

In addition to working with the college, CHA's Annual Conference was offered jointly with its member association in the province where the conference was scheduled to be held that year. In this way, the resources of its member association could be called on for support. In 1992, CHA's conference was held in St. John's, Newfoundland, jointly with the Newfoundland Hospital and Nursing Home

Don Roberts, Chair, CHA's Education and Conference Committee, 1986. Conference Attracted More Than 1,300 Delegates from across Canada.

Association, one of the last such joint sessions to take place.[5] CHA continued to explore options with both the college and other health organizations on how to cosponsor and deliver conferences in the future with partners.

As well as its annual conference, the association cosponsored three other conferences in 1992. Along with the Catholic Health Association of Canada, the Canadian College, the Canadian Long Term Care Association, the CMA and the CNA, CHA presented a conference on health care ethics. Working with the CMA, the college and a new partner—the Hospital Medical Records Institute—CHA delivered a conference on utilization and quality management. It also partnered with the CNA, the college, the Canadian Public Health Association and the Canadian Association of University Schools of Nursing to present a conference on nursing administration.

Collaborative efforts, partnerships and cosponsorships became the most effective and efficient method of developing and presenting conferences throughout the 1990s. The health system was undergoing significant change and had little financial resources to spend on workshops, seminars, conferences and other information sessions. However, health care professionals were supportive of joint efforts, which enabled them to budget to attend at least one major health conference. This also meant less time away from their jobs.

Due to economic constraints on health care facilities and the restructuring of the provincial health systems, registration at CHA's conferences continued to decline throughout the early 1990s. In 1994, CHA partnered with the college to deliver the first CHA/CCHSE Joint Annual Conference and Exhibition. Its purpose was to improve the governance and delivery of health services in Canada through the exchange of information, views on current issues and best practices, and develop networks among health service trustees, executives and researchers. The conference was designed for trustees and senior health care executives across the continuum of care. It was to be held in a different region and city each year.

The first conference took place in Halifax in June 1994 and focused on health reform occurring across Canada's health system. It included concurrent sessions on funding, governance and continuum of care issues, along with plenary sessions featuring keynote speakers. Considered a success by both partners, although there were growing pains with CHA handling the conference secretariat and the college managing the trade show for exhibitors, the partnership boded well for future collaboration in this area.

Then, in 1995, in order to reach out to other parts of the continuum of care, the two partners invited the Canadian Long Term Care Association (CLS) to participate as a partner. The conference program was expanded to include long-term care, home care and the home support sector of the continuum. Under the name of the National Healthcare Leadership Conference, this first tripartite conference was held in Calgary in 1995.

As is inevitable in any partnership, there were occasional differences among the partners about themes, whether the programs should be delivered entirely through plenary sessions or whether some concurrent sessions should be available. Each organization conducted its own separate business and annual general meetings prior to the start of the joint conference. Once these were finished, the participants were available to attend the conference sessions.

The National Healthcare Leadership Conference had proved to be financially successful for the three partners between 1995 and 2000. The master agreement between the partners specified that this arrangement was a business venture and provided for the secretariat to rotate among the partners. However, beside CHA, only the Canadian College was capable of planning and delivering the leadership conference, and by the beginning of the new decade, it was anxious to prove it could deliver on the success that CHA as the secretariat had achieved.

Over the next few years, the college pushed for CHA to relinquish the secretariat. CHA, its board and its membership continued to hold firmly to the belief that a stable secretariat, located at CHA, had enabled the three partners to establish a highly visible and financially successful conference over the years. This had paid profitable returns to each partner and maintained CHA's reputation as a capable conference planner. But, by the end of 2004, CHA agreed to relinquish the conference secretariat to the college, with the college taking over the secretariat for the 2007 conference. CHA remains firmly committed to supporting this major national health care conference, unless or until changing circumstances require that it rethink how it delivers conferences to and for its members in the future.

Summary

From the early days of the Canadian Hospital Council, hospital administrators and trustees had been gathering together in various Canadian cities to discuss issues impacting on the hospital. They heard presentations from experts, had an opportunity to question and debate the issues and network with each other to solve problems.

As the CHA biennial assembly meetings grew larger and the issues more complex, annual conventions were set up to enable hospital managers and other key personnel to connect with each other more frequently. Conventions became conferences with trade shows. Then, CHA's conference worked jointly with its active members to develop annual conventions. It was inevitable that CHA would join with other national health organizations to deliver conferences more economically in what had become a highly competitive field. Whether CHA continues in partnership arrangements, reverts back to managing an annual conference on its own or pulls out of the conference field entirely will be issues to be debated over the next decade by the membership.

Endnotes

1. These reports were also published in detail in *The Canadian Hospital*, the first one in December 1932 on hospital construction and equipment.
2. This international event would have seen three Canadians in leading roles—Dr. Malcolm T. MacEachern as president of the IHA, Dr. Agnew as president of the AHA and Dr. George F. Stephens as president of the council.
3. When CHA learned that the AHA was again holding its convention in Toronto in 1986, the board recommended that CHA hold its own conference in Edmonton as planned.
4. Future annual general meetings were held each year in March in Ottawa to coincide with the first board meeting of the year. Then, in 1996, the annual meeting was rescheduled to

take place at the same time as the joint National Healthcare Leadership Conference.

5. By the late 1980s, most of CHA's provincial member organizations no longer organized an annual convention. Among CHA's active members today, only the Ontario Hospital Association and the Saskatchewan Association of Health Organizations are in the conference business.

Part V

RESEARCH, POLICY, ADVOCACY AND REPRESENTATION

This section of the book presents an overview of CHA's research and policy development activities through the four key periods of its history. It also describes how the association developed its main role of representing the interests of Canada's hospitals to the federal government. As its provincial member associations established their own permanent organizations, CHA began to advocate on their behalf alone to provide a voice at the federal level for the institutional component of the health system. Readers are encouraged to review other chapters in various parts of the book as these also cover some of CHA's policy development and advocacy activities. (*See also* chapters 3, 4, 7 and 8.)

Chapter 14 provides an overview of the growth of research and policy development at CHA. Although neither of these activities was part of the hospital council's mandate, the association was asked to develop these areas to meet perceived needs either by its membership or by others, who believed CHA was in the best position to take the lead. The chapter outlines why the association set up a research department and some of the activities it undertook. The chapter also describes some of the key policy development areas that CHA became involved in during its history. While not every position statement and policy document is described in the chapter, a list of some of these key statements and papers is presented in appendix 5 for the reader.

Chapter 15 presents an overview of the CHA's advocacy and representation activities over the course of its history. This has been the association's main activity on behalf of its members. However, it has not been possible to describe every action that CHA took to represent its members' interests, so the chapter focuses on providing a chronological look at how representation evolved within the association.

It begins with the early activities of the council which represented Canada's hospitals both to governments and other health organizations. It then describes how this advocacy work progressed by highlighting some of the key areas where CHA has made a difference for Canada's health system.

14

SEARCHING FOR SOLUTIONS (RESEARCH AND POLICY DEVELOPMENT)

"CHA strives for excellence in policy development: CHA has a reputation for reasoned policy analysis. . . [which] requires sufficient time and resources to develop credible background policy documents."

(CANADIAN HEALTHCARE ASSOCIATION 2003C, 2)

The early hospital associations in Canada existed mainly to provide a venue for hospital superintendents to meet, discuss issues and exchange ideas about what was happening in their hospitals or their province. Extensive, investigative research activities as we understand these today were unheard of in virtually all the provincial associations and in many of those at the national level. Most of these associations had no full-time paid staff—only a voluntary secretary—and their funding was sporadic and dependent on voluntary donations from hospitals, if these were received at all. Without either staff or money, most hospital associations did little more than prepare an annual meeting and provide published material to support discussions.

Until the Canadian Medical Association (CMA) set up the Department of Hospital Service in 1928, research was not among the activities directed toward hospitals. The CMA focused on visits to hospitals to determine their suitability as locations for medical internships. But, with the hiring of Dr. Agnew, the hospital department did begin some minor research activities.

One of the first of these came at the request of the Department of Pensions and National Health. There was little or no information on how many hospitals were set up in Canada, where they were located or what type of beds they operated. As for an accurate bed count and the types of service, the information was sporadic and unreliable. Dr. Agnew wrote in his book that, in order to support a program to reduce maternal morbidity, the federal health department needed much more accurate information about Canada's hospitals and approached him for assistance in compiling a list of Canadian hospitals (1974, 4). In September 1929, he reported to a joint meeting of the provincial hospital and nurses' associations that the hospital department had "prepared a list as authentic as possible . . . and we find that Canada has now nearly 900 hospitals and over 74,000 beds. The annual maintenance budget is over $51,000,000.00 and the total capital investment is $214,000,000.00" (1930, 27). This list was published in the April 1930 edition of *The Canadian Hospital.*

The CMA hospital department was about to send out another survey questionnaire in 1931 in order to collect some statistical information on Canada's hospitals, when it learned that the Dominion Bureau of Statistics (DBS) was also conducting a nationwide survey. To avoid duplication, both questionnaires were combined and the results were to be made available through both organizations. The survey was being undertaken because: "It has become necessary to have complete, authentic, up-to-date and authoritative data relative to our Canadian hospitals" ("Your Cooperation" 1931, 12).

The survey was to collect information on the number of hospitals in operation in Canada, their ownership status, total bed capacity, collective days' stay as it was called and the average length of stay. The survey also asked for information on which hospitals had X-ray facilities, clinical laboratories and outpatient departments. Financial information on maintenance costs of public versus private hospitals and the total estimated costs of public hospitals in Canada would also be gathered.[1] The CMA Department of Hospital Service continued to operate on behalf of Canadian hospitals mostly in the area of approving hospitals for medical internships; a list of these first appeared in 1932 after investigation by the CMA Committee on Approval, of which Dr. Agnew was a member.

Council Research Activities, 1931 to 1952

With the establishment of the Canadian Hospital Council in September 1931, the delegates approved the formation of several committees to undertake studies in key areas of the hospital sector. These committees included: construction and equipment, public relations, administration and statistics, legislation, finance, medical relations, research, nursing, and small hospitals. Dr. Agnew had also been asked to investigate the impact of the British Preferential Tariff (of 10%) which was to be imposed on all hospital equipment imported under the tariff.

In late 1932, the Committee on Construction and Equipment delivered its report to the council's Executive Committee for approval. Its objective was to provide an overview of hospital planning, construction and equipment, and outline in considerable detail how a hospital should prepare for a major construction project by obtaining "authoritative data covering economic planning and costs based upon specialized research from those qualified by experience to supply it" (Parry 1932, 8).

The report detailed the types of questions that a hospital planner should ask about equipment in its facility, what should be looked at in constructing a power plant, in heating and ventilation systems, in fact, in everything from telephone systems to incinerators, elevators and lighting. The report was intended to assist hospitals, which were considering renovations, expansions or upgrades to their equipment and physical plant. Except in cities where hospitals might exchange information on such projects, in most parts of the country, every hospital was on its own when it undertook construction projects. Building standards were practically unheard of, national codes for electrical and other systems nonexistent, and safety and security were left to each hospital to implement as it saw fit.

Consistently throughout its history, the hospital council focused considerable time and resources on developing a uniform reporting system for accounting, statistics and records in Canadian hospitals. In 1931, shortly after it was created, the council asked the Dominion Bureau of Statistics to compile annual statistics on hospitals. This subject was once again on the agenda at the 1933 biennial meeting and the following recommendation was adopted:

> We would recommend, therefore, that a Special Committee be appointed to deal with the question of uniform accounting, statistics and records, that such a committee include representatives of the Provincial Governments, that it co-operate with the Dominion Bureau of Statistics, and that it then submit to this Council, details of a system for general adoption in the hospitals of Canada ("Uniformity" 1935, 20).

Although almost every province was collecting information, they all had different systems in place and used different terminology. As a result, comparisons between provinces were both difficult and worthless. The Dominion Bureau also studied the provincial annual hospital returns and recommended a standard schedule for information collection to meet all provincial needs. The Conference of Health Ministers unanimously supported this recommendation and a joint conference in 1935 of the Dominion Bureau, government delegates to the hospital council, and the members of the council's Committee on Accounting and Committee on Administration and Statistics amended the data collection forms and recommended their use in all provinces (Ibid., 21.)

The first official account of research activity conducted by the hospital council was reported at the 1937 biennial meeting. The council's Research Committee which had been struck in 1931, reported on the incidence of tuberculosis in nurses in training in public hospitals in Canada versus similar incidences in an average group of women of the same age. It was hoped that the results would help hospitals in dealing with TB outbreaks. The report presented a plan for testing both graduate and undergraduate nurses and recommended that testing be undertaken by the Canadian Tuberculosis Association. It also proposed better education for nurses about the disease and supported the implementation of preventive measures.

As for policy development, in 1941, the members of the General Assembly directed the council to cooperate with the federal Department of Pensions and National Health in any plan it developed for national health insurance. In order to be prepared for this eventuality, the council had set up the Committee on Health Insurance in 1937. When the federal health department announced the establishment of its Advisory Committee on Health Insurance, chaired by Dr. J. J. Heagerty, the council's committee appeared before it to present some key principles to be included in any national health insurance plan.

But the main thrust of the council's policy on health insurance came from its memorandum of 1943. In April, the council appeared before the House of Commons Special Committee on Social Security to present its position. After consultation with the provincial hospital associations, the council's Committee on Health Insurance had formulated the "Principles of Health Insurance as they Relate to Hospitals." This formed the basis of its submission to the House of Commons committee. These twenty key principles were highlighted in the document and included the following:

1.   Voluntary hospitals should be utilized.

2. Hospitalization should be through "public" hospitals.

3. Hospital benefits should be reasonably complete.

4. Facilities should be made available for all types of patients. (The council included chronic, convalescent, TB, mental disorders, observation, alcohol and narcotic addiction, homes for the aged and infirm.)

5. Hospitalization of "indigents", or those unable to pay, should be provided under the Plan.

6. Dependents of the insured should be included.

7. Remuneration of hospitals should be adequate.

8. Basis of remuneration should be fair to all parties concerned.

9. Hospitals should retain the right to determine their own staffing privileges.

10. Insured persons should have the privilege of taking higher priced accommodation by paying the difference in charges.

11. Health insurance should be on a provincial basis but under federal co-ordination.

12. Direction of the Plan should be strictly non-political.

13. Hospital representation on the Commission or Advisory Council.

14. The health insurance fund should be a contributory one.

15. Preventive medicine a major feature.

16. Research.

17. Teaching hospitals.

18. Voluntary hospital and medical care plans should be encouraged for those above the income level (if any).

19. Cash benefits.

20. Divulgence of clinical data (Agnew 1943).

Each of these key principles was explained in detail in the brief. The council informed the federal government that "The Canadian Hospital Council is *generally in favour of the principle of health insurance*" (Ibid., 18) and concluded that it wished to assist in any way that it could in working out a plan of health care for Canada (Ibid., 46). When the federal government eventually did establish the national hospital insurance plan in 1958, many of these principles were incorporated in it.

Between 1939 and 1945, the council members focused mainly on equipment, supplies and staff shortages. At the war's end, the council's attention turned to the reconstruction and expansion of the hospital sector after many years of neglect.

There was insufficient funding and few staff at the hospital council to undertake any in-depth research during these years, and what was accomplished was done mostly through committee work.

As for policy development, it was never on the council's agenda either in the 1930s or the 1940s, although the members passed resolutions that formed the basis for the council to formulate some positions on key issues that arose concerning hospitals. By the end of 1952, the council's agenda had been redirected to the development of educational programs, publishing activities, providing library services and ensuring the council's voice was heard at the federal government, speaking on behalf of Canada's hospitals.

Research and Policy Development at CHA, 1953 to 1977

As the newly named Canadian Hospital Association (CHA) settled into the 1950s, its focus continued to be on developing education programs, ensuring the success of its publications, working to set up an accreditation council for Canada and representing the hospitals' position to the federal government on the pending national hospital insurance program. Any conduct of research—what little was undertaken—was done through the various committees of the board, particularly the Committee on Accounting and Statistics; this committee was charged with developing the hospital accounting manual. (*See* chapter 16 for more information on this special project.) During this time, none of the committees dealt specifically with research or policy development but rather with specific issues either identified by the delegates at the general assembly meeting or, after 1959, at the annual meetings of delegates.

In 1960, the Education Committee recommended to the board that its name be changed to education and research. CHA records indicate that, for the most part, research consisted of work specific to the Education Department. No activities were assigned under the research umbrella and policy development was not considered or recommended at the board table or by the association's membership as part of CHA's mandate at the time. However, it did conduct representation activities (*see* chapter 15) and liaised with the federal government departments as needed.

In 1964, the board agreed to the suggestion that a Research and Statistics Department be set up to collect statistical information on nurses' salaries and the growth of training facilities in Canada. Dr. Piercey, CHA's executive director at the time,

Among Research Activities, CHA Published *Canadian Hospital Terminology and Definitions* with the Assistance of a Grant from National Health and Welfare, 1972.

proposed that the department collect, tabulate and distribute statistical information that would be useful for the management of hospitals. Such a department could also prepare and publish statistical studies, particularly on hospital trends, and provide a library service about the results of hospital research studies and surveys.

CHA's board agreed to establish the department but only approved two objectives: publishing reports and providing a library service. As for conducting research, the cost to staff the department with a full-time statistical officer and clerk was too prohibitive for the association at the time. However, the board did agree that a clerical assistant could be hired, who would report to the assistant director of education. The focus was on reviewing and revising lesson material for the education programs and collecting statistics on enrolment and the number of graduates.

On accepting the report of the Liaison Committee of the CHA-CMA-CNA at the February 1968 meeting, board members approved two recommendations from the committee: 1) a name change to Joint Committee and 2) the development of a research project to assemble a bibliography of facts concerning labor distribution and the transfer of functions between physicians and nurses. The board also approved new terms of reference, which included initiating studies of mutual interest among the three organizations and joint representation to the federal government on matters of common concern. It appears that, for the time being, the board was tying its research efforts to the joint interests of the three organizations.

The members of the Executive Committee raised the issue of policy development by CHA in 1968. Although the minutes do not say specifically who spoke about the issue, they show that one of the committee members pointed out that AHA prepared policy statements on subjects of particular interest to hospitals and the health field in general, outlining its position.[2] The minutes record that: ". . . it was the opinion of the Executive Committee that the Canadian Hospital Association should likewise study items of national interest in the health and hospital field and make known its stand or views through . . . appropriate policy statements" (CHA 1968a, 3). To this end, Dr. Brosseau was to write to a number of key individuals for advice on what study items might be significant. The list was to be presented to the Executive Committee, which would make recommendations to the board. The executive did identify the need for a CHA position statement on medicare.

This appears to be the beginning of CHA's focus on policy development, with a process set up to develop the activity at the board's direction. CHA did investigate timely issues that arose in the health care sector and reported back to the board on possible positions that CHA could take. For instance, in 1966, the Canadian Nurses Association (CNA) strongly supported phasing out nurse training at hospital schools in favor of nurse education at colleges and universities. The board directed the Nursing Committee to poll the membership and forward suggestions to the board for action.

Yet, despite the executive's directive to CHA to develop positions and policies, the focus continued to be on research. At the time, the intent of the Research Department was mainly to support the hospital information system (HIS) project, cosponsored with Statistics Canada. (*See* chapter 16 for more details.) CHA was to promote the project, undertake analysis and educate the hospital field about its application. A second task for the department was to produce and publish an annual trends chartbook. But the lack of resources curtailed the implementation of the department for nearly two years.

The early 1970s were a particularly unsettling time for the association. Its finances were under constant review, subject to audits by the federal government and close scrutiny—and much criticism at the time—by the Finance Committee. The provincial members were unhappy with increases in their fees, the fee structure especially and CHA's financial instability, so the Research Department was forced to switch its focus to concentrate on activities that would bring in revenues.

Many of CHA's special projects were being funded by grants from various federal government departments at the time. For example, any Research Department that was set up would be expected to oversee the development of the *Canadian*

CHA's Policy Development Included a Presentation to the Hall Commission, 1962.

Hospital Statistical Review book; support the work of the Committee on Accounting and Statistics, which developed and revised the accounting textbook (*CHAM*); publish control guides for the HIS project; and publish and distribute a booklet of instructions on HIS, as well as update the chartbooks. In 1969, Dr. Brosseau reported to the board that, in order to undertake the activities required by the HIS project and other research activities, he would be hiring an assistant director of research and statistics.

Finally, on 1 March 1970, CHA set up the Research and Statistics Department to oversee CHA's various government-funded projects and to respond to the many requests to conduct surveys. By the end of the year, Dr. Brosseau had proposed that CHA hire a research analyst to conduct market research for suppliers in the hospital field. At the same time, he suggested setting up a trust fund for education and research activities to support the additional demands in these areas; the board approved the request.

The Research Department did take on some policy development work for CHA at this time. At the October 1970 meeting, the board approved CHA's White Paper on Unemployment Insurance. After polling the members, CHA stated its opposition to the compulsory participation of Canada's hospitals in the plan; however, it would not oppose elective or voluntary participation by hospitals (CHA 1970, 17).

By 1972, the department was operating with a deficit and a cash shortage, so departmental staff began to explore ways in which the department could generate additional revenues. When CHA was forced to cut staff and eliminate the sales manager position, the Research Department ended up doing market research. It also tested, planned and undertook its own direct-mail sales campaigns, managed its own circulation and processed sales for its various products such as publications and metric kits.

By 1973, the department was spending considerable time developing grant applications to various federal departments to support CHA's many projects. These grant-assisted projects included 1) the cost analysis-based supplement for *CHAM*, 2) the HIS project, 3) the information system integration project, 4) the *Canadian Hospital Law Manual* publication and 5) research on primary care, another project of the Joint Committee of CHA-CMA-CNA. In fact, most of the department's focus was on market research to determine selling prices for its many print products.

In October 1975, the board approved setting up a Standing Committee on Research and Statistics to oversee these activities and approved its terms of reference in 1976. That same year, the Research Department was directed to publish the next edition of the *Canadian Hospital Statistical Review* in both English and French, and to monitor the federal government's Anti-Inflation Board's actions and decisions. Merging various research activities under one oversight committee was intended to enhance CHA's research capability. The committee also recommended that all hospital survey work, including that of other organizations, be consolidated in the department. But too many others were working in the field and they were not prepared to give up survey rights to CHA.

By 1977, the committee was becoming concerned about CHA's lack of visibility on the national scene, especially where its HIS project was concerned. CHA had withdrawn from the project and ceded involvement to the Ontario Hospital Association, which had more resources to move the project forward. It no longer provided input into the revision of the collection forms produced by Statistics Canada (i.e., HS1 and HS2), and the country's hospitals still lacked uniform statistical information for comparison purposes. The reasons: CHA was located in Toronto and not Ottawa, where Statistics Canada was headquartered; it had also cut funding allocations to the Research Department as a result of its financial difficulties during the 1970s. CHA's members were now expressing concerns about the association's lack of presence in Ottawa and outright criticizing CHA for the inadequacy of its research efforts on their behalf.

In a staff report submitted to the members of the board's Research and Statistics Committee in April 1977, titled "Future Options for Research and Statistics," it noted that little time had been spent in the department on research activities since

1972. Instead, the department's focus had been on generating revenue, carrying out some representation functions for CHA, and handling sales and distribution activities for its own products. In short, "the department is really a jack-of-all-trades operation responding to . . . current. . . priority needs which change quite often (Crysler 1977, 2). The report also explained that other departments within the association conducted research activities independent of the Research Department.

The report recommended that the department become actively involved once again with the hospital information system in developing standard definitions for reporting statistics, and liaise between Statistics Canada and the provinces in developing new data and comparisons. The proposed budget included senior, intermediate and junior analysts, as well as administrative support for these positions. The department's main activities would focus on research, representation and publishing. The committee did not take any action at this time because CHA was in the process of major change: 1) it was moving to Ottawa, 2) it had a new executive director and 3) the outgoing assistant director of research was leaving CHA. Any changes to the department's mandate, budget and staff would happen as the association settled in Ottawa.

Research Activities and Policy Development in the Capital, 1978 to 2006

In January 1978, the members of the CHA research committee met with the new executive director, Jean-Claude Martin, and his new director of research to look at the department's future and to establish relationships with the various board oversight committees that dealt with CHA's many special projects. Among the committees with research components, there was the Working Group on Terminology and Definitions, the Statistical Information Sub-Committee, the Accounting Committee (for *CHAM*), the Joint Committee of CHA-CMA-CNA and the HIS Committee.

The expectation was that the Research Department would become the liaison for all CHA committees, as well as a bridge between the federal and provincial governments regarding the collection of statistical information on hospitals. In addition, the committee recommended that several of the committees be integrated into one called the Task Force on Health Facilities Integrated Information Systems to lessen the number of committees whose activities would have to be coordinated.

The information systems integration project, which eventually led to the MIS Project, became a much bigger activity to manage than originally expected. Research Department staff worked on a proposal for funding and held many discussions with various officials at Health and Welfare Canada and Statistics Canada. These were much easier to organize and set up than previously now that CHA was in Ottawa. (*See* chapter 16 for details on both the HIS and the MIS Projects.) The project was complex in that it involved identifying management information needs, redesigning accounting procedures and developing a framework for a standard information module. The second area to be dealt with was whether Statistics Canada would continue to operate the Quarterly Hospital Information System (QHIS) or whether CHA would do this.

This project required both a Steering Committee and technical committees to support it and took up much of the Research Department's time. It was a three-year project, with funding in the range of more than $750,000, and needed extensive consultation and input from both CHA's member associations, the provincial governments, and both Health and Welfare Canada and Statistics Canada.

By the end of 1978, some board members began to urge CHA to find a way to include the interests of long-term care facilities in its research efforts. Increasingly, both nursing homes and acute care facilities were providing duplicate extended care services, which would continue to cost the health care system in terms of dollars and efficient use of staffing resources. CHA was directed to consult with its membership to explore ways to include long-term care facilities on its agenda. In June 1979, the board set up the Long Term Care Committee to investigate this issue further and determine objectives.

CHA's involvement in policy development under Jean-Claude Martin continued uninterrupted once the association settled in Ottawa. In fact, the process became more formalized. For instance, in preparing a major document such as CHA's brief to the Hall Review 1979, the process followed several steps. First, the issue was raised with the Executive Committee by CHA's executive director. If the committee members agreed that this was an issue of concern for the association, the members appointed a committee or individuals to follow up with recommendations. In this case, the Executive Committee appointed the chair of the board, Fred Lamb, and Jean-Claude Martin, the executive director, to explore the issue and bring recommendations for a procedure to the committee.

The plan of action, including an outline for the brief and a budget, based on each member's financial contribution, was presented at the next monthly meeting of the executive and referred to the board. The board then approved the plan and the budget, and set up a special meeting of the board for early January 1980 to review and approve the final submission to the Hall Commission.

The member presidents (today's chairs) and CEOs were then invited to take part in the discussions about CHA's brief. A member of CHA's Research Department, as the project coordinator, finalized the document, based on recommended changes from the special board meeting. Finally, the brief was presented to the Hall Commission in March 1980 and accepted by the board for information in September 1980.

This process ran into criticism from some member associations. In his report, the executive director explained "that two provincial associations were questioning the amounts they had been assessed" as part of their cost to develop CHA's brief, even though all provincial members had received the plan of action, along with the budget, prior to CHA's work on the brief. The board agreed that no written follow-up should occur at this time. But the executive director was to speak with his counterpart in each of the associations. This approach to policy development was beginning to cause problems for both CHA and its members.

Policy development in the early 1980s was still instituted primarily from board committees, especially the Long Term Care Committee and the Long Range Planning Committee. The Long Term Care Committee, which had been struck in 1979, was required to develop a survey to scan the long-term care environment in Canada and to liaise with the newly established Canadian Long Term Care Association. The committee's survey was developed and coordinated by CHA's Research Department.

There were also other board committees that could recommend policy to the board. These included board members and a staff support person assigned to each committee. The committee determined objectives, set priorities and made recommendations for board approval and for implementation by staff. Among the committees that provided input on policy development, the board received recommendations from the Research and Statistics Committee, the Joint Committee on CHA–CMA–CNA, the CHA Accreditation Committee, the Trustee Committee and the Long Term Care Committee.

Committee members directed staff to draw up a plan of activities that included priorities, a schedule and a budget. The Long Term Care Committee members also expected that research activities in the future would include projects with and for the nursing home sector, as many of CHA's members now included these among their membership. Its action plan would include a broader scope of activities. And parallel to this committee was the ongoing work of the Long Range Planning (LRP) Committee, which had been set up by the board in 1981.

By the early 1980s, CHA's members began to question the role of the Research Department in conducting surveys and collecting information directly from the hospitals. Several of CHA's provincial members were opposed to the association responding to requests from national organizations—or government bodies—seeking statistical information on Canada's hospitals. There had been requests for a survey of management salaries and CHA was committed to undertaking a trustee survey. Many of the provincial CEOs saw "CHA's Trustee Survey as an intrusion into provincial affairs" (CHA 1980, 3). Committee members were concerned about the ongoing disharmony between CHA and its members regarding the activities of the Research Department and directed staff to consult more frequently with the members and seek direction regarding various departmental activities.

In addition to the various requests to undertake surveys and market research, the Association of Canadian Teaching Hospitals (ACTH) expressed an interest in working with CHA's Research Department in 1981 to develop projects for teaching hospitals. However, since neither ACTH nor the Research Department had money, this alliance was quickly dropped. The department's staff continued to focus on updating the statistical compendium, working with the project director to launch the Canadian Hospital Association Job Exchange (*see* chapter 16 for details), and assumed responsibility for assessing CHA's internal computer needs and implementing a system. In 1982, a new vice-president of research was hired.

In 1982, CHA submitted a position paper on the Canada Health Act. CHA had met with Health Minister Monique Bégin to discuss the paper and had then asked the CEOs of its provincial member associations to review the document and provide feedback. The Canada Health Act would merge two previous pieces of federal legislation (EPF and CAP) but would not change any of them. CHA's position was unchanged from the past; it supported medicare and therefore this act. However, CHA raised concerns about whether the health department could actually include any of the EPF legislation under the Canada Health Act, as EPF was essentially financial and under the jurisdiction of the minister of finance. Nevertheless, the act was passed in 1984 and it did merge both acts and eliminated CAP.

In 1983, CHA endorsed one of many future joint statements with other national health organizations. Among these, there were joint statements on ethical issues in health care delivery (1983) and on terminal illness (1984). Another key area where CHA had needed to develop a position was on admission to nursing practice. CNA was proposing that, by the year 2000, the minimum requirement for admission would be a university degree. In late 1987, CHA sent a letter to CNA "stating that CHA recognizes that nurses have the right to set their own professional standards" (CHA 1987a, 7). CHA did ask the nursing association to consider several other issues, including the costs to hospitals. CHA was also directed by the board to work with the provincial members to set up further discussions at both the national and provincial level. CHA's members in Newfoundland, Ontario and Manitoba had already expressed their opposition to the CNA position on admission to nursing practice.

The issue of privatization of health facilities in Canada, especially their management by private firms or organizations, emerged in 1984 and 1985, with most governments assuming that the private sector was more efficient. The federal government appointed a task force to study the issue and report back to the House of Commons by April 1985. CHA investigated the evaluation methodology used to determine efficiency but did not present a position on the issue. The association did publish a document, titled *Privatize Hospitals/Privatisé les hôpitaux*, which the board approved in September 1985 as a discussion paper. It was referred to the provincial members for their feedback. By this time, several of CHA's provincial members had responded individually to the federal government's Sherman Report on privatization, universally criticizing its narrow base of recommendations. By now, policy development at the federal level was being conducted both by CHA and its individual provincial members.

In 1986, the Long Range Planning Committee adopted a procedure for CHA policy development. As a first step, an annual priority-setting exercise would be undertaken through a survey questionnaire to collect data on a range of potential priority issues. The process required that members of CHA's board, the CEOs of the provincial and territorial hospital and health associations, and CHA's executive staff assign scores to a list of possible issues. Weighted averages were used to determine the top five priorities for the association on which to focus its representation and policy activities each year (CHA 1987a, section 1, 3). Policy priorities would also be identified through resolutions from the membership, the board and its committees,

CHA staff and member organizations. The members of the LRP Committee reviewed the list of priorities at its fall meeting and recommended these to the board at the March annual meeting the following year.

CHA staff prepared draft documents for the members of the committee, which reviewed them and provided feedback for incorporation into the document. Then, the documents were circulated to the member associations for comments, endorsement or revision. The documents were resubmitted to the committee members and, on approval, the draft policy document was submitted to the board for its review and approval. Policy statements were then released in both official languages and sent to member organizations and a select list of key national health organizations, depending on the subject matter. A select list of federal ministers and other officials also received the statements automatically.

In 1987–1988, the board approved the following priorities for CHA: 1) the need for national health policies/objectives, 2) long-term care, 3) liability insurance/quality assurance and risk management, 4) bioethics and 5) funding issues. In 1985, the association had adopted the one-page policy statement format as a summary of the in-depth information contained in its position papers, briefs and reports. The association expressed its position through news releases and editorials. Then, in September 1984, CHA hired a vice-president of public affairs to increase its representation activities, to publicize and promote the association's efforts and to develop additional policy.

In 1987, the Long Term Care Committee recommended that CHA develop policy regarding uniform definitions for long-term care centres and types of care, and on improving access to transportation services for the elderly. The committee also recommended that CHA pursue research in this area. By the end of the year, the board had approved a policy statement on the development of uniform definitions.

In late 1987, the federal government announced its proposals for fiscal reform. Essentially, this included proposals on tax reform, especially the sales tax on health care facilities. CHA's brief, with input from the provincial and territorial hospital and health association CEOs, was presented to the Permanent Committee on Finance and Economic Affairs. It included four key principles: 1) full compensation to nonprofit health care facilities, 2) timely compensation, 3) administrative efficiency and 4) direct compensation. Furthermore, CHA recommended that health facilities should be zero-rated and CHA's preferred option was a national sales tax as in the past.

Then, in June 1989, the CHA board received the report of the Strategic Planning Committee, which had been struck in September 1988. The committee identified CHA's major role as advocacy. Some members wanted the provincial perspective presented in the association's lobbying and advocacy activities. The committee also recommended the merger of the research and development budgets into that of public affairs, which had been set up as a separate department in 1986. With this recommendation, the activities of the research department were effectively shut down. In fact, the 1990 budget did not include any funding of key research staff vacancies.

At the same time, CHA learned that the federal finance department had rejected its proposal for an exemption of health facilities from the sales tax. But it would implement a rebate system. CHA's position was to establish which health facilities were to be exempt and to negotiate the most favorable rebate level possible.

As the 1990s began, CHA's budget included an additional levy to the member provincial and territorial hospital and health associations to support the board-approved strategic plan—a plan that included some research activities supported by the CHA Foundation, including its setup. By 1990, however, the board's focus was on stabilizing CHA's finances and its member organizations were concerned with their own survival. Research activity ceased altogether and the new CHA president, Carol Clemenhagen, was to focus on representation and advocacy, and policy development. The CHA Foundation, which had also been approved in the 1990 budget with the objective of raising funds to support research activities, was also cut in early 1990 by the board. Nevertheless, CHA did receive considerable funding from Health and Welfare Canada in September 1990 to support a research project on stress management for caregivers treating HIV/AIDS patients in health care facilities. And the Finance Committee suggested that CHA staff should work more closely with its membership to develop research projects and pool resources to reduce costs.

Throughout the early 1990s, CHA staff focused on four major policy development areas as directed by the board. These were 1) national health policy and health objectives (*see* chapter 16 for more details about the Vision Project), 2) integration of mental health into the health system and 3) an ongoing focus on long-term care as part of the continuum of care. CHA also developed a policy on waste management for health facilities through the board's Ad Hoc Advisory Committee, including recommendations for action to be released in November 1990 in conjunction with the conference on waste management.

Between late 1990 and mid-1993, CHA's policy resources focused on developing the Vision Project, which was officially approved in March 1993 and released publicly in June to wide acclaim. For the next year, CHA's policy agenda centred on this project, with its key principle statements on the CHA federation's vision for the reform of Canada's health system. When Prime Minister Jean Chrétien set up the National Forum on Health in October 1994 to advise the federal government on how to improve Canada's health system, CHA urged forum members to use the Vision Report as a starting point for their investigative activities. (*See* chapter 16.)

With health reform proceeding at a rapid pace among all of CHA's provincial and territorial health and hospital association members, the association produced *Health Reform Update* to inform both members and other interested parties about the progress of reform activities across Canada.[3]

By the mid-1990s, the growing uncertainty among CHA's member organizations about both their survival and the nature of their funding began to have a considerable impact on the association's ability to focus on policy development. When Carol Clemenhagen resigned in January 1996 as CHA's CEO, policy development for the next eighteen months virtually disappeared off the board agenda as board members, the CEOs of CHA's member organizations and CHA staff, under Acting President Tim Julien, focused on downsizing, restructuring and redirecting the organization in order to ensure its survival into the next century.

By late 1997, CHA was both stronger financially and in terms of its relationship with its provincial and territorial members. The board had hired a new president in the person of Sharon Sholzberg-Gray, and with new staff in the Policy Development Department, CHA was ready to focus on its policy-driven agenda once again. In order to do this, one of the major support mechanisms for policy development in future would be the CEO Forum, which had been set up in 1995 as part of the bylaw revisions that had resulted in a name change for the association that year. The provincial and territorial member CEOs would discuss issues arising from and related to the roundtable updates, as well as provide advice on policy issues at the request of the CHA board. Policy development by CHA would be member-driven—at the very least member-reviewed.

In November 1998, the board unanimously approved a policy development process for CHA, which included a review of the strategic directions of the association every three years and the identification of key issues at each fall board meeting through a brainstorming- and-prioritizing exercise using the dot system. CHA staff presented an extensive list of health issues for review. Each member of the board was provided with a set of colored dots. The major policy subjects were written on tearsheets taped up around the board room. Each voting member was asked to place a dot—representing the level of importance—beside an issue. CHA staff counted the dots and provided the list of policy issues for the board to formally endorse.

Once the priorities had been approved, these were adopted by the Policy Development Department as its action plan. A progress report and update were presented at the late winter board meeting to determine whether any shifts or changes were required. A special joint meeting of the board members and the CEOs and chairs of the member organizations was held at the time of the annual general meeting in June. This meeting provided an opportunity for CHA staff to refine and review policies, and to receive input from its members. This process was followed consistently for the next several years as CHA developed key policy statements and position papers.

Funding Canada's health care system—and influencing the federal government to restore the cash floor to its transfers to the provinces and territories for health—became one of the major policy focuses for CHA during the late 1990s and for much of the period between 2000 to 2004. The board, with input from the membership, also identified the recruitment and retention of physicians, nurses and other health professionals, and the issue of accountability in the health system as key priorities for CHA policy development. These issues became the dominant policy issues and the main focus for much of the early part of the twenty-first century for CHA's policy agenda.

CHA had developed and presented its funding brief titled "Preserving and Strengthening Our Healthcare System" to the Standing Committee on Finance in August 1998 in which it asked for the Canada Health and Social Transfer (CHST) cash floor to be raised by $2.5 billion. CHA had also asked for an escalator to the cash component of the CHST to sustain the current health system.[4] To support its position further, policy staff developed a detailed funding brief to inform board members, provincial and territorial member organizations and other interested parties on how Canada's health system was funded. The document also presented background material that would enable CHA to continue to develop sound policy in the critical area of health system funding.[5]

Rather than concentrating entirely on funding and health human resources, the board broadened CHA's policy agenda in March 1999 to focus on the issue of sustainability of a publicly funded health system. This umbrella issue included each of CHA's key policy priorities at the time, many of which were often ways in which the health system could be sustained. The board directed CHA staff to develop a framework for a sustainable health system. This document was published as a second major policy brief in 2000 and provided discussion points for both its members and others. CHA also contributed to the development of the funding brief to be presented by The Health Action Lobby, or HEAL, to the federal finance committee.[6] CHA staff then developed discussion kits for each of its policy positions and discussion papers. These could be used by the member organizations in getting the message out in each of the provinces and territories. Policy development on funding remained a priority on the agenda for the next four years.

At the same time, the accountability issue emerged as a priority for the federal government, particularly with the release of the Social Union Framework and the Health Accord. The issue also began to dominate the CHA policy agenda increasingly beginning in 1999 and over the next few years. In fact, it had moved up on the board's list of policy priorities by 2000. Identified as a two-pronged issue, it involved both identifying who was accountable for what and to whom, and then finding a way to measure health system performance and its impact on the health status of Canadians.

In 1998, as the issue was emerging on its agenda, CHA initially partnered with the University of Ottawa's Centre on Governance and the master of health administration program to apply for research funding from the National Health and Research Development Program (NHRDP) of Health Canada. But the funding proposal was turned down. CHA staff next developed a framework for collecting information on accountability initiatives within each province and territory through its member organizations. Leading from the issue of accountability was the need for quality national health system information to support evidence-based decision-making. This information would become a core component of any accountability process (CHA 1999, 8).

In response to discussions at the CEO Forum and following recommendations at the June 2000 Annual General Meeting that the CHA board develop specific actions in the area of accountability, CHA staff prepared a draft document on accountability and role definitions. The issue was also the focal point of a joint meeting of the CHA board and its member organizations in June 2001. This issue was not only about who was accountable but about the perception that the health system in Canada was not either well-managed or well-governed. CHA's members were concerned that such perceptions be dealt with in a document written in a firm but friendly tone that promoted cooperation and openness, and a willingness to work with governments at all levels to resolve concerns around health system accountability.

In June 2001, the board approved the policy brief titled *Towards Improved Accountability in the Health System*. While it was not expected that the document would lead to any policy changes in Canada's health system, or changes in practice for that matter, it was intended to be used widely by all interested parties to generate discussions. It was hoped that a joint statement could be released in collaboration with the Canadian Council on Health Services Accreditation and the Canadian Institute for Health Information. Unfortunately, the three organizations could not agree on a final policy statement. (A special project on accountability and governance is highlighted in chapter 16.)

The ever-expanding policy agenda grew to include aboriginal health, core services and public expectations, home and long-term care, and privacy and protection of health information. Both the board and the CEOs of its member organizations began to question how CHA would carry out its policy agenda with its current resources. The board asked CHA's president, Sharon Sholzberg-Gray, to prepare a document on value-added in being a member of the federation for discussion at the March 2000 board meeting. In June 2000, the board approved a five-percent increase in the membership fees to support the ongoing work of the president's office and CHA's policy, advocacy and communications staff.

The board also fine-tuned the review process for determining CHA's strategic directions in November 2001. Policy staff would propose a list of strategic directions, based on both an internal and external scan of existing and potential health system issues. The board would review the list and determine if new issues should be added or incorporated elsewhere. It would prioritize the list, approve the top three to five issues to focus on in the coming year, and review the specific actions related to each direction. In this way, CHA continued to develop its policy agenda on a consistent and firm foundation, tied in to its advocacy and communication strategies and activities (*see* chapter 15 for details on the advocacy and communication).

The seven components of CHA's sustainability framework remained the core of the association's strategic directions for both policy development and advocacy over the coming years. These seven components as discussed in the policy brief were:

1. Responding to the Changing Health Needs of Canadians.
2. Realizing the Vision of an Innovative and Integrated System.
3. Ensuring the Availability of Appropriate Health Human Resources.
4. Developing and Implementing Appropriate Accountability Mechanisms.
5. Advancing Health System and Health Services Research.
6. Contributing to the Productivity of Canadian Society.
7. Providing Sufficient and Long-Term Funding (CHA 2000, vi).

The framework document, published as a Policy Brief, was to be used by both CHA and its member organizations to encourage public discussion and to demonstrate the need for adequate long-term funding for Canada's health system.

In late November 2001, CHA released one of its most significant policy documents at a press conference held in Ottawa. CHA's Ten Point Plan laid out a no-nonsense approach for revitalizing Canada's health care system. The plan identified ways to ensure "a responsive, sustainable and publicly funded health system in Canada" (Health 2001, 2.). The plan was based on the association's ongoing policy research and development, including its brief on the private-public mix in health delivery. While CHA was fully supportive of Canada's health system, it believed that it must be appropriate, improve quality care, ensure public accountability and embrace the entire continuum of care.

In meeting with the Romanow Commission in October, CHA had based its presentation to the commissioners on this plan and had suggested that any reform of Canada's health system, as well as any future directions, would need to:

1. Reflect Canadian Values.
2. Embrace Appropriate System Change.
3. Address Critical Health Human Resources Issues.
4. Support Needed Health Infrastructure.
5. Examine the Private-Public Mix in the Funding and Delivery of Health Services.
6. Ensure Adequate, Predictable Public Funding.
7. Improve Performance Measurement.
8. Ensure Public Accountability.

9. Involve Health System Managers and Trustees.
10. Improve Federal/Provincial/Territorial Relations.

These ten points formed the central core of the association's policy and public position on health system reform throughout 2002. All of these points continued to be relevant as a base for developing policy for almost any area identified by the membership over the next two years. Whether CHA was presenting its position to the Romanow Commission or the Kirby Senate Committee, this key policy document outlined precisely where the association stood. It also assisted the members in their advocacy efforts at the provincial or territorial level.

Through the latter part of 2002 and into mid-2003, the Policy Department suffered from staff shortages as key positions within the department either remained vacant or as new staff were oriented to their job. Staff refocused their time on representation and advocacy activities with the release of the Romanow and Kirby reports in 2002 and follow-up to these key reports. The CHA president also decided to merge the Communications Department with the Policy Development Department to create the Department of Policy and Public Affairs in 2003.

Policy staff continued to present issues of the day and note areas where an issue could rise to the top of the policy agenda at any time, as was the case with patient safety and quality care in 2001. Staff were directed to produce a background document to identify key issues in the area of patient safety; the complexity of the issue meant that collaboration among many organizations would be important for finding solutions and developing guidelines in this area. In 2002, CHA prepared a Provincial/Territorial Comparison Grid, which summarized health reform reports and provided an overview of the similarities and differences among the various recommendations in the reports; the grid was posted on CHA's Web site for access to members and other interested parties.

One area that the board did recognize as relevant for policy development was that of the long-term care component of the continuum of care. While the board had approved short and issue-specific statements regarding long-term care in the past, it had not developed a position regarding the many issues related to facility-based long-term care. The issue received no attention—or very little—at the federal level during this time. Staff recommended to the board that CHA develop a position paper on facility-based long-term care. Not every member of the board was convinced that this was necessary. Nevertheless, through consultation and review, following the established board policy development process, CHA released its fifth Policy Brief in 2003 titled *Facility-Based Long-Term Care within Continuing Care*. The brief was widely circulated and its recommendations were supported by the National Advisory Council on Aging. (*See* appendix 5 for a list policy/position statements.)

In 2003, CHA's board approved the development of a major policy project on governance and accountability as one of its key strategic directions. By 2004, CHA's list of key strategic directions included accountability, patient safety, wellness and population health, health human resources and knowledge transfer and its update. Pharmaceutical issues were also quickly moving up the list as an issue to be watched in the future. Between 2004 and 2006, the board and the CEO Forum readjusted the list of policy priorities as needed to reflect shifts that were occurring either at the federal level or within the provinces and territories. As more funding was restored to Canada's health system, CHA redirected its policy focus to specific areas that required attention. The core business of policy development continued to dominate CHA's agenda and the board's attention as the association celebrated its seventy-fifth birthday.

Summary

The early years of the Canadian Hospital Council were focused on its survival. Policy work was done through special studies identified at the general assembly or by the Executive Committee. With the name change in 1953, the dominant focus of the organization was on the growth and stabilization of its distance education programs and its publishing activities, as well as establishing an accreditation council in Canada and a hospital administrator organization to set standards for a rapidly expanding health system.

The turning point for CHA's policy and research activities appears to be 1968 when the board supported some research and development work—albeit mostly in the area of distance education programs. Much of CHA's focus throughout the 1970s and 1980s was on its special projects to support and improve Canada's health system. Research was conducted in some key areas in the 1980s and then disbanded by the beginning of the 1990s as the organization focused on survival and meeting its members' needs in advocacy and representation at the federal level. Policy development also gradually moved to the top of the CHA agenda as its membership identified key areas where work was needed.

By late 1998, the organization had refocused on developing a board-approved, member-driven policy agenda, with supporting advocacy and communications activities tied to key position statements and policy briefs. By 2006, the Canadian Healthcare Association had developed a reputation for well-researched, credible policy development to support its commitment to speak on behalf of Canada's health system and to represent its members' interests on the national health scene.

Endnotes

1. The 1932 Census of Hospitals, released in April 1935, reported 860 hospitals in Canada, 589 public, 214 private, 35 dominion and 22 incurable with a total bed capacity of 51,577 beds excluding mental and incurables ("Recent" 1935, 14).

2. Judge Chaiker Abbis was CHA's president at the time and both he and Dr. Brosseau attended the AHA annual meeting and convention. Other members of the 1968 Executive Committee were R. Alan Hay, C.E. Barton, G. Massue and Dr. Brosseau, CHA's executive director.

3. Today, CHA provides periodic updates through its Web site and sends out an electronic newsletter monthly.

4. The development and presentation of a funding brief to the federal Standing Committee on Finance, in collaboration with its members and on approval by the board, is an annual policy and advocacy activity for CHA.

5. This brief was the first in the Policy Brief Series created by the department to promote CHA's policy positions. (*See* chapter 16 for more information.)

6. HEAL was a coalition of several national health organizations that worked together to lobby the federal government to ensure adequate and stable funding for Canada's health system.

15

MAKING OUR VIEWS KNOWN (ADVOCACY AND REPRESENTATION)

*"It was felt that, as a national association, there should be
more consultation and liaison between the C.H.A. and the
government in matters affecting the hospital field, and that
such liaison should be a continuing one so that discussion
could take place before policies were set by the government."*

(CANADIAN HOSPITAL ASSOCIATION 1954)

The earliest record of the Canadian Hospital Association (CHA) role in advocating on behalf of Canada's hospitals is mentioned in 1912. The CHA appointed a committee, whose members were "to appear before the Tariff Commission to press for the abolition of duties on hospital supplies" (7). It is important to remember the many obstacles that existed in Canada during these years that made undertaking representation to the dominion government in Ottawa both a costly and time-consuming activity.

To seek an interview with the Tariff Commission was not an easy task for the members of CHA's committee to undertake. They could not simply call a minister (few or no phones) or book a flight to Ottawa to meet (no planes). As of 1913, they had still not succeeded in setting up a meeting. Finally, in 1914, the Executive Committee decided to seek advice from the larger Ontario hospitals to ask for their suggestions on the matter of tariffs on hospital supplies. Since this early CHA never met again after the war, it is unknown what the outcome regarding tariffs was.

When the Department of Hospital Service of the Canadian Medical Association was set up, it was not intended as an advocacy body. It had been established to study hospital problems and to act as a consultation bureau to hospitals, hospital superintendents and the existing provincial hospital associations. However, Dr. Agnew, the department's secretary, did spend much of his time between 1928 and 1930 visiting every hospital in Canada and working as closely as possible with the existing hospital associations. In fact, he criss-crossed Canada several times during these two years, a formidable undertaking even today with modern transportation available.

Dr. Agnew actively advocated for the American College of Surgeons' standardization program to be supported, especially by physicians working in Canadian hospitals. He reported in his book that he personally spent one week in Chicago studying the program first-hand "and returned to Canada convinced that the program—albeit one originating with an outside organization—was the best thing that had ever happened to Canadian hospitals" (Agnew 1974, 67). While he supported this program at the time, he also firmly believed that Canada would set up its own standardization program some day.

Often, he accepted speaking engagements in order to promote the work of the CMA's hospital service department. In October 1928, he was the keynote speaker at the Ontario Hospital Association (OHA) dinner at which he described the department's objectives and activities. He appeared at the inaugural meeting of the Nova Scotia Hospital Association in August 1929, again discussing how the department could assist both the association and the provincial hospitals with their problems. In fact, he addressed as many annual meetings of provincial associations and Catholic conferences as possible, carrying the message of the department, identifying hospital issues and problems, and encouraging support for the department and its work on behalf of hospitals.

In a June 1930 article in *The Canadian Hospital*, the writer describes advocacy actions by the hospital department. "Representation to the Advisory Board on Tariff and Taxation was made last Fall by the Department of Hospital Service . . . embodying suggested revisions of the Tariff Regulations affecting certain types of hospital supplies and equipment" ("Further" 18). Dr. Agnew sent a list of revisions to each hospital in Canada to keep them up to date on the changes. He also informed journal staff, so that the information could be published. These early efforts by the CMA hospital department to represent the interests of Canada's hospitals laid the foundation for the future work of any proposed national hospital organization.

Advocacy and Representation, 1931 to 1952

Among the objectives spelled out in the constitution of the Canadian Hospital Council, which was approved at its founding meeting in 1931, is the following:

> (2) To represent the hospitals of Canada in those matters of general or national interest which concern the welfare of the hospitals or the sick public whom they serve; . . .

> (3) To co-operate with the governments, federal and provincial and with the municipalities and with any other body or organization in promoting public health and welfare and in furthering the purposes and objects of the Council herein set forth; . . . ("Incorporation" 1937, 11).

Although, today, this bylaw would be seen as trespassing into provincial members' jurisdiction, there was clearly little hesitation on the part of provincial delegates at the 1931 assembly in directing the council to advocate on their behalf. Most of the provincial hospital associations and Catholic conferences had no staff—or only part-time volunteers—to undertake their work. At least the council was in a position to identify issues and work with its members to represent hospital interests through both Dr. Routley (the council's president) and Dr. Agnew. In fact, in 1935, delegates supported a resolution directing the council to ". . . urge passage of legislation, in those provinces not having done so already, providing for reciprocal recognition of the accounts of hospitals in other provinces for [nonpaying] patients" ("Canadian" 1935, 5).

At this same meeting, the delegates also approved a resolution directing the council to submit a request to the commissioners of the Employment and Social Insurance Act to exempt all public hospital employees from paying unemployment insurance. On 29 December 1937, the members of the council's Executive Committee presented a brief to the Royal Commission on Federal-Provincial Relations in Ottawa, which discussed two issues: 1) paying hospitals for indigent care and 2) exemptions from unemployment payments.

The brief noted that "[a]s the Canadian Hospital Council represents all of the thirteen provinces and other hospital associations in Canada, it may rightly claim to represent the official viewpoint of the public hospitals of this country" ("Brief" 1938, 32). The council was especially concerned to relay to the federal government the financial burden that was being carried by the voluntary hospital sector for patients who could not pay for their care. The council lobbied for ". . . ADEQUATE state assistance. . . to cover the hospitalization not only of indigents or non-pay patients of fixed residence, but also of transients. . ., of immigrants with less than three years' residence in Canada, of old age pensioners, . . . and of other groups . . ." (Ibid.). The council wanted to ensure that these costs were covered under any state health insurance plan that might be set up in the future by the dominion government. It was acting at the direction of its membership, based on a resolution passed at the 1937 assembly meeting.

The brief addressed the issue of unemployment insurance as well and requested that, if it became a federal responsibility, provisions should be made for meeting the full costs of hospitalized recipients who received such a benefit. Copies of the brief were sent to the provincial member associations after it was presented to the commission. This process was followed for many years by the council, as there were no provincial association staff, who could be consulted prior to presenting briefs and position papers to the federal government.

In 1937, the delegates also directed the council to make plans to take part in any consultation process that the federal government might enact in the future regarding a possible national health insurance plan. Such a plan was to have gone into effect in 1937 in British Columbia but the legislation was never passed. Nevertheless, the delegates and officers of the hospital council expected that the federal government would act at some point to implement a national plan. In a motion, the membership firmly expressed their opposition to any legislation that did not support the voluntary hospital system in Canada. A Committee on the Relationship of Health Insurance to Hospitals was set up by the delegates. Its work led to a document titled "Principles of Health Insurance as they Relate to Hospitals" which was eventually used to form the basis in later advocacy efforts. (*See also* chapter 14.)

In 1939, Dr. George Stephens, the council president, went to Ottawa to discuss with officials of the Department of Pensions and National Health what role Canadian hospitals could play in the war effort. In September, he reported to the delegates at the Fifth Biennial Convention: "We [the hospitals of Canada] should have direct representation in an advisory capacity with the Department of Pensions . . ., so that the hospitals may be continuously informed as to needs and plans [of the dominion government]" (CHC 1939, 9-10). Dr. Stephens firmly believed that public hospitals should make the final decision when it came to providing both beds and staff that would be needed to care for civilians during the war.

Speaking in 1941 on representation to federal officials during wartime, Dr. Stephens expressed his frustration at the government's lack of consultation. The council did manage to win an exemption for hospitals from paying unemployment insurance with what is surely an unusual argument. Dr. Stephens stated that: ". . . there is no unemployment in hospitals. Therefore, hospitals and hospital employees would be penalized in being required to pay towards a fund from which they could not at any time hope to receive a return benefit" (CHC 1941, 8). As he reported to the delegates, this argument was accepted by government officials.

Three key health associations discuss joint programs and approaches to Task Force

Back row *(left to right): Dr. A. F. W. Peart, General Secretary, CMA; Dr. A. Mercer, CMA; Miss E. L. Miner, President Elect, CNA; Dr. B. L. P. Brosseau, Executive Director, CHA; Dr. Gaston Rodrigue, President Elect, CHA; Miss M. McLean, 2nd Vice President, CNA; Mr. Chaiker Abbis, Executive Committee Member, CHA; and Dr. D. L. Kippen, President Elect, CMA.*

Front row *(left to right): Dr. Helen Mussallem, Executive Director, CNA; Mr. L. R. Adshead, President, CHA; Sister Mary Felicitas, President, CNA; and Dr. R. M. Matthews, President, CMA.*

The Executive Committee had also written to the prime minister, expressing the council's concerns about the intrusion of federal government into the local hospital scene during the course of the war. The Defence Department was establishing military hospitals across Canada to care for members of the armed forces. Council representatives met with the medical directors of the three armed forces and the health department to work out a suitable arrangement. The council successfully represented hospital interests in limiting the number of hospitals to be constructed by the department. They worked out an arrangement that required the Defence Department to either contract with a public hospital for its services or to build annexes or wings on public hospitals. At the end of the war, these would be turned over to local hospitals.

One of the council's major advocacy efforts occurred on 9 April 1943. The hospital council's president, Dr. George Stephens, as well as other representatives of the membership, along with Dr. Agnew, presented a Memorandum on Health Insurance to the House of Commons Special Committee on Social Security. The document had been prepared by the Executive Committee, "[a]fter consultation with, and acting on what is believed to be a large majority of opinion of [the council's] member associations" (Stephens 1943, 31). The brief spelled out fourteen essential principles and six general recommendations. (*See* chapter 14 for details.) In making their presentation to the special committee, the council advised that it was *"generally in favour of the principle of health insurance"* (Agnew 1943, 18, italics in orig.) and that any plan should include these "essential principles." Much of the work in preparing this brief was undertaken by Dr. Agnew, who frequently compiled the council's major policy and advocacy documents.

During the course of World War II, the council's representation focus was on how Canada's hospitals could assist in the war effort. But the council was also concerned to keep civilian hospitals informed about the many controls that the federal government had established to conduct the war. At the September 1943 biennial meeting in Ottawa, president Dr. George Stephens brought the members up to date on the various wartime boards and the exact areas for which they were responsible.[1] The council also protested to the federal government about the lack of consultation in setting up some of these control boards, which had directly impacted hospital operations with no input from either the hospital sector or the council acting on its behalf.

Dr. Stephens also outlined to the delegates what he believed were the four major areas that the council would need to watch during the next two years, that is, between 1943 and 1945. He identified utilization of data from the council's health survey as an area for study and suggested it should be "continuously watchful over social security legislation" that was being drafted. The council should also support and encourage the voluntary hospital service at every opportunity, and both continue and expand its study committees and their work (Stephens 1943, 72).

In 1945, council advocacy focused on representing the postwar needs of Canada's hospitals. The hospital system had suffered from considerable neglect during the years 1939 to 1945. The council identified two specific areas in which to concentrate its lobbying efforts: 1) acquiring capital investment money to rebuild and expand the hospital infrastructure, and 2) finding ways in which to resolve shortages of nurses, other hospital personnel, medical equipment, drugs, foodstuffs and many other major hospital supplies. Canada's hospitals essentially needed to be rebuilt from the ground up and this was going to take considerable financial support from the local, provincial and federal governments. Despite the failure of the Dominion-Provincial Conference in 1945, governments would have to find a way to support the reconstruction of the hospital system, as well as meet Canadians' demands and expectations for access to health care in a country for which they had sacrificed much over the last several years.

In 1947, the council sent a memorandum to the Dominion Council of Health to address hospital shortages. The dominion council was made up of representatives from the federal Department of National Health and Welfare—as it was now called—and provincial health department officials. It was chaired by Dr. D.G.W. Cameron, the deputy minister of health. In its presentation to this group, the hospital council pointed out that there were now significant demands being placed on Canada's hospitals. First, the hospital was now the choice among women in which to deliver their children. Second, with more and more cars on the road, traffic accidents were on the rise and emergency rooms needed to be expanded to handle these cases. The council also noted that "the crowding of people into cities and towns and the increased financial ability of a large section of the population to finance short hospital admissions" (Agnew 1947, 25) were driving up the demand for more hospital beds. The council brief went on to describe Canada's hospital situation as bordering on the critical:

> . . . Today many hospitals are operating with an average census exceeding 100 per cent of normal and some are operating at 130 to 140 per cent of normal capacity. This means, of course, that not only in periods of peak demands but in normal relatively slack periods no beds are available on short notice" (Agnew 1947, 26).

The memorandum asked the members of the Dominion Council to seriously consider providing assistance to build more hospitals for the country. The hospital council representatives concluded their address by stating: "If the Provincial Governments and the Federal Government jointly, or in whatever manner would seem best, could make substantial capital grants for approved construction, a tremendous step forward would have been taken . . ." (Ibid.).

In 1948, on failing to reach an agreement with the provinces on cost-sharing, the federal government proceeded on its own to set up the National Health Grants

Program, which included hospital construction grants. Dr. Cameron addressed the council's biennial meeting in May 1949, describing in detail the intent of the grants and the amount of money available in each of the various programs. He noted that, at the time of his address, well over fifty percent of the available $30 million had been allocated to hospital construction projects. He advised the delegates that some of the council's proposals for these grants had been accepted by the department and incorporated in the health program. While the delegates commended the deputy minister and the department for the program, they also adopted a motion asking the department to extend the grants program "to cover part of the cost of construction of nurses' residences and other essential and supporting services, . . ." ("Resolutions" 1949, 45).

Much of the advocacy and representation work of the council was being carried out by one person—Dr. Harvey Agnew. Members of the Executive Committee had become more and more concerned that this activity was becoming too much for one person to undertake. The chair of the Finance Committee, Dr. A.L.C. Gilday, spoke at length to the delegates in 1949 on the need for more money and additional staff to relieve Dr. Agnew's duties. He noted that ". . . for two decades the burden of the Council's work has rested largely upon Dr. Agnew, . . ., who frequently visits Ottawa guarding the interests of the field in legislative matters, and who travels widely throughout the year, . . . coordinating the work of various associations" (Fraser 1949, 70). Dr. Gilday advised the membership that, if Dr. Agnew was to continue his work, he would need an assistant secretary, more staff and additional office space. This, of necessity, meant more membership financing.

To support the comments of the finance chair, Dr. Agnew reported to the delegates and guests at the meeting on the many representation activities in which he had been involved. He had consulted with the federal health department at meetings and had written letters to the provincial members on their opinions regarding the National Health Grants. He had worked closely with the Defence Department to study defence measures against foreign attack. At the request of the federal health minister, he helped to set up the Canadian Arthritis and Rheumatism Society and was a member of its board. He also established the Department of Hospital Administration at the University of Toronto and taught in the program. He attended as many provincial meetings as possible. Dr. Agnew also had represented the council's interests at Canadian Blue Cross Plan meetings, the Canadian Red Cross Society Outpost Branch Committee and the C.M.A. Committee on Approval for

Internship. He maintained close contacts with the American Hospital Association and the American College of Hospital Administrators.

As the council continued its representation activities in the 1950s, it had to do so without the knowledge, expertise and limitless connections of Dr. Harvey Agnew, who retired from the position of executive secretary in 1950. The new executive director, Dr. Leonard Bradley, took over the representation role. He reported to the Executive Committee in 1951 on a meeting he had attended in Montreal to discuss the issue of nursing shortages. This resulted in the establishment of the Canadian Commission on Nursing with two representatives each from the CNA, the CMA and the council, with an outside chair. Dr. Bradley was also involved in establishing the Canadian Commission on Accreditation. His term with the council was shortlived and it was left to the next executive director to move the council's advocacy efforts forward.

Advocacy and Representation, 1953 to 1977

By 1953, with its name changed to the Canadian Hospital Association (CHA), its main areas of focus were governance and adequate financing for the association, accreditation, setting up an equitable fee structure and promoting the use of the accounting manual in Canadian hospitals. However, the executive director, Dr. Arnold Swanson, did continue to carry out his responsibilities to represent CHA at its provincial member meetings and on various other committees, including close work with the federal government when needed.

The board spent considerable time at its June 1954 meeting discussing CHA's relations with the federal government. There was a serious lack of coordination between government policies and the hospitals in Canada. The board believed there should be more consultation and liaison between the two groups. It also established a committee that was directed to interview the federal health minister at least twice a year. At the next board meeting, the chair of the committee reported that the meeting with the minister had been cooperative and he had assured the committee members that CHA would not be bypassed in matters pertaining to hospitals.

By this time, Dr. Douglas Piercey was CHA's new executive director. Although he was heavily involved in developing more distance education programs, he found time to present a brief on accreditation to the health minister in July 1955. He was also caught up in questions such as the fluoridation of water, the revision of the

Opium and Narcotic Act and never-ending requests from the many new professional and disease-related national organizations that were continually springing up and seeking membership in CHA. He was also expected to work with the membership to seek their input and feedback on CHA's brief to the federal government on the pending national hospital insurance plan. (*See* chapter 14 for details on the policy developed.)

In 1958, with the Hospital Insurance and Diagnostic Services (HIDS) Act passed, CHA was once again pulled into the debate over unemployment insurance. This time the initial request to pursue the issue came directly from Dr. Bradley, who was now the executive director of the Winnipeg General Hospital. He asked the association to seek exemption status for Canada's hospitals, as CHA had managed to do in the past. In May 1958, the assembly delegates reaffirmed their belief that there should be no changes to the current unemployment insurance legislation.

CHA's lack of a presence on the federal scene surfaced at the May 1958 board meeting. Dr. Piercey had been invited to attend a meeting of the Dominion Council of Health but, when he asked to attend a dominion-provincial meeting, CHA was turned down. The board directed Dr. Piercey to meet with the Dominion Council's members to express the board's disappointment at being excluded from this joint meeting.

By the late 1950s, the executive director, the assistant director and the president of the association carried the bulk of advocacy and representation work on behalf of CHA. In 1958, Dr. Porter, CHA's president, reported to the biennial meeting delegates that he had attended several provincial association and Catholic conference meetings during his term of office. He had also participated in the Western Canada Institute meeting, the annual meeting of the AHA and had met with the Comité des Hôpitaux du Québec to discuss their fees.

On 6 June 1958, CHA representatives met with Prime Minister John Diefenbaker and Health Minister J. Waldo Monteith to submit a brief requesting changes to the HIDS Act. CHA's membership had asked for an amendment to allow hospitals to include interest on debt and depreciation on buildings as part of a hospital's operating costs. The members were also concerned about the numerous requirements for statistical reports. There was an urgent need for a schedule to be developed in close consultation with provincial governments.

In late 1959, the Department of National Health and Welfare set up an Advisory Council on Hospital Insurance and invited CHA's president, Stanley Martin, to attend the inaugural meeting. Many of CHA's members, including those on the board, wanted CHA to have permanent representation on this advisory council. The association spent many hours over the next several years advocating for a seat at the table. But the advisory council comprised members from the federal health department, the provincial health ministries and the provincial hospital insurance commissions. It was chaired by the deputy minister of health, who firmly believed that the voluntary hospital sector, as represented by CHA, should not attend these meetings.

By the mid-1960s, the issue of relations between hospitals and governments had moved to the top of the CHA board agenda. Hospitals were now required to submit budgets for approval and statistical reports to both provincial health ministries and the federal health department, as well as statistics to the Dominion Bureau of Statistics. Because of this constant interaction at some government level either by hospitals or its membership, CHA's board struck a committee at its May 1960 board meeting to develop a guide on hospital-government relations.

By late 1961, the Executive Committee recommended the fifth draft of the document for approval by the board. The board directed that the document then be distributed to the member associations and conferences and any others who may be interested. The "Guide to Hospital-Government Relations" spelled out the philosophy behind the guidelines, noting that the intent of the document was to improve relations between all levels of government and the voluntary sector.

The document clearly identified which groups should interact with each other and at what jurisdictional level. Both the process for approving the document and the intrusion into local and provincial affairs by the national body was a common practice at this time. The guide provided the following recommendations for interaction:

3. Individual hospitals, in dealing with provincial governments or other organizations on matters which affect other hospitals in their province, should consult with their provincial hospital association. . . .

5. Provincial hospital associations should, whenever feasible participate in the drafting of any legislation, rules and regulations affecting hospitals and hospital services by provincial governments. . . .

6. In matters of national interest and of federal jurisdiction, the federal government and the Canadian Hospital Association should work together in all matters concerning legislation, rules or regulations which may affect hospitals and hospital services.

7. Provincial hospital associations should consult the Canadian Hospital Association in all matters of federal jurisdiction and should keep the Canadian Hospital Association informed in respect of developments in provincial legislation and regulations pertaining to hospitals (CHA 1961a, 2).

In 1961, Prime Minister John Diefenbaker appointed Justice Emmett Hall to chair the Royal Commission on Health Needs. Again, CHA lobbied for a seat on the commission. Barring that, the association offered to help by providing information to the commission. Regardless of whether CHA's offer was accepted, the Executive Committee directed staff to prepare a submission to the royal commission. CHA sent a copy of its brief to the commission in April and made its presentation in May 1962 in Toronto. The brief reflected the input and advice of the CHA member association and Catholic conference boards of directors and that of the CHA board. The letter to the commission mentioned that, although the CMA was an active member, it had not taken part in the preparation of the document. The views and the sixteen recommendations were solely those of the CHA representing the hospitals of Canada. When the commission released its report in 1964, CHA's board set up a committee to respond to it.

In 1961, CHA established regular meetings with the provincial hospital secretaries (today's CEOs) to exchange information and as a mechanism for the members to provide feedback to the board. The members continued to be concerned about the lack of a national hospital presence in Ottawa and the lack of influence the hospital sector had with the federal government. This issue was raised frequently at the board table. CHA's members needed the association to work more closely with the federal government, particularly to improve the construction grants program for hospitals and to develop a uniform system of reporting on hospital finances. The federal government was now a major player in Canada's hospital sector. CHA's members needed a strong voice on the national scene to watch over and guard their interests and those of Canada's hospitals.

Several of the resolutions approved by the 1966 assembly directed CHA to "make the strongest possible representation to the Federal Government that it undertake a more realistic sharing of costs of hospital construction at the earliest possible date" (CHA, 1). CHA was also asked to work with the Department of National Revenue to acquire a sales tax exemption for nonprofit nursing homes on purchases of goods and services, and to seek a simplified method for computing the hospital excise exemption.

When Dr. Bernard Brosseau became the executive director of the CHA in mid-1966, the main priority for his representation and advocacy activities was to improve relations with the federal government, especially with the department of health. This priority was reaffirmed in a recommendation of the 1968 Aims and Objectives Committee Report, which was approved by the assembly. This required identifying key federal officials, arranging to meet with them and rebuilding communication links.

Before 1968 had ended, Dr. Brosseau was able to report to the board that "[r]elations with various Federal Government Departments and, in particular, with the Department of National Health and Welfare, have improved considerably over the past year" (CHA 1968b,7). He advised that this had occurred as a result of "frequent liaison visits" to Ottawa. In fact, Dr. Brosseau went to Ottawa once a month to meet with federal officials either at the health department or with CHA's traditional federal partner, the Dominion Bureau of Statistics. CHA continued to meet with the deputy minister of health twice a year and CHA's Executive Committee met with the federal health minister annually, along with the deputy minister and other senior health department members.

By the end of the 1960s, Dr. Brosseau had managed to change CHA's lack of visibility at the federal level to one of ongoing meetings and communication with many government departments. As a result, CHA benefited in a number of ways. For the first time, CHA was invited to make a presentation to the federal Advisory Committee on HIDS. Since the implementation of the HIDS Act in 1958, CHA had been seeking a seat on this powerful oversight committee but had been continually turned down because its membership was restricted to government representatives only. Being asked to appear before the committee was a major coup for CHA as a national health organization and for Dr. Brosseau personally.

CHA also reaped financial benefits from its improved relations with federal officials. The deputy minister of health had informed Dr. Brosseau during a meeting that he believed the department should provide grants to organizations like CHA to set up national programs. As a result, CHA received considerable project money to support several of its activities. This included funding national symposia on computers in hospitals, on group purchasing and on hospital responsibility for drug users. (*See* chapter 13 for details.) CHA also received grants for the revision of its accounting manual and the publication of a supplement, as well as funding for a joint research project with the CMA and CNA on the transfer of functions among health professionals. In fact, by the end of 1969, CHA had obtained four grants, one of which was used to revise the HOM distance education course. However, this generosity was subject to the whims of both the minister and deputy minister, and the political party in office in Ottawa at the time.

CHA also prepared an annual brief for the federal health minister—and his officials—who attended the first board meeting of the year to speak directly about the department's work and to learn about CHA's concerns regarding Canada's hospitals. This had been an ongoing practice for many years and was often the only opportunity for CHA's board as a whole to communicate directly with the health minister.

By the beginning of the 1970s, CHA was faced with two challenges in its representation and advocacy activities. First, it had to respond to the report of the Task Force on the Cost of Health Services in Canada, which had delivered its final report in late 1969, with some major recommendations that would have far-reaching effects on the health system.

CHA responded to the federal task force report in two ways. It worked closely with both the CMA and the CNA, through a working party, to reach a consensus on the impact of the recommendations and to develop a final report on priorities for presentation to the health minister in April 1970. The association also presented its own separate brief to Health Minister John Munro in May. While in agreement with most of the 328 recommendations, CHA disagreed with the recommendation that medical staff should be appointed to hospital boards. Nor did CHA support the development of home care programs under public health departments; CHA believed these should remain as part of the hospital service and, thus, under the umbrella of universal coverage.

The second challenge for CHA's advocacy efforts occurred with the appointment of Dr. Maurice LeClair to the position of deputy minister of health. Relations between CHA and the health department were about to take a turn for the worse. Working relations with Dr. LeClair did not start out well. One of the more frank exchanges between CHA and federal health officials took place at the 1971 February board meeting in Toronto.

CHA expressed concerns that the department had not renewed funding for some of its projects. Dr. LeClair explained that he had asked for a more impartial selection and approval process for projects. As a result, a committee of outside representatives—rather than health department staff—now recommended projects for approval. CHA pointed out that the committte consisted mostly of representatives from teaching hospitals; the majority of hospitals in Canada did not fall into this category.

The deputy minister promised to look into the matter. Health Minister John Munro also promised to consult with his deputy and expressed his regret over the apparent breakdown in communications between the two groups. To improve relations, Deputy Minister LeClair designated the assistant deputy minister as the direct contact for CHA's executive director. This meeting had not been as cordial or as cooperative as in the past.

In the spring of 1970, CHA and several other national health organizations were invited to attend the National Conference on Price Stability, organized by the federal Prices and Incomes Commission. Prime Minister Trudeau addressed the participants and outlined the government's efforts to control prices and wages. CHA was included among the many health professional organizations as the representative of the hospitals of Canada. In support of the other health organizations, CHA agreed to urge hospitals—through its membership—to do their part to keep costs under control.[2]

CHA's relations with the federal health department were about to undergo further changes. Under Health Minister Marc Lalonde, the federal health department was now working on implementing the recommendations outlined in his report entitled *A New Perspective on the Health of Canadians*. This meant that the department's focus was on developing health prevention and protection measures.

At his meeting with CHA's board in March 1975, the minister sought CHA's assistance in developing a plan of action to work with Canada's hospitals both to develop and promote public and preventive health programs, and health evaluation measures. The minister also informed CHA's board that the National Health Grants Program was now to be called the National Health Research and Development Programs (NHRDP); it would give priority to funding public health and prevention projects.

CHA planned its 1975 convention program around the Lalonde document and sent copies of the booklet to all its member hospital associations on its release. CHA had also advised both the minister and his officials that it would do what it could to push the proposed philosophy of the document forward to hospitals and its own member organizations. At the 1975 Annual General Meeting in Ottawa, the members supported a resolution to prohibit smoking in all patient areas and to ban the sale of cigarettes on hospital premises. CHA also implemented a no-smoking policy at its board meetings.

Senior health department staff were also deeply involved in discussions with their provincial counterparts on the new financial arrangements for health funding that the federal government was intent on implementing. These new fiscal arrangements would bring about a decreased role for the federal government in tracking how funding was being applied by the province and whether transfer payments were, in fact, being used to support health care delivery. There was an urgent need for CHA to advocate on behalf of its members.

CHA continued to hold regular meetings with the provincial hospital association CEOs, who, by 1976, were concerned with the impact of anti-inflation legislation and the federal Anti-Inflation Board. To address member concerns, the Executive Committee recommended to the board that it set up an anti-inflation committee to study the legislation and "make whatever representations are deemed necessary . . ." (CHA 1976b, 11). The board assigned the task of monitoring the Anti-Inflation Act to the Research and Statistics Committee instead. CHA staff would consult with the provincial hospital secretaries to obtain their input.

In the late 1970s, CHA representation was frequently sought in establishing technical standards for hospital equipment and medical devices. Dr. Brosseau reported "that CHA activity in the field of standards-writing was increasing at a considerable rate; there was more and more demand for participation in standards preparation and in standards implementation" (CHA 1976b, 12). CHA had managed to find local resource people in some cases. Unfortunately, many of these appointments required the association to pick up the costs for its representatives.

Dr. Brosseau informed the board that the Canadian Standards Association (CSA) had twelve technical committees, a steering committee and an implementation committee; CHA had been asked to send representatives to most of these. The board did approve the cost of this representation activity in the 1977 budget. But, with the association about to incur major expenses in a move to Ottawa, both this cost and the issue of these types of representation requests would have to be closely monitored in the future.

At the March 1977 board meeting with Minister Lalonde, CHA was able to report that the members had approved resolutions at the 1976 AGM to support the compulsory use of seatbelts in vehicles and to ban all print and broadcast alcohol advertising. These resolutions had gone even further than what the minister had

The Advisory Council on Health Care Technology, a new component of the Canadian Standards Association, has begun its work. Some members of the council are, from left: Dr. B.L.P. Brosseau, Chairman; A.M. Dolan, Manager, Health Care Technology Program, Canadian Standards Association; George F. Klein, Biomedical Engineering Consultant, B.C. Ministry of Health; and Paul Brown, Assistant Executive Director, Canadian Hospital Association.

expected. In return for CHA support for his health agenda, the minister and senior health department officials indicated their willingness to assist CHA in its efforts to acquire funding for some of its projects and help it to establish links with the Health Protection Branch, the Health Programs Branch and the Medical Devices Branch, where federal department activity was now happening.

The matter of CHA's liaison and representation efforts was raised once again at the March 1977 board meeting by Judge Chaiker Abbis, chair of the Committee on the By-Law and Regulations. He believed that the committee should "review the structure of the Association and recommend whatever changes should be made to provide better representation, more involvement of the membership, and better continuity of reporting to the membership" (CHA 1977a, 5). The issue would continue to dominate the association's board agenda even as CHA made plans to move its operations to the nation's capital.

Advocacy and Representation in Ottawa, 1978 to 2006

As CHA settled into its headquarters in Ottawa, it had already established a considerable presence at the federal level with representation on several key federal bodies. CHA attended meetings of the Metric Conversion Commission. The Research and Statistics Department director, along with the CHA executive director, represented the association on the Federal/Provincial Advisory Committee on HIDS, and the association was the alternate representative to the Federal/Provincial Sub-Committee on Quality of Care. CHA had also established contacts with the federal departments of labor, national defence, national revenue, and manpower and immigration. But the association's major linkages continued to be with Statistics Canada to work out the problems associated with the statistical reporting system (QHIS) and the integrated hospital information system.

By now, CHA's new executive director, Jean-Claude Martin, had settled into his role at the helm of the association. He had been given a clear mandate to maintain a strong advocacy and representation role as it had been developed by his predecessors. In a major coup, he had succeeded in persuading Health Minister Monique Bégin to address CHA's annual conference in 1978 in Calgary. In her address to the delegates, she presented her vision for the development of Canada's health system in the 1980s. This included areas where CHA and its representation efforts would no doubt be most helpful and effective.

Another area where CHA continued to advocate on behalf of its members was that of tariffs. For many years, Canadian hospitals were exempted from paying tariffs on certain scientific equipment and laboratory supplies. CHA opposed moves by the Tariff Board to withdraw hospitals' exemption status in 1979. Unfortunately, it was not successful in rolling back the tariff on these particular goods. Nevertheless, it continued to appeal to Finance Minister Jean Chrétien on behalf of Canadian hospitals to reopen the discussions. Working with other national associations, CHA did succeed in persuading the Canadian Transport Commission to deny Air Canada's request to increase its prices by twenty-five percent for the transportation of hazardous material, much of it coming from the hospital sector.

One of CHA's major advocacy efforts in the late 1970s was to work closely with government officials to move the hospital information system project forward. CHA had representation through its Research Department on the Federal/Provincial Sub-Committee on Hospital Information. This committee was working out a standard set of data that could be exchanged between provinces. In fact, hospital information systems in every province needed to be upgraded to accommodate the new fiscal arrangements under the 1978 Established Programs Financing (EPF) Act. In addition, the Federal/Provincial Steering Committee on Workload Measurement Systems was reviewing proposals on these systems for use by hospital management and provincial health ministries.

When the Health Services Review '79, headed by Justice Emmett Hall, was set up by the federal government, one of the first steps CHA took, at the board's direction, was to meet with the commissioner. The meeting included representatives from other national health organizations and Justice Hall was explicit in his directions that each organization should present a concise picture of the impact of current health programs and the public they serve. CHA presented its brief to the Hall Commission in late 1979. One of the reasons for the Hall Review was to examine the issue of extra-billing by physicians.

CHA was not in favor of user fees if these prevented Canadians from accessing necessary health services. The association brief recommended ways to ensure that national health standards were not lowered, defining these standards and exploring other ways to meet them. CHA did support the need for remuneration to health care professionals to be approved by their professional associations.

The issue of CHA's involvement in the long-term care sector was discussed by the Executive Committee early in 1980. The new Canadian Long Term Care Association had been set up and CHA's members expected it to work with this new organization on matters in this area. To assist staff, the executive recommended that a long term care committee be established; the board approved this at its February meeting. Among the terms of reference for the committee, the board directed that it was to revisit the board's 1974 decision that CHA would only become involved in long-term care through its provincial associations.

The board received the report of the Special Committee on Role and Communcations in September 1980, which recommended that CHA play a more adequate role in representation. CHA's president, Jean-Claude Martin, advised board members that this would require the association to develop positions on a number of issues. Both he and CHA's senior vice-president agreed to undertake the task of developing discussion and position papers for presentation to the board; the board would review these, or direct others to do so, and approve the paper before it could be released and used as the basis for representation activities to the necessary parties or federal bodies.

Many of CHA's interactions with the federal government in the 1980s involved applying for grants to move several of its projects—the integrated hospital information system, InfoHealth, the hospital of the future project and others—from the planning and development phase to the implementation stage. The Research Department interacted with various federal bodies to report on these projects. Many of these projects had been developed to help health care facilities adapt to the rapidly changing environment.

Unfortunately, the impact of so much involvement in project development began to affect CHA's finances. These projects involved considerable time, staff and money and CHA's commitments were becoming worrisome both for the board and the membership. In fact, much of the board's time during these years was spent receiving updates on these projects, reviewing their impact on CHA, determining the extent of CHA's continuing support and deciding how much longer the project could continue before it became detrimental to the association.

In 1984, CHA's president had hired a vice-president of public affairs. She assumed some of the representation duties that had been carried by the president and other senior staff. Much of the portfolio involved working with various organizations on standards, medical devices and bar coding. She also worked closely with various board committees and joint committees involving other national health organizations to develop position statements in areas such as ethics.

By the late 1980s, system change was beginning to have an impact on CHA's membership and, thus, the association itself. The work of the Long Term Care Committee continued to drive much of CHA's involvement in this sector. As the health system restructured to integrate services across a broad continuum, including long-term care, this committee provided a valuable link for the association to its members. Some of the provincial members had included long-term care facilities in their membership for many years; CHA's long-term care agenda through the board committee provided visibility in this area.

Throughout the 1980s, CHA had also extended its advocacy and representation activities to many other nongovernmental organizations. This included the Conference Board of Canada, the Canadian Comprehensive Auditing Foundation, the Law Reform Commission of Canada, the Institute of Donations and Public

CHA's annual general meeting received national media coverage. Being interviewed are CHA president, **Carol Clemenhagen** (above left), CHA Chair, **Gaston Levac** (above right).

CHA's Annual General Meeting in 1995 in Calgary Received National Media Coverage.

Affairs Research and several other groups. Much of its advocacy work was conducted by two staff: the CHA president and the vice-president of public affairs. While it was not always easy to document the results of these activities, nevertheless, they remained the backbone of CHA's efforts on behalf of its members.

When Carol Clemenhagen became CHA's president in January 1990, the board had established that her main priorities would be financial management of the organization, governance, long-term care, evaluation and ethics in that order. The first two areas required a focus on the internal structure of both the organization and the board. These areas took up much of the president's time and, given the directive to stabilize CHA financially, this did not leave much time for external advocacy efforts.

CHA joined The Health Action Lobby (HEAL) Coalition in 1991, in which several national health organizations worked together to influence the federal government to ensure adequate and stable funding for Canada's health system. CHA also vigorously lobbied for exemption for Canada's health facilities from the Goods and Services Tax (GST) which the government had implemented in 1990. CHA also successfully delayed its implementation for the health sector until 1991.

The early 1990s were a time of reassessment of both the Canadian federation—with the failure of the Meech Lake Accord in 1990 and the referendum on the Charlottetown Accord in October 1992. CHA's federation was also under review with downsizing and shifting of various provincial hospital structures across the country. In many ways, the tensions in the country were mirrored in CHA's federation and at the board table.

Among CHA's other advocacy and lobbying efforts in 1992, the association presented briefs to various standing committees of the House of Commons, including finance, liability and compensation in health care, and hazardous materials in the workplace. CHA also wrote to several federal ministers about biomedical waste, regulations on the transportation of dangerous goods and enhanced its communication activities with its membership. Believing that there was much to be gained by lobbying and advocating CHA's positions to the federal finance department, CHA's president invited Finance Minister Michael Wilson, as well as Health Minister Perrin Beatty, to address the annual general meeting in Ottawa in March 1992, thus opening up lines of communication with this powerful and influential federal department.

In addition to lobbying efforts at the federal government level, CHA held several bilateral meetings with other national health organizations. The association met with the Canadian Medical Association and the Canadian Nurses Association to discuss issues that continued to arise from the turmoil in the system and to cosponsor conferences on utilization and quality management, as well as nursing management.

As Canada's health system continued to reorganize and downsize, the impact of financial cutbacks moved like a wave across the federation affecting, first, CHA's members and, then, CHA. For almost two years, between late 1995 and late 1997, CHA almost disappeared from the national health scene. Its advocacy and representation efforts were drastically cut back as both its board and its members reviewed its operations and redirected it for the future.

Then, in November 1997, CHA's board and the membership began to focus once more on the association's core business of advocacy and representation. The board approved strategic directions for the advocacy agenda and directed the association to express its support for 1) a strong federal presence in the Canadian health system and 2) accessibility to services and care, both of which were to be maintained and improved. CHA was also expected to respond to operational issues that impacted on or, in turn, were impacted by the health system.

By the end of the year, CHA's advocacy and representation role was set for a new direction in a significant way. CHA now had a fully staffed Department of Policy Development and a new president in the person of Sharon Sholzberg-Gray. She was well informed about health policy, well connected in political circles in Ottawa and extremely articulate in explaining the federation's position on health care issues. When CHA arrived back on the national scene, it did so with the intention of representing its membership effectively and making a difference for Canada's health system.

Some of CHA's major advocacy efforts in late 1997 and early 1998 were linked to the HEAL Coalition. In November 1997, HEAL submitted its pre-budget brief to the Ad Hoc Standing Committee on Finance. Members made the point that the $12.5 billion in the 1997 budget had really been a cash floor, not a ceiling, as the federal government was promoting it.[3] The coalition called for an escalator for the Canada Health and Social Transfer (CHST) and identified the increase in passive privatization that was occurring in Canada's health system as a result of the federal government's funding cuts. The members of HEAL raised concerns that these cuts had resulted in service cuts across the system. As a result, the door had been opened to the private sector to step into the vacuum.

In November 1998, for the first time in a long time, the federal minister of health, Alan Rock, attended a CHA board meeting. The discussion allowed both sides to present their priorities and concerns. CHA's focus was on funding issues and the minister spoke about his wish to support a national plan for home care. The exchange boded well for CHA and its advocacy efforts to the federal government.

To ensure that there were clear lines of understanding about advocacy, CHA's board approved a policy titled "The Advocacy Role of CHA and Its Provincial/Territorial Members" at the November 1998 meeting. The intent of the document was to ensure that CHA spoke with one voice whenever any one of its member organizations initiated contact with a federal minister, its provincial members of Parliament or addressed a special commission, task force, standing parliamentary committee or communicated in other ways with federal officials. The document provided guidelines to ensure that neither the provincial nor territorial organization, nor the CHA, was expressing an opinion or presenting a position that was contrary to what had been approved at the board table.

The document proposed six principles for the advocacy process or framework. CHA would, as a general rule, advocate on behalf of the provincial/territorial members at the federal level. Its position would reflect the majority opinion or consensus adopted by CHA's board. In this way, CHA could rightly claim to be representing the national voice of the federation. The provinces and territories would advocate on behalf of their members at the provincial and territorial government level. The membership was asked to let CHA know if it would be contacting any officials at the federal level simply to keep it informed.

The document spelled out in clear terms what CHA's advocacy role at the federal level was; it was seen as ". . . the promotion of the policy goals of the CHA federation, maintaining a high degree of visibility for health care as a national issue, securing adequate funding . . ., preserving and strengthening Canada's health system," (CHA 1998a, 2). Of course, all of CHA's advocacy efforts were intended to enhance the organization's mission. This policy was approved by the board at the November 1998 meeting and remains in place today.

At the same meeting, the board agreed to the recommendation of the CEO Forum to disband the Policy and Advocacy Committee. Originally intended to provide input into the policy development process and support advocacy, the board had agreed to a much broader process. CHA staff had also provided a document for the board's approval, which contained suggestions for representation requests from both the federal government and other national health associations. CHA staff spelled out seven steps that could be followed in addressing each request, determining its relevance to the CHA goals and priorities, and dealing with requests that were inappropriate. The board supported the process and requested that it be brought back to the board only if substantial changes occurred in future.

Throughout 1999, CHA undertook aggressive and intense lobbying activities to the highest levels of the federal government, and through the media to the Canadian public, to secure more money for the health care system in the federal budget. Its efforts focused on increasing the amount from $1 billion to $3.5 billion and on raising the cash floor from the proposed $12.5 billion to $15 billion. As a result, when the 1999 budget was presented to the House of Commons in February, CHA's president was interviewed extensively leading up to and after the budget was delivered. CHA's messages seemed to be reaching the federal government's ears as various phrases and expressions about the health system were adopted by both the health minister and the prime minister in speaking about the health system.

To address funding issues, health system change and sustainability of the system, CHA developed its Ten Point Plan in 2001, which became the basis for much of its advocacy and representation activity for the next five years. The plan was officially released in November 2001 at a press conference in Ottawa to considerable national coverage by the media. Both CHA's president and its chair, Ken Ezeard, were interviewed extensively on the day of the plan's release. CHA continued to receive media requests the rest of that week about its plan. This extensive media coverage enabled CHA to deliver its message across the country. While CHA supported system change, its key message was for strong leadership, appropriate system change and adequate funding to sustain Canada's health system into the future (CHA 2001b, n.p.). In fact, this plan became CHA's rallying cry for the next several years.

A form of CHA's Ten Point Plan was submitted in detail in October 2001 to the members of the Romanow Commission, which had been set up by Prime Minister Jean Chrétien in April 2001 to look at future directions for the health system. CHA presented its brief titled, *A Responsive, Sustainable, Publicly Funded Health System in Canada: The Art of the Possible,* to the commission.

The association continued to deliver its message whenever and wherever it was invited to speak. In fact, the board had reiterated that CHA should continue to advocate on all the issues outlined in the Ten Point Plan, with adequate and predictable funding at the top of the list. In March 2002, CHA's president responded to the Standing Senate Committee on Social Affairs, Science and Technology—the Kirby Committee as it was known—in a speech on the health of Canadians. In April 2002, CHA was asked to address the Romanow Commission once again.

By the spring of 2002, CHA's advocacy efforts were paying off in significant and ongoing media coverage. There were numerous requests for background information from the media on funding issues and for comment on the various commissions and task force reports that were being released during this period.

When the federal government announced the 2003 Health Accord, CHA alone, among the major national health organizations, was critical of the agreement. The association believed that the accord had not gone far enough to address health system problems and reiterated this view when the federal budget was announced in February 2003. CHA's press release stated that both "CHA and our provincial and territorial members will continue to advocate for adequate and predictable levels of funding to stabilize the existing system and support needed health system reform" ("CHA" 2003a, n.p.). Eventually, many other national health organizations came around to CHA's point of view.

Prime Minister Paul Martin called another First Ministers Meeting in September 2004 to address the continuing criticism of the federal government for its inadequate support of the health system. By this time, CHA had joined with the Canadian Medical Association (CMA), the Canadian Nurses Association (CNA) and the Canadian Pharmaceutical Association (CPhA) in what was called the Group of Four or G4. This strategic alliance proved to be very effective. It successfully advocated for an agreement that resulted in significant federal investments in health care over the next ten years.

Perhaps, one of CHA's most significant lobbying coups was actually being present in the meeting room at the Conference Centre in Ottawa for the September 2004 First Ministers' Meeting as they negotiated the Health Care Plan. CHA's president successfully acquired credentials for representatives from all four organizations in the Group of Four. During the two days of meetings, CHA was front and centre and took part in extensive media interviews, both live broadcasts on what was happening inside the meeting room and in the media debriefings afterward.

CHA's advocacy efforts in the coming years will focus on closely monitoring the federal government's efforts to implement its ten-year health plan. While the 2004 health accord did not entirely meet CHA's vision for the health system, it did provide a foundation on which to build a better, more effective health system for Canadians. CHA and its members could take considerable satisfaction from the results of these advocacy efforts to guard Canada's health system.

Summary

In 1931, the first representation activities were spearheaded by Dr. Harvey Agnew, who travelled across Canada to promote the council, and assist and advise provincial member associations and Catholic conferences on hospital matters. When required to do so, the council ensured that Canada's hospitals were heard by the federal government. CHA's visibility at the federal level improved significantly during the late 1960s and 1970s, as Dr. Brosseau worked very hard to establish cordial relationships with the federal government; CHA's main handicap was its location in Toronto. This problem was solved with its move to Ottawa in early 1978.

Once in Ottawa, CHA's focus in the 1980s was on effectively lobbying the federal government to support many major projects. If these proved to be successful—and several did—the benefits for Canada's health system would be considerable. By the 1990s, CHA was becoming caught up in the effect of health reform that was sweeping across provincial health systems. For a brief period, its advocacy efforts had to move to the backburner, so that CHA could refocus on what its core business would be in the future. But, by 1999 and over the next several years, CHA became ever more influential both alone and working with others to advocate on behalf of the health system. In fact, every federal election between 1999 and 2005 was fought on a health agenda, with CHA playing a key role to keep health issues in the public forum. At the beginning of the twenty-first century, CHA can rightly say that it has become the undisputed voice for Canada's health system.

Endnotes

1. These boards included the Wartime Industries Control Board, the Wartime Prices and Trade Board, the National Selective Service, the National War Labour Board and the Foreign Exchange Control Board.

2. The other organizations that were invited by the federal government to attend the conference included CMA, CNA, the Canadian Institute of Chartered Accountants, the Canadian Council of Professional Engineers and the Royal Architectural Institute of Canada.

3. A cash floor for the CHST of $12.5 billion had been recommended by the National Forum on Health in the 1996 final report. The CHST is a block fund that provides transfers—both cash payment and taxpoints—to the provinces and territories to support health care, post-secondary education, social services and social assistance programs. The provinces and territories can direct the money to their priorities.

Part VI

LOOKING AHEAD

While every organization has a primary responsibility to fulfill its current mandate and objectives as set by its board, it also needs to plan for its future. To ensure that it will be viable for its members, a healthy and vital organization looks forward. This part of the book presents some key projects that the Canadian Healthcare Association undertook over the course of its history to help Canada's health system move forward or to meet the wishes of its members to look ahead to a preferred future.

Although some of these projects have been described in chapter 10, the intent there was to look at the events that led to the establishment of an independent health organization, CHA's role in its setup and the relationship of the two organizations today. This chapter details the actual project, its purpose and the output or product that resulted from the development of the special project. While there is some duplication, the intent of the two chapters is quite different.

Chapter 16 describes some of the major projects that the association undertook in order to prepare hospitals—and in turn its members—for the future. While some of these had a major impact on the health system in Canada (e.g., the development of the accounting book and the MIS Project), others struggled for several years and were finally shut down either from lack of money or lack of interest. Others went into limbo but were eventually resurrected by the federal government to meet a current need.

16

PREPARING FOR THE FUTURE: THE ASSOCIATION'S SPECIAL PROJECTS

"In futures thinking, it is necessary to anticipate change and to ask what are we going to do about it."

(BEZOLD 1985, 42)

Along with its services and programs, the Canadian Healthcare Association (CHA) was also involved in many special projects. Some of these proposed new methods or processes to improve the efficiency and effectiveness of health services management; others supported a special celebratory event, the implementation of a new system, task force or foundation or produced documents and special conferences on issues either identified by the government or by CHA's member organizations.

All of these projects required the input and a considerable investment of CHA's resources in order to bring them to fruition. Some were developed solely by CHA and some required the financial support of the federal government through its various funding mechanisms. Others received the financial assistance and support of CHA's membership and, occasionally, support and assistance were sought from the private sector.

Eventually, some of these projects became part of the services offered by the association. Others were shut down either because they had served their purpose or because they lacked adequate financing and were no longer supported by potential users or customers. Several of these projects were transferred to newly created autonomous organizations and have become powerful organizations in their own right and make valuable contributions to Canada's health system today.

Looking to the Future, 1931 to 1952

The Canadian Hospital Council was considerably limited in its ability to undertake any major projects because it lacked both full-time staff and financial resources. Nevertheless, in 1931, the assembly delegates were informed that the council would study issues that might impact on Canada's hospitals. All major issues for study were assigned to a council committee that included Executive Committee members, member representatives and experts in various fields. Often these studies were conducted with the secretarial and financial support of the Canadian Medical Association's Department of Hospital Service. By 1933, several studies were underway with some reports due for presentation at the 1935 general assembly meeting.[1]

One of the hospital council's main concerns had been the collection of information on Canada's hospitals. Dr. Harvey Agnew had worked closely with the federal government in the late 1920s to collect information on their location and size, the type and number of beds, as well as their budget. By 1931, the Dominion Bureau of Statistics (DBS) had taken on the role of compiling annual hospital statistics "at the urgent request of the . . . Council" ("Uniformity" 1935, 20). But the requirements for reporting to the bureau and to the various provincial governments differed considerably across the country. There was an urgent need for a uniform reporting system for Canada.

Uniform Financial and Statistical Information

It was this need to report uniform information that resulted in the 1933 assembly delegates approval of a special study to be undertaken by the council. This special committee, which was "appointed to deal with the question of uniform accounting, statistics and records" in Canada's hospitals, included hospital superintendents and accountants, two hospital auditors, a member from DBS, two members from the provincial departments of health and one hospital secretary ("Uniformity" 1935, 20). They were to report back at the next assembly.

The 1935 general assembly delegates accepted the committee's recommendation that public hospitals in Canada adopt a standard form for reporting their financial and statistical returns. Their report also contained complete accounting forms and schedules for hospitals to use. The form had been approved by the council after extensive consultation with the federal bureau, provincial governments and hospital personnel. In fact, the general assembly of 1935 spent considerable time meeting with representatives at DBS discussing how to develop a uniform system to collect data on Canada's hospitals.

The public hospitals in Canada did not react positively to this recommendation. Many smaller hospitals found the form too complex to use, so the form was modified in 1941. However, larger hospitals reported that it was not complete enough for their more complex services. By 1943, seven of the nine provinces—only Ontario and Alberta did not use the form—had adopted the system and DBS was collecting information based on it. By 1945, Alberta agreed to adopt the form as well, and Ontario was using the reporting system by 1947.

In 1947, the chair of the council's Committee on Accounting and Statistics was prepared to move to the next phase in a uniform financial reporting system, that is, the development of a standard accounting manual. Over the decades, each hospital in Canada had developed its own process, which responded to its needs and requirements, for recording financial information. But there were considerable disparities in this information, which rendered comparisons among hospitals and across provinces difficult, if not impossible. Various manuals were being used across the country, including one from the American Hospital Association. But there were serious problems in the way of developing the manual: 1) small hospitals still had little expertise in reporting all but basic financial costs, 2) few hospitals in Canada had trained financial experts on staff and 3) many hospitals didn't use standard financial terminology.

By 1949, another player had entered the field of setting uniform accounting standards. Compulsory hospital insurance plans, Blue Cross plans, the professionalization of accounting practices and the increasing complexities of larger hospitals were impacting the collection of financial information for hospitals. For these reasons, the federal government had held a Dominion-Provincial Conference on Hospital Statistics in 1949 and essentially took over the role that the hospital council's Committee on Accounting and Statistics had played for almost two decades. The council conceded that the federal government should be involved in this area, as long as hospitals had a significant say in accounting procedures.

By 1952, four provinces in Canada had developed their own accounting manuals and DBS had published definitions and instructions for completing their reporting schedules. But a standard working manual that would be "a guide in setting up hospital accounting systems and . . . a reference text in their operation" (CHC 1950, 275) was needed for Canada's public hospitals. Described as a "formidable undertaking," nevertheless, the Executive Committee decided that the hospital council should provide the leadership to Canada's hospitals and investigate developing a manual.

In May 1951, the Executive Committee directed council staff to develop an accounting manual at a cost not to exceed $25,000, provided that funds were available through the federal health grants program. The council received the funding, with the understanding that it would manage all aspects of the project, including promotion, distribution and revision of the manual as needed.

With the publication of the *Canadian Hospital Accounting Manual (CHAM)* in 1952, it became one of CHA's major contributions to hospital management. The main objective of *CHAM* was to provide a guide on accounting matters in hospitals "to assist hospital management in the planning and control of hospital operations" (*CHAM* 1968, 1). Minutes of board meetings record that there was widespread acceptance of the manual by hospitals in Canada.

National Hospital Day

National Hospital Day was first suggested in an editorial in an American journal called *Hospital Management*. It was endorsed by President Warren G. Harding and first celebrated on 12 May 1921 to commemorate the birth date of Florence Nightingale, considered the founder of modern nursing. The purpose of the event was to promote awareness of health issues and the hospital to the local community. The date was quickly adopted in the United States and fully supported by Dr. Malcolm T. MacEachern, the hospital superintendent of the Vancouver General Hospital. The British Columbia Hospitals Association was the first provincial association in Canada to endorse the event.

On his election as president of the American Hospital Association (AHA) in 1924, Dr. MacEachern directed that a committee, which he chaired, be set up to promote hospital day; he regarded this as one of his most important duties. In 1930, the Canadian Nurses

Dr. Malcolm T. MacEachern, Superintendent, Vancouver General Hospital, circa 1921, Was the First Hospital Superintendent to Celebrate National Hospital Day on 12 May.

Association adopted a resolution at their annual meeting favoring the celebration of hospital day on 12 May. By 1931, the Maritime Conference of the Catholic Hospital Association, as well as the provincial hospital associations in Nova Scotia and Prince Edward Island, and Saskatchewan were working closing with the AHA to promote and celebrate the event in their provinces.

Not every province was prepared to adopt 12 May as a suitable date for celebrating hospital day. In some parts of Saskatchewan in early May, many local communities were in the middle of seeding operations—as was the case in parts of Alberta—and they favored the date of 19 June. This date reflected the work of Sister Jeanne Mance, who founded the Hôtel-Dieu de Québec in Quebec City in 1639, the oldest health institution in North America. A number of Quebec and Maritime hospitals also celebrated National Hospital Day in June.

There is little or no mention of the Canadian Hospital Council's support or involvement in this event, although it was covered extensively in the council's journal *The Canadian Hospital*. Throughout most of the 1930s and 1940s and well into the 1950s, the event was promoted across North America by AHA with what appears to be token support by the hospital council. The AHA sent bulletins to all the hospitals in both Canada and the United States advising them about the types of activities that would be appropriate for them to develop.

In 1953, the Canadian Hospital Association (CHA)'s board directed Dr. Swanson, the executive director, to send a questionnaire to the provincial association members "to ascertain their reaction to National Hospital Day and whether or not their support could be expected" (1953a). There is no indication in the record exactly what CHA intended to do with the information it collected. Nor is there any mention of CHA's activities regarding the event. In the same year, National Hospital Week was celebrated as a result of the efforts of the hospital auxiliaries, in cooperation with AHA.

By 1964, Dr. Piercey had determined that the only support for a week-long celebration in Canada was in Saskatchewan and Manitoba. He didn't recommend that CHA become involved, as he seemed to regard this as an American event. But a resolution was passed that same year at CHA's assemby for the organization to become more involved in implementing a Canadian National Hospital Week. However, it appears that the provincial hospital associations and individual hospitals continued to be the driving factors in Canada for the event.

In his report to the board in late 1969, Dr. Brosseau, CHA's executive director at the time, confirmed that National Hospital Day "has more often than not been given little notice at the national level" (CHA 1969b, 5). He stated that CHA intended to give considerable attention to the event, including asking the federal minister of health to issue a statement. The association was also going to undertake a major public relations program to support and promote the event.

By 1972, Dr. Brosseau was able to report to the board that CHA was now actively involved in promoting National Hospital Day and had persuaded the federal minister of health to issue a proclamation on 12 May. CHA worked very closely with the Ontario Hospital Association to develop materials such as place mats and brochures for hospitals. The two associations also developed mailing kits for provincial associations to use to promote the event.

In 1981, the event was renamed Canada Health Day and CHA became heavily involved in promoting the event in partnership with the Canadian Public Health Association (CPHA). Both associations agreed in 1982 to work closely together to cosponsor the celebration. CHA arranged national media coverage in cooperation with its member associations. The association produced posters, buttons, place mats and brochures for sale to Canada's hospitals and developed annual themes to celebrate the date. Eventually, the distribution of these items was taken over by CPHA. By the mid-1990s, as its priorities and finances underwent considerable refocusing, CHA gradually reduced its involvement in the event.

CHA's Special Projects, 1953 to 1977

Canadian Hospital Accounting Manual (CHAM)

By 1953, the association's main concerns regarding its successful accounting manual were how to reprint and revise it, as there were limited financial resources available to undertake either of these activities. The CHA's Committee on Education was also under considerable pressure at the time to develop a course for hospital accountants, so that they could learn how to apply the

CHA's *Canadian Hospital Accounting Manual* Was the Forerunner of the M.I.S. Project.

CHAM guidelines in their hospital. The lack of money, in-house expertise and agreement on exactly how the course would be delivered eventually forced the association to drop this idea. As well, small hospitals in Canada were finding the guidelines in *CHAM* too complicated to implement.

In 1955, CHA's board had decided that any revision of *CHAM* would be fully funded by CHA under the publications umbrella without any government assistance. However, a third party had now entered the field of collecting hospital statistical information. With the implementation of the Hospital Insurance and Diagnostic Services Act of 1958, the Department of National Health and Welfare would determine what information would be collected, what form it would take and what would be done with the information before it was sent to DBS. CHA needed to obtain input from this new player for the next *CHAM* revision, which it did. It then succeeded in putting together a second edition of the manual which was released in 1959.

In order to revise the manual for a third edition, CHA's Accounting Committee undertook an extensive consultation process that included its provincial member associations, the provincial hospital plan authorities, the federal government and a sampling of hospitals. The committee also placed an ad in *Canadian Hospital* seeking feedback from all hospitals on what purpose the manual should play and what should be added or dropped from it. A third edition was released in both official languages in 1968, with an expected shelf life of five to ten years. But the revision and rewriting process was both lengthy and costly for CHA.

In 1974, CHA proceeded to develop a *CHAM Supplement*, which was published in 1975, with funding support from the federal health department. The supplement was to be used by all types and sizes of health organizations and agencies, and paid special attention to nursing homes, small hospitals and newly emerging health centres, as well as new programs such as self and crisis care. It was also intended to respond to recommendations from various task forces across the country that had studied rising health care costs in Canada and suggested the need for such a supplement.

CHAM had proven to be a highly successful undertaking for the association. By 1977, the manual was being used by ninety percent of Canada's hospitals, in more than forty percent of nursing homes, and as a textbook for most university health administration courses. Its use was mandatory in Quebec and government reporting in Ontario was based on it (CHA 1977c, 7).

CHA's Committee on Research and Statistics was again studying the need for a revised version of the manual by 1979. But there were considerable barriers to overcome in undertaking this process: 1) the large hospitals of Canada were much more complex facilities and no longer used *CHAM*, 2) the federal and provincial governments were moving forward to implement electronic information collection systems and 3) accounting principles had become much more complex. A complete rewrite of the manual would require extensive consultation, be costly to do without federal government support and would require considerable CHA staff support, which was already heavily committed to other key projects.

In the late 1980s, the board decided to cease publishing *CHAM* as other financial information systems were being developed that were much more sophisticated in assisting hospitals to manage information.

Hospital Information Systems

With the implementation of the national hospital insurance plan in 1958, the public hospitals of Canada were required to report financial information to the federal health department. To do this, hospitals used the DBS Annual Return of Hospitals, Forms HS-1 and HS-2. By 1966, reports from DBS were three years behind schedule and CHA's members directed it to discuss with the federal health minister how to speed up the release of information from DBS. The members had also requested that CHA study and recommend uniform definitions for hospital terminology.

Arising from the Aims and Objectives Committee report of 1968, the general assembly approved the following recommendation: "The Canadian Hospital Association must undertake the collection and interpretation of statistical data in the health field and should distribute this material to Member Associations" (CHA 1967, 4). CHA's Statistics Committee was charged with finding out from Canada's hospitals 1) what information was needed, 2) what information was available and 3) how to interpret statistical information.

The committee recommended to CHA's board in 1968 that the association develop a hospital information system (HIS) to further assist hospitals in their management responsibilities. The project consisted of two parts: 1) a quarterly statistical reporting system (QHIS) and 2) an annual report on health expenditures, published under the title *Trends in Health and Hospital Care*. The federal statistics bureau, later renamed Statistics Canada, would process the information and distribute quarterly reports to the provincial hospital plans, as well as individual hospital profiles, so that hospitals could participate in the program at no direct cost to them. In turn, CHA would distribute information to its member associations.

But there were problems. Often, the hospitals were either late in responding or submitted incomplete forms. Statistics Canada was frequently late in processing results and some of the provincial hospital plans were decidedly "cool" or opposed to the information collection system outright. The OHA was one of the more supportive member associations; it promoted the system within its province and used the federal report to generate an Ontario-focused report for its members. CHA was dependent on each of its provincial members to promote the system within its province. Without this support, the HIS would not work.

By 1970, approximately 630 hospitals were part of the HIS. But there was still considerable dissatisfaction with the system, especially among specialty and teaching hospitals. In 1971, the federal government set up a working party which included representatives from the Department of National Health and Welfare, Statistics Canada, the provincial hospital plans and CHA's member associations, to review the system. As a result, CHA implemented various changes, published a third edition of the *Chartbooks on Trends in Health and Hospital Care* and released *Management Control Guides* in 1973. These guides covered the major hospital departments such as radiology, obstetrics, housekeeping, dietary, physical plant and engineering, and were intended to assist hospital management in using the QHIS reports more effectively.

The implementation of the HIS had improved the collection of hospital financial and statistical information in Canada considerably. In 1973, the federal health department, Statistics Canada and CHA's member in Quebec asked CHA to explore how an integrated information system, which included *CHAM*, could be developed for the country. New computer technologies now made this type of system much more feasible than in the past. An integrated information system would also be much more efficient than the duplication of reporting that was currently required.

CHA did apply for a grant to develop such a system but little progress was made either at the federal level or by the association itself. The federal government was involved in negotiations with the provinces between 1974 and 1976 over the new financial arrangements it was implementing under the Established Programs Financing (EPF) legislation in 1977. From 1972 to 1976, CHA was dealing internally with serious financial problems, which were being reviewed by the board and its membership. Preoccupied by the review process and running significant deficits, CHA was not in a position to develop an integrated reporting system on its own.

The association had also reduced its role in HIS and its relationship with Statistics Canada had suffered as a result. In a meeting with Health Minister Marc Lalonde in March 1977, CHA asked what had happened to its proposal to integrate the financial information system. Federal officials assured CHA's board that the project would receive due consideration because the new financial arrangements would require a different type of information collection system. The minister urged CHA to reconnect with his department when its move to Ottawa was complete.

CHA's Special Projects in the Capital, 1978 to 2006

With CHA's move to Ottawa, its board and members expected the organization to establish much closer ties to the federal government and its agencies, and to work closely with federal officials to resolve problems in areas that impacted the hospitals of Canada. These new directions for CHA meant that it had to find more resources for its Research and Statistics Department, as well as increase its representation activities. (*See* chapters 14 and 15 for more details on these activities.) Its limited resources over the past five years had meant that CHA had provided little or no feedback to Statistics Canada on QHIS or on the development of an integrated information collection system. How information was to be reported to the various levels of government would change significantly with the passage of the EPF legislation in 1977.

Management Information System (MIS) Project[2]

Management processes in hospitals rely heavily on information. Planning, resource allocation, productivity analysis, medical and nursing quality control, statistical reporting, research requirements and program evaluation all require relevant, accurate and timely information. Data collection and reporting must be uniform throughout a facility and the health system in order to be useful for decision-making.

This system—the Management Information System (MIS) Project—evolved from a growing recognition within the health care field that national financial accounting guidelines, as represented by CHA's *Canadian Hospital Accounting Manual* and its hospital information system, were no longer meeting the needs of Canada's hospitals and the provincial health ministries to which they reported. Rising health care costs were forcing hospitals to use more sophisticated technologies to manage their information requirements. Hospitals were now making increasingly more difficult resource allocation decisions, which needed to be based on the integration of financial, statistical and clinical data. Historically, these data had been collected, processed and reported separately.

The federal and provincial governments were also supportive of a national framework and had held discussions in the spring of 1978 on how to improve the quality of health information systems. In an editorial in the journal *Dimensions*, CHA's executive director noted that: "A fundamental concept guiding these discussions was that of an 'information pyramid', where information required by provincial and federal authorities would flow in increasingly aggregrated form from the data generated by the institutions. . ." (Martin 1979, 6).

The MIS Project was designed to develop national guidelines for the integration of all information required for the effective management of health care facilities. One of the most important innovations in the design of this system would be the inclusion of clinical data. CHA supported the initiative and suggested that work begin immediately to design such a framework to avoid the development of different systems across the country. This would hinder the ability to collect and analyze comparable information from province to province and from facility to facility.

The term "hospital management information system" implied a computerized data communication and storage network to handle all clinical, statistical and financial information in the hospital. A fully integrated system would include the following elements: on-line entry, the retrieval and display of information via specialized terminals, automatic information communications throughout the hospital, a system that supported daily operations in the hospital and the use of a fully integrated approach.

A preliminary analysis of the systems in place at the time indicated that the development of an integrated hospital system had been slow in Canada. Five factors were identified as having hindered progress. These were: 1) technological—an inadequate understanding and analysis of hospital information needs; 2) economic—development efforts were often underfunded; 3) external—the demand on hospitals to report to external agencies was growing rapidly; 4) conceptual limitations—systems were often designed solely to collect data for statistical reporting purposes, with no consideration for how they could support decision-making; and 5) managerial education—insufficient educational opportunities.

In an effort to address these problems, CHA sought financial support from the federal government to initiate a project to develop information tools to improve management control and generate more efficient and effective internal processes for Canada's health care facilities. Thus, the focus was on the institution and the specific needs of its managers for timely, valid, comparable and reliable performance indicators. The project would identify a standardized basic framework for use by all institutions that could be modified to meet individual needs. The core data to be collected would not only meet internal needs but also external agency requirements. This would considerably reduce the duplication of work being done at the time.

An important component of the project was to produce a data dictionary to provide standard definitions for all data elements in the system. This would be necessary for interhospital and interprovincial comparisons and to satisfy virtually all health-care-related information requirements on a national basis. The process was expected to lead to the development of a new chart of accounts and would replace *CHAM*.

This initial stage was developed and supported by CHA's Research and Statistics Department staff, with the support of a committee of experts from the health sector. CHA also financed all the developmental costs for the preparation and submission of a funding request to the Federal/Provincial Advisory Committee on Institutions and Medical Services in 1980 to implement what was now being referred to as the MIS Project. In the first year of the project, MIS was to develop an information framework. Springing from that, the project staff identified more specific products for development to support the framework. Work proceeded in the areas of workload measurement in hospital nursing and diagnostic and therapeutic departments.

In November 1981, CHA announced that funding had been approved for the next phase of the project. The federal and provincial ministries of health, acting through the Federal/Provincial Advisory Committee on Institutions and Medical Services, were prepared to underwrite the one-million-dollar cost of this phase, which was to be completed by 1984. At the time, the provincial ministries paid eighty percent of the project costs and the federal government supported the other twenty percent. A national steering committee to oversee the project was appointed in 1982 with representation from the provincial health associations, CHA and the federal/provincial advisory committee.

Both a project director and professional staff were recruited. CHA provided the necessary office space and administrative support for the project, with CHA's vice-president of research representing CHA on the steering committee. Throughout this phase of the project, MIS staff developed guidelines for hospitals to ensure that whatever systems were implemented would meet their internal and existing needs.

During the following eight years from 1984 to 1992, the MIS Project completed significant work in developing a set of guidelines. These were produced in binder format under the title of *Guidelines for the Management of Information Systems in Canadian Hospitals*. The guidelines consisted of nineteen manuals: a core manual called *Frameworks and Functions*, a glossary of terminology, an accounting guidelines manual to replace *CHAM* and sixteen service or departmental manuals. The manuals were all published in loose-leaf format for easy update.

Each manual included the recommended statistics and indicators for the service, the workload measurement system that would apply to the service, appropriate audit tools and directions for management's use of the information. While the focus was originally on the hospital, eventually the MIS Project encompassed the provision of similar guidelines and measurement tools for long-term care facilities and community health organizations. For several years, CHA managed the inventory and distribution of these products for the MIS Project through its Publications Department. Along with the guidelines, MIS staff also implemented programs and provided educational, consultation and audit services for hospitals.

In 1985, the MIS Project staff completed work on the guidelines and started implementing them in ten Canadian hospitals. Work in these test sites was to be completed by the end of 1987, with the initial testing focused on financial systems and workload measurement systems at the department level.

In November 1988, the federal-provincial advisory committee approved the establishment of a three-member task force, composed of representatives from Health and Welfare Canada, the MIS Project and the advisory committee. Its mandate was to establish an integrated steering committee to direct the activities of both the National Hospital Productivity Improvement Program (NHPIP), a separate organization under the jurisdiction of Health and Welfare Canada, and the MIS Project. Following deliberations, the two projects were merged to form a new corporation called The MIS Group in 1990.

The new MIS Group, which had been located at CHA's headquarters at 17 York Street, moved into space at 24 Clarence Street, a building CHA shared with another national organization. As the project continued to expand and to increase its staff, mandate and funding, the project was eventually merged with other organizations to form the highly visible and influential Canadian Institute for Health Information (CIHI). (*See* chapter 10 for the chronology of events, including the challenges and barriers to its success, that led to setting up The MIS Project and its evolution into CIHI.)

CHA had successfully managed to provide leadership for Canada's health system in developing not only a uniform accounting system but an integrated framework, including guidelines, that enabled the health care facilities in Canada to collect information on their services and how cost-effective they are and, thus, to enable the system's managers to determine the best way in which to allocate funding resources to provide quality care for Canadians.

Task Force on Energy Management in Health Care Facilities in Canada

By the late 1970s, the world's oil-producing countries had banded together to raise the cost of oil and to cut production. This decision triggered a worldwide energy crisis that resulted in a rapid increase in energy costs, especially for oil, based on the assumption that the resource was declining much more rapidly than originally anticipated. Because Canada's health care facilities were important and significant consumers of energy, it was important to investigate the magnitude of increasing energy costs on them and to determine what was being done by health facilities and CHA's provincial member associations to address this crisis. This included looking at what efforts facilities were undertaking to conserve energy and cut consumption.

Many of the other sectors in Canada had already implemented energy conservations guidelines and processes. CHA's member organizations in New Brunswick, Nova Scotia, British Columbia and Ontario had already taken steps to assist their members in finding ways to save on energy consumption. CHA proposed to take the lead at the federal level to provide guidelines for the health sector. In a special supplement on energy, published in its journal, CHA presented five recommendations "to strengthen [the] energy conservation program within the health care industry in Canada" (Martin 1980, E2). These included 1) conducting an energy audit, 2) making energy conservation a high priority in facilities, 3) investing in capital spending projects that resulted in energy cost-savings, 4) implementing energy conservation measures that required little direct capital expenditures and 5) continuing to support energy conservation for the long term.

CHA presented a proposal in 1980 for funding to support a project on energy conservation to the Federal-Provincial Subcommittee on Health Facilities Planning and Construction. This committee struck a Task Force on Energy Management and mandated it to develop and support the CHA proposal. The autonomous Task Force included representatives from hospitals—either independently or through their hospital associations—and from both the federal and provincial governments. Its objectives were to promote energy conservation, provide information on current conservation programs, promote new ideas and initiatives and exchange information on projects.

To support the administration of the Task Force, CHA received a grant from the Department of Energy, Mines and Resources Canada to assist the association in providing secretarial services. The Task Force would function as a clearinghouse to coordinate research development through demonstration projects, publications, symposia and workshops. The Task Force delivered a Canadian Conference on Energy Conservation in April 1981 in Ottawa, with a focus on the Canadian viewpoint, including innovations and new designs, financial incentives for energy conservation and motivating staff to conserve energy.

In 1983, the federal energy department renewed funding for a further two years for what was now called the Energy Task Force. As more and more health care facilities across the country became sensitized to the energy conservation issue, and as local and provincial initiatives were increasingly being developed, CHA's involvement decreased significantly. By the mid-1980s, the Task Force secretariat worked independently, although it continued to pay for financial services and office space from CHA until 1996, when its operations were shut down.

Canadian Hospital Association Job Exchange Project (CHAJE)

The Trans Canada Job Exchange (TCJE), which had developed a computerized personnel recruitment system, had been operating in the commercial field in Montreal for more than a year by 1980. In the process of expanding its operation across Canada, the company had approached CHA with the offer of a partnership arrangement to implement a similar national clearinghouse system for the health care field.

The Executive Committee directed CHA to investigate the need for such a system of health care career recruitment in Canada and to seek the input of member associations. The expectation was that the system would produce a profit for the organization. Trans Canada Job Exchange demonstrated to the committee members how the project might work for hospitals to enhance and streamline their staff recruitment process. With the development of new computer and communications technologies for health facilities throughout the 1970s, this provided an additional opportunity for CHA to implement the job exchange project. Pending the results of a market survey to be conducted that year, the committee recommended that CHA undertake this project.

After negotiating a partnership agreement to share revenues with the firm, CHA announced the creation of a computerized personnel recruitment service, known as the Canadian Hospital Association Job Exchange (CHAJE), in October 1981. The system proposed to bring together health care facilities searching for experienced administrative and technical health professionals and individuals from across Canada who met those requirements. The databank of qualified candidates was the nucleus of the system. Health care facilities paid a membership fee to belong to the Job Exchange rather than the individual candidates. The most important features of the system at the time were its speedy response, low cost, national coverage and confidentiality.

There were operational difficulties including the fact that CHA would be dealing directly with institutional members and bypassing its member associations. CHA would also have to pay for software modifications to accommodate the needs of the hospitals.

In January 1983, CHA added an additional new service called the Health Consultant Referral Service (HCRS), which would provide interested health institutions with a list of consultants who specialized in specific management areas. Unfortunately, economic times were especially difficult for both Canada's hospitals and for CHA; the association was unable to sign up sufficient subscribers to support the project financially. There had always been an expectation that the project would generate revenue for the association, particularly for its Research Department. But these expected revenues did not materialize and, by the end of 1984, CHA officially informed its partner, Trans Canada Job Exchange, that it could not continue to use their program and provide the prescribed services. The project was shut down at the end of the year.

InfoHealth/InfoSanté Project

By the early 1980s, more new and improved technologies in computer and communications applications were being developed for the health system. Leaders both at

CHA and within its membership believed that it was time for CHA to investigate how these new tools and technologies could improve operations within Canada's health care facilities. To assist in this activity, CHA launched the Telidon Project in 1983.

This project was developed as a videotext network. This network connected five provincial associations to a database held at CHA in a host computer. The database included medical device alerts, descriptions of CHA and its members, and samples of other databases that might prove useful to health care facilities. The system could also provide electronic mail and messaging among the various users in the provincial associations (Cameron 1985, 4). Telidon, delivered through a Telecom Canada service, acted as a gateway to information sources. CHA completed an analysis of databases available in North America for health care facilities. It was hoped that the facilities would advise CHA which databases were important and then pay a fee to access them through Telidon.

Following up on this project, both the American Hospital Association State Hospital Association Review and Evaluation (SHARE) Program and the report of CHA's Long Range Planning Committee recommended that there was both a need and a place for CHA in the development of national communications strategies for Canada's health system. In September 1983, CHA's board approved the SHARE recommendation that CHA "develop an electronic telecommunications strategy that will express the requirements of the Association and hospitals as they begin to acquire and use this developing technology" (CHA 1983b, 3). The board struck a Communications Committee to oversee the development of a strategy and set priorities, as well as to act as the oversight committee for the current network project.

By the end of 1984, the CHA board had approved the implementation of a project called the Canadian Hospital Association Information Network (C.H.A.I.N.) and the establishment of the Information Systems Department. Although CHA had staffed a director of communications position prior to this, when the incumbent left, this presented CHA with an opportunity to provide a broader commitment to communications and information systems strategies.

The board directed the Information Systems Department staff to produce a feasibility study document outlining a strategy to establish the proposed network called C.H.A.I.N. This was a complex project and the feasibility study described thirty-two separate stages, each with its own specific time frames, that would need to be implemented.

Originally, the project was to be operated entirely by CHA with the majority of the work to be carried out by Information Systems staff. At various stages, additional staff and the services of provincial hospital/health member associations would be recruited. When CHA's staff did not have the necessary time or technical expertise and knowledge, then external consultants would be hired. The feasibility study was presented to CHA's board in June 1985 and approved, along with a motion for the department to provide a business plan that included details on financing, marketing and the participation of CHA's member associations. The business plan was accepted and endorsed by the board in September 1985, when the project was officially renamed InfoHealth/InfoSanté.

Because of the complexity of the project, it was expected that CHA would need to involve many other organizations in the development of InfoHealth. The board directed CHA to develop an additional strategic document outlining how CHA proposed to deal with suppliers, telecommunications carriers and information providers, and what areas would need to be covered in these complex negotiations. For example, on the question of telecommunications, there were only two providers in Canada at the time: Telecom Canada, which was a consortium of all Canadian telephone companies based in Ottawa, and CN/CP based in Toronto. Eventually, Telecom Canada became the partner communications carrier in the project.

As part of the strategic planning and preliminary work to be done before the project was launched, CHA needed to find out who had what information and identify and analyze the information needs of current and future users. In conjunction with the provincial member hospital and health associations, CHA staff conducted nine workshops in 1985 with health care administrators and other professionals to determine precisely what types of on-line information would be useful to these potential users. A top-ten list identified information on Canadian health and hospital statistics as the number one issue. Other areas included newsletters on new developments and activities in the health system; information on medical and hospital equipment, computer hardware and software, and drugs; and several other types of information.

CHA had also identified key information sources that maintained databases at the time. These included government agencies, private companies, universities and hospitals themselves. Some of these were delivered through database brokers or gateway communication companies who provided access to users. CHA next explored the various organizations and database delivery options and their costs, and defined those who could adequately fulfill the needs of future users at a reasonable cost.

The InfoHealth/InfoSanté communication network was officially launched by CHA and Telecom Canada in March 1986. As described in an editorial in *Dimensions*, InfoHealth was "a modification of the iNet 2000 service, which [was] provided nationwide by the member companies of Telecom Canada. InfoHealth [was] specifically customized for use in Canada's health care system" (Cameron 1985, 4). Essentially, it was designed to provide faster access to information sources, save time and find solutions to problems (Ibid.). The idea was to enable both health facilities and individuals working in them to log into various databases; retrieve, edit and file information in an electronic workspace; or send the information to CHA, its member associations, other organizations or individuals through the InfoHealth electronic message service.

InfoHealth/InfoSanté had a long and difficult history between 1986 and 1990 because it was both innovative and complex to develop and implement. This was also a very costly project with a budget of almost $400,000 over the next five years. This amount would include administration, marketing and promotion, research and training, telecommunications and technical support, database development and a newsletter. Each hospital would pay a member fee to access the network, with user fees for other services. Other revenue sources might come from database royalties, an enquiry service and volume discounts.

The board had approved the budget with the understanding that there would be no increase in membership fees to support InfoHealth. At the time of the official launch in 1986, there were 141 subscribers to the service. Financing for the project was to come from CHA's line of credit. But, by the end of the year, projected growth had not materialized and revenues were far short of budget projections.

One of the main reasons for the shortfall in revenues was the difficulty initially in obtaining a commitment from Telecom Canada. They had committed to certain obligations, including delivery rates, discounts, and deploying a sales force across Canada to market the product to the health system. But Telecom Canada also had to be careful not to violate the Canadian Radio Television Commission (CRTC) regulatory body, a federal body that set telecommunications rates for the industry. As a result, Telecom Canada had not dispatched the required sales force needed to reach revenue targets for the end of 1986.

By the end of the year, the board raised concerns about the impact of continuing low revenues from the project and the potential of jeopardizing CHA's financial viability. The board decided that CHA would link into Telecom Canada's system and cut staff in the Information Systems Department in order to reduce the deficit. Revised marketing plans were to be created with the assistance of CHA's Information Services Department and board committee members. CHA was also to seek input from all the provincial hospital/health associations and all of Telecom Canada' members. Senior management were to monitor the project on a monthly basis as well.

CHA wrote to the CEO of Telecom Canada asking for clarification of their role and ongoing commitment to the project, meeting most of CHA's requests to the end of 1987. CHA approved the terms of the letter of understanding which were to be implemented immediately. The project director was asked to produce a document called "Options for the Future of InfoHealth/InfoSanté." Six options were discussed in the final report submitted to the board in October 1987 in which concerns were expressed about the ability of Telecom to deliver on the promised sales targets.

CHA and the members of its board made every effort to save this project. It was monitored throughout 1988 but continued to pile up significant deficits for the association. Members of CHA's board met with senior management at Telecom in May 1988 to find ways to make the project work for both partners. In November 1988, CHA was informed that Telecom had created a new department, called Mediatel, with a mandate to take over all network services under Telecom's jurisdiction, which included InfoHealth/InfoSanté. CHA began a new round of negotiations with representatives from Mediatel to revise all previous agreements between CHA and Telecom.

After considerable communication between the two organizations, Mediatel sent an offer to CHA in May 1990 to pay annual royalties for the use of the InfoHealth/InfoSanté trademark. Mediatel stated in their letter that the majority of InfoHealth/InfoSanté end users had been developed and recruited exclusively by the Mediatel team. Therefore, the company was not willing to pay CHA a percentage of the revenues from the customer base.

The InfoHealth/InfoSanté project was a traumatic experience for CHA. The project seriously impacted the association finances almost from its startup. The upfront funds required for the project were much larger than anticipated and the budgeted revenues did not materialize fast enough, thus leaving CHA in a precarious financial position throughout much of the late 1980s. There were many problems during the implementation period which were not resolved adequately and on time. The selection and contract negotiation with the telecommunication supplier was complex, arduous and at times unproductive. While the senior staff at Telecom Canada were interested and supportive of the project, the marketing and operational staff regarded InfoHealth/InfoSanté as a minor project. The selection and recruiting of on-line information and database suppliers were very time-consuming activities, which further delayed the ability of the two partners to generate revenues and increase the customer base.

Finally, CHA's member provincial hospital/health associations and their health care facilities were experiencing their own financial difficulties at the same time. They could not provide the necessary involvement and support to the project to accelerate the participation of potential user-customers for the electronic telecommunications network. Yet, despite all these factors, many senior health administrators regarded the InfoHealth project as being ahead of its time.[3]

In many ways, this prophecy was right. In 2000, in response to a commitment of Canada's First Ministers, Canada Health Infoway was created "to accelerate the development and adoption of electronic health information systems in Canada" (www.infoway-inforoute.ca/). By 2003, there was more than one billion dollars in capital investment available to Canada's health care system through this federal body.

The CHA Foundation

The idea of a foundation was recommended to the CHA board of directors in 1983 in the report of the Long Range Planning Committee, chaired by Sister Lucy Power. Board members and members of the committee believed the foundation could be a funding resource for some of CHA's programs, particularly for the Research Department. The board agreed in principle to set up a foundation at their March 1984 meeting. After reviewing a proposal prepared by an ad hoc committee and presented to the board in June, the CHA Foundation was officially incorporated in November 1984.

Under its Letters Patent, the objectives of the foundation were to raise money for the purposes of the Canadian Hospital Association as follows: 1) to promote research in the health field; 2) to work with governments, individuals, corporations and other associations, national or provincial, to improve the health of Canadians;

3) to provide education in the health field; and 4) to do all such things as are incidental or conducive to the attainment of the above objects. The members of the foundation would be all the past presidents or chairs of both the CHA and the Canadian Association of Hospital Auxiliaries; however, the foundation was a separate organization from CHA.

At the March 1985 meeting, the members approved By-Law I, which described more specifically the objectives, mandate, structure and obligations of the foundation. The members also elected the three officers of the foundation: David Innes as president, Marjorie Crawford as vice-president and Jean-Claude Martin as secretary-treasurer.

The first proposed fundraising activity of the foundation was to support CHA's Hospital of the Future Project (*see* chapter 10). The foundation met annually over the next few years and regularly reported on its activities to the CHA board of directors. In 1987 and again in 1989, the foundation was discussed by the board in negotiating and ratifying the president's contract, although the board record does not indicate that the foundation was actually contributing funds to the association.

One of the recommendations from CHA's strategic planning project, which had been launched in 1988 and approved by CHA's board in November 1989, included the foundation as a central element of the association's future. The board directed the newly appointed director of development for the foundation, Jean-Claude Martin, to prepare a business plan. The comprehensive plan included potential donors, methods for fundraising, an action plan, a timetable and a budget, which were presented to CHA's Finance Committee in March 1990.

The board of directors reopened the discussions on the future of the proposed foundation at this meeting. Several of CHA's member organizations had serious concerns about both the foundation and the special levy that had been included in the 1990 CHA budget. With their organizational futures somewhat uncertain, these members did not believe they could support the additional costs of the foundation. Although there had been some improvement in CHA's own financial situation, both its board members and the member CEOs believed that the association could not afford to support the foundation at this time. After extensive discussions, the board agreed to withdraw CHA's financial support for the foundation and its chair was so advised. As a result of this decision, the directors decided to dissolve the CHA Foundation at the annual meeting held in June 1991 in Toronto and transfer its assets to CHA.

National Health Policy Reform Project (the Vision Project)

In March 1990, the board agreed that one of CHA's policy priorities was the need for national health policy and objectives. Canada's health system was still undergoing rapid restructuring and reform as a result of the extensive reviews that had been conducted at both the federal and provincial levels durng the 1980s. But the recommendations from many of these task forces and commissions had been directed at the provincial and local level. A major vacuum remained at the national level. CHA was directed "to identify the key issues facing the Canadian health system and to articulate a clear 'vision' or goals for health reform" (CHA 1993b, v).

This two-year project, known as the National Health Policy Reform Project, was overseen by a fifteen-member National Steering Committee, chaired by Jacques Brunet from the Université Laval. In addition, four Expert Working Groups were established with membership drawn from across Canada. Membership included CHA's provincial member organizations, the academic sector, health facilities, health ministries, other health organizations, as well as consultants and economists. A draft workplan, with a proposed budget, outlined the framework, scope and process to be followed to complete the project; it was approved by the board in March 1991.

The final report of the Steering Committee synthesized the input from key informants and wide-ranging cross-Canada consultations, special submissions from several of CHA's provincial members, briefing reports and the vision statements and recommendations of the National Steering Committee.

The full report, titled *An Open Future: A Shared Vision*, was approved by the board in March 1993 and released at the annual conference in Vancouver in June to widespread media coverage. CHA's shared vision encompassed the following key vision statements:

- A System Guided by the Needs of the Citizen Consumer;
- The Citizen-Consumer as an Active Partner;
- A System Based on National Principles;
- A Goal-oriented System;
- A Sustainable and Affordable System;
- A System Where Appropriate Providers Deliver Service;
- A Research-supported System;
- Valued Partners in a Community Network of Health Services; and
- Innovations for Improving the Quality of Service (CHA 1993b, 4).

Published in both official languages, the document outlined CHA's nine vision statements for future reform of Canada's health care system. As well, the document became the focus of the association's policy directions for the next few years and placed the organization at the forefront in voicing its members' concerns for a reformed Canadian health system. CHA had also developed a bilingual Dialogue Kit for use by its member organizations in their meetings with provincial health ministries, their own members and local communities to develop an ongoing dialogue about health reform. The kit was also intended to influence political decision-making and candidates during elections.

One of the largest projects undertaken by CHA during the 1990s, the Vision Project encompassed a broad consultative process with health facility CEOs, managers and other health providers; consumer groups; futurists and academics; business and labor groups; sister national health organizations; CHA's members; and its board of directors. The briefing and component reports, produced by the four Working Groups, were published in a companion document called the *Briefing Report for the National Health Policy Project*. The reports that resulted from CHA's Vision Project remain a key contribution to the health care literature about one of the most turbulent periods in the reform of Canada's health system of the 1980s and early 1990s.

Waste Management Project

In September 1986, a resolution was presented to the CHA board from the British Columbia Health Association (BCHA) regarding the improper transport and storage of hazardous waste. At the time, most of this type of waste was dumped into landfill sites. Internationally, both the United States and some European countries had passed legislation to encourage on-site recycling and destruction of hazardous waste. BCHA requested that CHA lobby the federal government to negotiate with the provinces to develop similar legislation that would favor incineration and recycling programs. Uncertain whether this was the best way to deal with the issue, it was referred to CHA's Executive Committee for study.

The executive reported back to the board in March 1987 recommending that CHA participate in the development of a definition of hazardous waste for hospitals and laboratories and encourage adequate procedures for hospitals in dealing with waste products. CHA was to call in technical expertise through its provincial members.

In 1989, CHA's board struck an Ad Hoc Committee on Waste Management to develop a policy statement on the issue. The Canadian Standards Association was also formulating a code of practice for handling biomedical waste at the request of Environment Canada. CHA's member associations were worried about the lack of input from the health sector in this process. The ad hoc committee members suggested that CHA write to Environment Canada and send a copy of the letter to each of its member CEOs. They, in turn, should approach their provincial ministries of the environment with their concerns.

On recommendation of the committee, the board approved a motion that CHA plan and deliver a conference on waste management in late 1990 subject to receiving funding. The successful conference was delivered in Ottawa in November 1990 and CHA's policy statement on Waste Management in Health Care Facilities: Recommendations for Action were released at the same time.

AIDS Video Project

In 1987, CHA received minimal funding from the Federal Centre for AIDS to develop an educational AIDS video for health care workers. CHA had hired a film company, prepared a draft outline and was working with both the centre and the Canadian Public Health Association to complete the project, when the funding budget for the film ran into a snag late that year. As the situation regarding AIDS became more urgent for Canada's hospitals, CHA urged Health and Welfare Canada to reinstate funding or it would seek corporate funding to complete the project. Finally, in December 1989, CHA received the required funding for the project.

CHA hired a communications consultant in early 1990 to oversee the project and to work closely with the film company. Extensive interviews were conducted with health care workers in four hospitals across Canada. The video, along with a teaching guide for in-service educators, was produced in both official languages and released in 1990 with considerable success. As a result, CHA was again awarded significant funding from the Federal Centre for AIDS in late 1990 for a research project on stress management to reduce staff absenteeism and turnover among health workers involved in care delivery to AIDS patients. This project resulted in publishing the document titled *Caring for HIV/AIDS Caregivers* in 1992.

As CHA's mandate from late 1997 onward focused much more on lobbying and advocacy, and much less on specific project development, the organization has been involved in relatively few special projects during the early years of the twenty-first century. But there are three special projects that should be mentioned.

Policy Brief Series Project

CHA's board agreed in late 1998 that some of its key internal policy documents such as the funding brief, which had been written to build CHA's case on the need for more money to be injected into Canada's health system, merited a much wider distribution. Many of the issues and background documents prepared to brief the board, with extensive input from the CEO Forum and the Joint Meeting of the CHA board and the CEOs and chairs of member organizations, provided detailed information on complex issues. These documents also presented CHA's formal position on key issues identified as priorities by both its board and its member organizations.

To ensure widespread distribution and a longer shelf life for these position documents, a new Policy Brief Series was developed in collaboration with CHA Press, CHA's publisher. The first of these documents titled *Funding of Canada's Healthcare System* was released in January 1999. It provided a much-needed overview to clarify and simplify the complex issues around funding Canada's health system and outlined CHA's position on this issue. This first brief was well received and became an additional reading source for several health administration programs and CHA's distance education courses.

Because of its success, the board approved the release of several more CHA position documents. Policy Briefs have been published on issues such as the sustainability of Canada's health system (in 2000), the private-public mix in funding and delivery of health services and issues around accountability in the health system—both released in 2001—and an extensive review of facility-based long-term care in 2004. The latter document includes twenty-nine action statements as recommended by CHA and its member organizations to improve Canadians' access to a broad continuum of care. The recommended actions were also endorsed by the National Advisory Council on Aging.

Interprofessional Education for Collaborative Patient-centred Practice (IECPCP)

In December 2003, CHA submitted a proposal for a workshop on interprofessional education for collaborative patient-centred practice to the Office of Nursing Policy at Health Canada at their request. The federal department had approached CHA to deliver this workshop "because of its unique role as an association representing the health system, as opposed to one particular profession" (CHA 2004). Health Canada also believed that CHA had the organizational and policy expertise to both implement and deliver the project.

This project involved setting up a national stakeholders' workshop on issues related to interdisciplinary education and collaborative best practices. CHA would be expected to plan, organize and facilitate the preplanning sessions and arrange two study tours. The project had to be delivered by the end of March 2004 and involved considerable work on the part of staff from CHA Learning and Conferences, as well as from Policy and Communications.

In February 2004, CHA staff, along with researchers, Health Canada officials and members of the National Expert Committee met to review the research and discuss the implications of the findings. On 31 March 2004, a successful workshop was held in Ottawa with over 110 representatives in attendance from academia, health care, governments, health organizations and other national stakeholders. The discussions around interprofessional education and collaborative patient-centred practice identified barriers and issues, and proposed solutions for action. CHA submitted a final report to Health Canada on the project, which it had delivered on time and on budget; this successful collaboration further enhanced CHA's reputation in the conference field and also contributed unexpected and unbudgeted revenues to the association's operations in 2004.

Governance and Health System Effectiveness Project

By 2002, CHA's member CEOs were increasingly voicing their concerns both at the CEO Forum and board table about the intrusion of government into the management and governance of the health system. The CEOs, as well as CHA's board, were particularly concerned about the need for independent community representatives on both regional health and hospital boards. There was a widespread and growing tendency for provincial governments to appoint more and more directors to regional boards and to recruit CEOs for the regionalized health authorities, with the requirement that the latter report directly to a deputy minister of health. Throughout its history, CHA had always supported a health system based on community involvement and governed by volunteers.

The board set up the Health System Effectiveness Working Group in February 2003 to direct a project to identify key principles for effective governance, management and accountability in the health system. The Working Group was to seek the assistance of an independent third party to develop a list of principles. CHA was also to develop a position statement on community governance for approval by the board.

By June 2003, CHA had entered into a partnership with CCAF (formerly the Canadian Comprehensive Auditing Foundation) to develop a key principles document. This draft document was circulated to CHA's member organizations for feedback and was the subject of discussion at the 2004 Joint Meeting of CHA board members, and the chairs and CEOs of its member organizations.

Feedback from this in-depth discussion session helped to focus how the principles document could be used for advocacy and in developing advocacy materials. In the fall of 2004, the board approved suggested changes to the principles document, including adopting it as a position paper rather than a discussion paper. It was also renamed *Excellence in Canada's Health System: Principles for Governance, Management, Accountability and Shared Responsibility*.

The "document outlines a set of principles to guide thinking and practice in relation to the governance, management and accountability of the health system" (CCAF-CHA 2004, 1). The final version of the monograph was released in January 2005. As future follow-up, CHA's board approved motions urging the association to seek a research partner to study governance, management and accountability models in Canada's health system and to find funding to support the study. There is no doubt that this issue will surface in the future among CHA's members and at the board.

Summary

This chapter has presented some of the major projects—but by no means all of them—that CHA has launched at the direction of its board to meet a strategic priority or the needs of its membership. Some of these projects were immensely successful and enhanced CHA's credibility as a leader in resolving problems and moving Canada's health system forward. Projects that were less successful were dropped. Some projects made money for the organization and others proved to be a considerable financial burden and were either shut down or handed off to others in a position to commit more funding and staffing to continue them. These special projects were intended to assist Canada's health system. Whether the project was successful or not, it was CHA's leadership and forward thinking throughout its history that created innovative solutions and moved Canada's health system forward into a preferred future.

Endnotes

1. The study committees included small hospitals, hospital finance, legislation, health insurance, nursing, medical relations, accounting and statistics, construction and equipment and hospital administration. Reports from all these committees were presented to the delegates at the general assembly, after being reviewed by the Executive Committee. Final reports were usually published in issues of *Canadian Hospital*. In fact, the October 1937 issue carried many reports from these committees, providing considerable information and guidance on these subjects to hospital administrators across Canada.

2. The chronology of events and the involvement of many others, including significant input from CHA's provincial member associations, is described in detail in chapter 10. This section outlines what the MIS Project intended to do and its end products.

3. CHA did continue to use the trademark InfoHealth/InfoSanté to market its label and list services from the healthcare database for the CHA *Guide to Canadian Health Care Facilities*. In 2005, CHA decided to relinquish the trademark as too many organizations were using the name to market a variety of health products in North America; it was simply too costly for the association to defend it.

CONCLUSION

"Without a knowledge of history there can be no intelligent appreciation of the contributions of the past; there can be no intelligent assessment of the present; and no intelligent planning for the future."

(McGugan 1960, 7)

Guarding Canada's Health System describes some of the achievements of the Canadian Healthcare Association (CHA) during its seventy-five-year history and shows how the association has influenced various segments of the health care system throughout its own development. It also provides an opportunity to pay tribute to the many people who have worked long and hard to ensure both the survival and continuation of the association over the decades. Many of these individuals—often unknown and unacknowledged publicly—dedicated many years of their lives to CHA and this book points out some of their accomplishments on its behalf. Publishing this history book has also been part of the celebrations in 2006 to commemorate CHA's seventy-fifth anniversary.

It has not been an easy history. Organizations such as CHA, which are not-for-profits and dependent on their members for support, must endure the ups and downs of what is often uncertain funding. When its provincial members have been hit by funding cutbacks, creating uncertainty about their own futures, this often forced CHA to look to its own means to ensure its survival. Sometimes, it did so with the full and enthusiastic support of the membership, particularly during the founding years, when provincial hospital associations were little more than volunteer secretariats set up to organize an annual conference and business meeting. At other

431

times during its past, CHA leaped forward with a less than enthusiastic commitment from its membership. More often than not, whatever decisions it has made or directions it has taken, they have resulted in interesting times for both the member organizations and CHA.

This national hospital association has survived in spite of itself. From its tentative beginnings as an ad hoc group of hospital superintendents and physicians in 1931, it has developed into a strong federation seventy-five years later. It can rightly and proudly say today that it is widely recognized as an impartial voice speaking on behalf of Canada's health care system.

Seventy-Five Years of Service

Getting from there to here, with all the ups and downs of its various advocacy efforts, is a large part of CHA's history. In 1931, the responsibility of representing the hospitals of Canada was considered one of the council's primary roles. At the time, this task mainly fell to two people—the president and the secretary-treasurer—both of whom were volunteers and elected members of the hospital council executive. Along with their own full-time jobs, they worked tirelessly between 1931 and 1945 to ensure the council became visible and completed its work on behalf of its members. The work of these individuals both for the council and Canada's hospitals cannot be underestimated.

As the times changed and the workload became more than one person could ever hope to carry out, CHA's member organizations—many recognizing at their own provincial level how demands were increasing on them—agreed that the council needed to expand to carry out their expectations and designated activities at the national level. Throughout the 1960s and 1970s, universal hospital and medical care insurance had created a whole new set of problems and complex issues for the provincial members and, in turn, for CHA. The need for a spokesperson for the health system at the federal level sat squarely on the shoulders of CHA's executive director and other key staff.

But the real change for CHA as a voice for the health system came when it finally moved to Ottawa to take its place among the many other national health organizations that had set up their headquarters in the capital. Establishing closer ties with federal health officials, parliamentary standing committees, and many other national health organizations took considerable time and effort during the 1980s and 1990s. Either working on its own or in partnership with sister organizations, CHA began to make an impact for its members in priority areas, where these had been identified, and to speak on behalf of its members whenever and wherever their views should be heard.

Advocating on behalf of Canada's health system is the organization's core business today. Its members' fees support policy development and representation exclusively. The organization's policy staff and president work closely with the member CEOs and the board of directors to arrive at positions that reflect the views of the federation. Its well-researched position papers, briefs and statements have helped to build CHA's reputation as a credible, honest and knowledgeable voice on the national scene. How it arrived at this position is a considerable part of the history of this organization.

Nor have CHA's contributions to Canada's health system been limited to advocacy, representation and policy development. The association has also been deeply commited to delivering quality educational programs; publishing accurate and current information on the health system in journals, guides and books; planning and delivering conferences and other national symposia; and creating and implementing projects to improve the system. Sometimes, these activities were developed to fill a gap that had been recognized by other health organizations, the federal and provincial governments or by its own members as areas in which CHA needed to be involved. All of these services and programs have added to the organization's credibility and visibility over the years as a leader. Over several decades, they have carried the association financially when additional revenues were needed to maintain its stability.

During the founding years, the Canadian Hospital Council's provincial and Catholic conference members came to recognize the value to them of good communications with their own member hospitals. At the time, the best mass communication tool available was a journal titled *The Canadian Hospital*. It played a critical role for these early associations in keeping hospital superintendents and their staff up to date on what was happening provincially and at the federal level.

The council's member delegates had the foresight to see the importance of and need for a similar communication vehicle for their national hospital organization. They were fully supportive of the council's decision in 1936 to negotiate an arrangement with the owner of *The Canadian Hospital* for the council to take over its editorial direction and management. Eventually, CHA came to own it outright. By doing this, the council had a way to deliver its messages and a revenue-generating service that supported its growing advocacy mandate. The journal also provided the council—and later the association—with a reserve fund to support increasing secretarial requirements. Without the journal and the revenues it provided for several decades through subscriptions and advertising, the council may well not have survived through the 1930s and 1940s, especially during the difficult years of World War II.

By acquiring and supporting a hospital journal, CHA has created and provided a rich and extensive literature on Canada's hospitals and its health system for more than sixty years. These journals have also recorded the historical growth and background of the association's provincial and Catholic members from their earliest establishment in the 1920s until well into the late 1970s. The journals also documented historical federal and provincial legislation, significant federal-provincial meetings, described conferences and annual meetings of many major Canadian health organizations, and provided commentary and editorial on significant events that have impacted Canada's health care system during the twentieth century.

By keeping copies of these journals, some dating back to the mid-1920s, CHA has preserved an important historical record on the growth of this sector through what could rightly be described as the century of Canada's hospitals. These journals also contain a photographic history of CHA, its leaders and its member organizations, some of which may not be available anywhere else in the country.

CHA was also instrumental in urging the federal government to collect and store information about Canada's hospitals—who they were, where they were located and what kinds of services they provided to Canadians. When the federal government was unable to release hospital information in a timely manner, CHA decided that it would collect, maintain and publish its own facts and figures annually. In 1953, the association published its first record of Canada's hospitals in the *Canadian Hospital Directory*. It has continued to do so for more than fifty-three years now.

This information has often been the only accurate and up-to-date record available. Today, the healthcare database, which evolved to support the publication of the annual health care guide, provides an unlimited opportunity for electronic updating in the future, and for the collection of and access to other information on Canada's health facilties and regions that will meet user needs. The association is still regarded as the most credible national organization to collect basic information on the regional health authorities, health care facilities, where these are located, what types of services and programs they offer and who works in them.

Through its research activities and with the publication of the *Canadian Hospital Accounting Manual*, CHA inadvertently entered the book publishing field. As the demand for information on statistics increased, CHA published the statistical review. When hospital bylaws, terminology and definitions, and policies and procedures were required by Canada's hospitals, the association filled the gap by publishing books on these subjects. By the middle 1980s, health care book publishing had been identified as a potential growth area for CHA. Between the early 1980s and well into the late 1990s, the association has added more than two hundred book titles to the literature about Canada's health system. Many of these books have been used in health administration programs in universities and colleges in Canada and have often provided the only Canadian textbook available on the health system.

One of the asssociation's most significant contributions over its history has been in the field of education. CHA's involvement in this area came about more at the urging of others than as a result of an internal decision or recommendation by its staff. In the late 1940s, CHA's own active provincial members, administrators in many of Canada's hospitals, and members of both the provincial and federal government believed that the association was the most appropriate organization at the national level to launch education programs for personnel currently working in hospitals. These groups urged CHA to enter the education field.

In 1951, CHA first offered the extension course in hospital administration. From there, it provided educational opportunities for medical record librarians, head nurses, food service personnel and nursing home administrators to increase their knowledge, enhance their understanding of administration and improve their chances to acquire national certification in their professional association. For more than fifty-five years, the association has provided distance learning to thousands upon thousands of individuals working in the health care field, in both the federal and provincial governments, in Canada's military and in other health agencies, as well as in almost every province and territory in the country.

By developing and delivering distance education courses, CHA opened up the door for many who would not have been able to advance their knowledge and skills. CHA's programs offered nonmedical personnel a chance to learn on the job and to improve their opportunities for advancement within their chosen field and within their facility. In some cases, these educational programs have achieved both national and international recognition for the quality of their course content and the currentness of their curriculum.

Over the years, CHA's distance learning programs have generated hundreds of thousands of dollars in revenue for the organization. As a result of this, CHA was able to support the work of its research department during the 1960s through the 1980s. This revenue often supported CHA's investment in workplace technology in the mid-1980s and again in the late 1990s, and enabled the association to pay off the mortgage on its building at 17 York Street in 1999. These programs have also provided health personnel from across Canada with a chance to meet annually to exchange ideas and experiences at intramural sessions. At the same time, the sessions enabled health professionals to network and interact with each other in Ottawa, discuss new ideas and best practices and, in some cases, build relationships with colleagues across the country that might not have happened otherwise.

And from its earliest days, the hospital council established a time and a place every two years for hospital people to assemble, discuss issues of the day, deal with council business and review and approve the council's future agenda. By the late 1950s, as the membership became more permanent, with its own full-time staff and many more demands on it, there was a need for both provincial member associations and hospital administrators to meet more often to resolve the growing and more complex issues that were developing in the health system. By the 1960s, CHA was holding annual meetings and tying these into annual conferences, with keynote speakers, plenary sessions and more educational workshops for health personnel.

Through the years, CHA was asked by others—the federal government, its membership or other health organizations—to deliver specialty workshops, seminars or symposia on key issues of the day. Either on its own or in partnership with others, CHA delivered conferences on hospital-medical staff relations, computer use in the health field, on trusteeship, and on health and the law. In the heyday of delivering conferences, CHA was attracting over two thousand delegates to cities across the country. Often partnering with its member association in that province, CHA offered health personnel throughout Canada an opportunity to meet, exchange information and ideas, and build linkages with each other for the future.

CHA can rightly boast that it never gave up on the idea of developing a Canadian-made accreditation program for the country's hospitals. From very early on, its leaders and staff supported standards for Canada's hospitals. Working closely with its traditional health partner, the Canadian Medical Association—and others—by 1960, Canada had its own accreditation program well underway. And CHA did much more than merely assist in getting the accreditation council set up. Through the council's own difficult founding years, CHA picked up its deficits periodically and ensured that capable and knowledgeable individuals were appointed to serve on its board. Today, Canada has a highly respected voluntary accreditation program that CHA can be proud to have assisted in implementing for hospitals.

Sometimes, CHA was in the forefront in leading its members to places where they were not yet prepared to go. As it became ever more certain by the late 1940s that the federal government would eventually establish a universal hospital insurance plan, the need for uniform accounting standards and guidelines for Canada's hospitals became even more urgent. In 1952, the hospital council released the *Canadian Hospital Accounting Manual* to assist hospitals in implementing standard financial procedures. Although it took more than twenty years from 1931 to 1952, Canada's hospitals finally bought into the idea of a standard financial reporting system that would enable them to compare themselves with other hospitals of comparable size and with similar services.

CHA's commitment to uniform accounting standards did not end with the manual. The association continued to push for an integrated hospital information system through the late 1960s. By the late 1970s, the association was actively and heavily involved in trying to persuade both its member organizations and the federal government that there was an even more pressing need for a national management information system. More and more money had been invested in Canada's health system, yet no one was able to say for certain what the impact of this investment had been, which parts of the system were working well and in what ways, and which were not.

CHA risked much to persuade the federal government to provide grants, so that the association could explore ways to set up a management information system and develop guidelines. It had to win over both its members and the hospitals and persuade them that there were benefits in adopting such a management system. By the late 1980s, The MIS Project was well underway, CHA's membership was deeply commited and many provincial governments and hospitals were beginning to adopt the M.I.S. guidelines.

Today, another national health organization provides statistical and comparative analysis of health care facility and hospital performance. However, it took more than sixty years—often over a rough and risky path—before CHA realized its dream, started by the Canadian Hospital Council in 1931, of ensuring that Canada's hospitals had uniform financial reporting systems in place that would enable them to accurately compare their performance to that of other health institutions in the country.

Every now and then, CHA has not only been ahead of the health system and its provincial members, but it has also been ahead of itself. Projects such as InfoHealth/InfoSanté, the Health Computer Information Bureau, the Institute for Health Care Facilities of the Future, the Telidon Project and the CHA Foundation had immense potential for both Canada's health care facilities and the health system. Had these projects succeeded, they would have provided considerable benefits to CHA's members, as well as opportunities for CHA to become a leader on the cutting edge of some of the new communications technologies. They may even have made much money for the organization. But CHA had neither the financial resources, the know-how or the time to build on these visions and future thinking. Nevertheless, CHA can take considerable pride in knowing that Canada Infoway and the Health Council of Canada were envisioned by its own leadership long before these organizations were eventually created by the federal government early in this century.

Summary

By writing CHA's history, it has given the organization an opportunity to assemble in one place a record of its accomplishments and successes, as well as its disappointments and failures over these first seventy-five years. This book has described the actions—or lack thereof—of some of the many individuals who have served the organization during these past seventy-five years. It has presented the consequences of some of these actions and described the not-so-successful efforts that the association occasionally undertook. Sometimes, by reading about what others did during similar circumstances in its history, leaders and staff, who come along in the future, may be spared from making similar mistakes. If a history book does nothing more than record what failed or was unsuccessful, then it will have accomplished some of what it is intended to do.

In providing this history, it may also have helped to put CHA into perspective by reminding readers—and those connected with CHA over the many years—that the organization did not arrive at where it is today entirely under its own steam. Organizations must persuade, cajole, negotiate and partner with many others over time in order to succeed. And CHA has learned how to do this throughout its history without losing a sense of who it is, where it has come from and where it may be going. By working and interacting with many other health associations, especially its own provincial/territorial member organizations, CHA has enriched and broadened its own knowledge, experiences and influence. As part of the national health Group of Four, the association has positioned itself today to work on behalf of the health system to find solutions that include these key health partners. Together, they work toward the ultimate goal of maintaining an affordable health system that meets the needs of Canadians wherever they reside in this country.

It seems most appropriate to end this history of the Canadian Healthcare Association as it began, with a quote from Dr. Harvey Agnew. In concluding his own book, he noted the many problems in Canada's hospitals at the time, which remained to be solved, and pointed out that there had been considerable successes. But, he wrote, "there is still much to be done." This is still true today. With the support and commitment of its members, its current and future staff, and its present and future leaders in whatever capacity they serve in the association, CHA should be well positioned to watch over and guard Canada's health system for the next seventy-five years.

APPENDIX 1
CHA's FOUNDING MEMBERS

Hospital Association of Nova Scotia and Prince Edward Island
Maritime Conference of the Catholic Hospital Association
New Brunswick Hospital Association
Montreal Hospital Council
Ontario Hospital Association
Ontario Conference of the Catholic Hospital Association
Manitoba Hospital Association
Saskatchewan Hospital Association
Alberta Hospital Association
British Columbia Hospitals Association
Department of Hospital Service of the Canadian Medical Association

NOTE: In 1936, the Letters Patent were signed by Dr. Fred Routley, Walter R. Chenoweth and Dr. G. Harvey Agnew.

APPENDIX 2
WINNERS OF THE GEORGE FINDLAY STEPHENS MEMORIAL AWARD

This award is now called the CHA Award of Excellence for Service and Leadership.

1949	Dr. Alfred K. Haywood	British Columbia
1950	Dr. Frederick William Routley	Ontario
1951	Dr. A. L. C. Gilday	Quebec
1952	Dr. A. F. Anderson	Alberta
1953	Dr. Harvey Agnew	Ontario
1954	Mr. A. J. Swanson	Ontario
1955	Mr. Percy Ward	British Columbia
1956	Reverend Mother M. Ignatius	Nova Scotia
1957	Mr. Roy Fraser Armstrong	Ontario
1958	Mr. J. H. Roy	Quebec
1959	Dr. Angus McGugan	Alberta
1960	Judge John Milton George	Manitoba
1961	Right Rev. John G. Fullerton D.P.	Ontario
1962	Mother M. Berthe Dorais	Quebec
1963	Dr. J. Gilbert Turner	Quebec
1964	Mr. Stanley W. Martin	Ontario
1965	Judge Nelles V. Buchanan	Alberta
1966	No award given	
1967	Father Hector Bertrand	Ontario
1968	Dr. J. E. Sharpe	Ontario

1969	No award given	
1970	No award given	
1971	Judge Chaiker Abbis, Q.C.	New Brunswick
1972	No award given	
1973	Mr. R. Alan Hay	Ontario
1974	Mr. L. R. Adshead	Alberta
1975	No award given	
1976	Mr. Paul-Émile Olivier	Quebec
1977	Mr. Murray Ross	Alberta
1978	Sister Mary Fabian Hennebury	Newfoundland
1979	No award given	
1980	Dr. L. O. Bradley	Alberta
1981	Dr. Gustave Gingras and Justice Emmett M. Hall	Prince Edward Island and Saskatchewan (jointly)
1982	Mr. Andrew Pattullo	Michigan
1983	Dr. James D. Galloway	Ontario
1984	Mr. Claude Castonguay	Quebec
1985	Mr. A. G. Ayers	Saskatchewan
1986	Mr. Gordon Campbell Eaton	Newfoundland
1987	No award given	
1988	Mr. William A. Kilpatrick	New Brunswick
1989	Dr. Hugh McDonald	British Columbia
1990	Mr. Roger Larose	Quebec
1991	Mr. John MacKay	British Columbia
1992	Mr. Gordon Cunningham	Ontario
1993	Mr. Ralph Coombs	Alberta
1994	Mr. Ralph D. Moore	Newfoundland
1995	M. Claude E. Forget	Quebec
1996	Mrs. Margaret L. (Peggy) Davison	Nova Scotia
1997	No award given	
1998	Miss Muriel Jarvis	Saskatchewan
1999	No award given	
2000	Ms Brenda Montgomery	Nova Scotia
2001	Sister Elizabeth M. Davis, RSM	Newfoundland
2002	Mr. Michel C. Leger	New Brunswick
2003	Mr. Kenneth J. Fyke	British Columbia
2004	Ms Joan D. Dawe	Newfoundland
2005	M. Jean-Claude Martin	Quebec

APPENDIX 3
CHA's Presidents/Chairs

1931–1935	Dr. Fred W. Routley*	Ontario
1935–1937	Walter R. Chenoweth*	Quebec
1937–1938	Father Georges Verreault*	Ontario
1938–1945	George Findlay Stephens, MD*	Manitoba 1938-1939
		Quebec 1939-1945
1945–1949	Arthur J. Swanson*	Ontario
1949–1951	R. Fraser Armstrong*	Ontario
1951–1953	Owen C. Trainor, MD*	Manitoba
1953–1955	Angus C. McGugan, MD*	Alberta
1955–1957	J. Gilbert Turner, MD*	Quebec
1957–1959	Donald F.W. Porter, MD*	New Brunswick
1959–1961	Stanley W. Martin	Ontario
1961–1963	Judge Nelles V. Buchanan*	Alberta
1963–1965	Arthur H. Westbury*	Quebec
1965–1966	Charles E. Barton	Saskatchewan
1966–1968	Judge Chaiker Abbis*	New Brunswick
1968–1969	R. Alan Hay*	Ontario
1969–1970	L. Reginald Adshead*	Alberta
1970–1971	Gaston Rodrigue, MD	Quebec
1971–1972	William A. Holland	Ontario
1972–1974	Mr. Justice Edward N. Hughes	Saskatchewan
1974–1975	Leo P. Chiasson, PhD	Nova Scotia
1975–1976	George C. Sherwood	Alberta
1976–1977	Lucien Lacoste	Quebec
1977–1978	Gordon Frith*	British Columbia
1978–1979	William A. Kilpatrick	New Brunswick

1979–1980	Fred W. Lamb*	Alberta
1980–1981	Sister Mary Lucy Power (now Dobbin)	Newfoundland
1981–1982	A. G. (Bert) Ayers	Saskatchewan
1982–1983	J. David Innes	Ontario
1983–1984	Mme Claire Labrèche	Quebec
1984–1985	Gustave Gingras, MD*	Prince Edward Island
1985–1986	T. I. (Ted) Bartman	Manitoba
1986–1987	Peter Carruthers	Ontario
1987–1988	Jacques Nolet	Quebec
1988–1989	Margaret (Peggy) Davison	Nova Scotia
1989–1990	Thelma Sharp Cook, PhD	British Columbia
1990–1991	Elma Heidemann	Ontario
1991–1992	André Brousseau	Quebec
1992–1993	Michel C. Leger	New Brunswick
1993–1994	Robert J. Smith	British Columbia
1994–1995	James Saunders	Alberta
1995-1996	Gaston Levac	Ontario
1996–1997	Dan de Vlieger, PhD	Saskatchewan
1997–1998	John Baker	Newfoundland
1998–1999	Jean Graham	Alberta
1999–2000	Garth Pierce	Ontario
2000–2001	Edward Bergen	Manitoba
2001–2002	Kenneth W. (Ken) Ezeard	Prince Edward Island
2002–2004	Lorraine Grant	British Columbia
2004–2005	Mary Lapaine	Ontario
2005–2006	Alex Taylor	Saskatchewan
2006–2007	Garnet Burns	Nova Scotia

NOTE: Dr. Stephens was elected president of the council both for Manitoba and Quebec between 1938 and 1945.

*Deceased

Appendix 4
Titles Published by CHA

Between 1952 and 1975, many of the titles published by CHA were handled through the Research Department. CHA did not enter into book publishing until 1986, when the Publications Department set up a book unit.

In addition to conference proceedings, textbooks and "how to" manuals listed here, CHA Press published thirty-three executive briefs between 1986 and 2006, several titles in the Medical Devices Guidelines Series for Health Canada's Bureau of Medical Devices, colloquia for the Université de Montréal and many major policy documents, including the Policy Brief Series.

1952–1953

Canadian Hospital Accounting Manual

Manuel de comptabilité des hôpitaux du Canada

1959

Canadian Hospital Accounting Manual, 2d ed.

Manuel de comptabilité des hôpitaux du Canada, 2d ed.

1968

Canadian Hospital Accounting Manual, 3rd ed.

Manuel de comptabilité des hôpitaux du Canada, 3rd ed.

Trends in Health and Hospital Chartbook, 1968

Tendances en matière de santé et de soins hospitaliers cahier-graphique 1968

1972

Canadian Hospital Terminology and Definitions, 1972

Trends in Health and Hospital Care Chartbook, volumes 1 and 2 (revised)

1974

Canadian Hospital Accounting Manual Supplement, 1974

Canadian Hospital Law: A Guidebook

1975

Papers and Proceedings of the National Conference on Health and the Law

1977

Canadian Manual on Hospital By-Laws

1979

A Zero Base Budgeting Primer

1981

Developing Policy and Procedure Manuals

Health Care Institutions: Terminology and Definitions / Terminologie et définitions des établissements de services de santé

1983

Hospital Medical Staff Organization: An Annotated Bibliography

Hospital Manuals: Model Tables of Contents

Hospital Departmental Operations

The Financial Health of Canadian Hospitals: A Financial Ratio Analysis

1984

The Canadian Health Care System (5 volumes)

A Canadian Telehealth Sourcebook

1985

Introduction to Nursing Management: A Canadian Perspective

Introduction au management des soins infirmiers: une perspective canadienne

Hospital-based Quality Assurance

Quality Control Appraisal and Assurance for Quality Management in Health Care Institutions

The Patient's Right to Know the Truth

Handbook for Health Care Communicators

1986

Papers from the Third National Conference on Long-Term Care

Objective: A Health Concept in Quebec

Non-Chew Cookbook

1987

Managers as Strategists: Health Services Managers Reflect on Practice

Medical Care Quality and the Public Trust

The Health Care Auxiliary: A Practical Guide for Volunteers

Women under Stress

1988

Developing Policy and Procedure Manuals, Revised Edition

The Human Act of Caring: A Blueprint for the Health Professions

The Regulation of Emerging Health Care Occupations

Disaster Planning for Health Care Facilities

Hospital Departmental Operations: A Guide for Trustees and Managers

The Management of AIDS Patients

1989

Risk Management: A Practical Framework for Canadian Health Care Facilities

Governing with Distinction: Evaluation Models for Hospital Boards

Marketing Health Care in Canada

Hospital-based Health Promotion

1990

Canada's Health Care System: Its Funding and Organization

Capital Funding of Canada's Hospitals

Marketing Strategies for the Health Care Administrator

Privilege and Quality Assurance: The Issues for Canadian Hospitals

Marketing Health Care in Canada

1991

Review of Significant Health Care Commissions and Task Forces in Canada since 1983-84

Compte rendu des commissions d'enquête

et d'étude significatives en soins de santé du Canada depuis 1983-84

New on Board: Essentials of Governance for Hospital Trustees

Feeling the Squeeze: The Practice of Middle Management in Canadian Health Care Facilities

Managed Care in Canada: The Toronto Hospital's Proposed Comprehensive Health Organization

La gestion de l'information dans les établissements de santé: L'expérience québécoise

Disaster Planning for Health Care Facilities, Revised Edition

1992

Case Studies in Canadian Health Policy and Management, Volume 1

Case Studies in Canadian Health Policy and Management, Teaching Notes, Volume 2

The Human Act of Caring: A Blueprint for the Health Professions, Revised Edition

Managing Information in Canadian Health Care Facilities

1993

Hospital Waste Audit Manual

Guide de vérification de la gestion des déchets dans les hôpitaux

The ABC of Drug Utilization Review

1994

Recruiting a Health Care CEO: The Definitive Guide for Boards

Canada's Health Care System: Its Funding and Organization, Revised Edition

Policies and Procedures: Producing Manuals That Work

The Reuse of Disposables: A Discussion Paper

Strategy Planning, Program Evaluation and Public Accountability for Health Service Professionals

The Elimination of CFCs in Canadian Health Care Facilities

Quality Management for Health Services

1995

Gestion de qualité pour les services de santé

Developing Clinical Protocols in Rehabilitation

Rédaction des protocoles cliniques en réadaptation

L'élimination des CFC dans les établissements de santé

Disaster Planning for Health Care Professionals, Third Edition, Revised and Expanded

1996–2006

Continuing the Care: The Issues and Challenges for Long-Term Care

The Reuse of Single-Use Medical Devices

La Réutilisation des instruments médicaux uniservice

Regional Governance: A Resource Guide for Trustees

Guidelines for the Management of Latex Allergies and Safe Latex Use in Healthcare Facilities

Integrating Clinical Practice Guidelines into Canada's Healthcare Facilities

Anthology of Readings in Long-Term Care (1997)

Anthology of Readings in Long-Term Care, 2nd ed. (1998)

Managing Missing Patient Incidents: Prevention and Response (1999)

Customized Manuals for Changing Times (1999)

The Evolution of the Vancouver/Richmond Regional Health Board, 1992–1998 (2000)

The Canadian Health Care Glossary (2000)

Don't Shoot the Messenger (2001)

Continuing the Care, Rev. Ed. (2002)

Caring, The Human Mode of Being (2002)

What Good Is Health Care? Reflections on the Canadian Experience (2002)

Anthology of Readings in Long-Term, 3d ed. (2002)

The ABC of Drug Utilization Review, 2nd ed., 2000 (2003)

Strengthening the Quality of Cancer Services in Ontario (2003)

Governance for Health System Trustees (2004)

The Road to Eden North (2004)

Anthology of Readings in Long-Term Care, 4th Ed. (2005)

Change and Continuity in Canada's Health Care System (2006)

Guarding Canada's Health System (2006)

APPENDIX 5
CHA POSITION STATEMENTS, POLICY BRIEFS AND SUBMISSIONS

This is a partial list of some of the key documents, position statements and policy briefs developed by CHA over its seventy-five-year history. It was not possible to include all of them due to space limitations.

1938
Brief submitted to the Royal Commission on Dominion-Provincial Relationships (the Rowell-Sirois Commission)

1943
"Memorandum on Health Insurance" presented to the House of Commons Special Committee on Social Security

1950
Brief to the Unemployment Insurance Commission requesting that public hospitals be excluded from coverage under the Unemployment Insurance Act

1955
Brief on National Health Services submitted to the Minister of National Health and Welfare

1962
Submission to the Royal Commission on Health Services (the Hall Commission)
Supplementary Submission re: Hospital Construction Grants to the Royal Commission on Health Services

1964-1965

Brief to Minister of National Health and Welfare re: Amendments to the Hospital Insurance and Diagnostic Services Act, jointly with the Catholic Hospital Association of Canada

1966

Brief to the Minister of National Health and Welfare re: Recommendations from the General Assembly

Brief to the Provincial Associations and Catholic Conferences re: Approval of the American Hospital Association proposal on Canadian membership

1968

Presentation to the Minister of National Health and Welfare re: Recommendations to revise the hospital construction grant formula, depreciation on buildings, grant assistance for educational programs

Trends in Health and Hospital Expenditures

1970

Brief to the House of Commons Standing Committee on Labour, Manpower and Immigration on the White Paper entitled "Unemployment Insurance in the '70s"

1972

Brief to the Minister of National Health and Welfare and the Provincial Ministers of Health re: The Voluntary Trustee System in Canadian Hospitals

"Report on the Transfer of Functions between Doctors and Nurses in the Hospital" from the Joint Committee of the CHA-CMA-CNA

Brief to the Federal/Provincial Ad Hoc Committee on Plasma Fractionation

Brief to the Deputy Minister of Health on a National Health Accrediting Agency

Response to the Recommendations of the Hastings Report

1978

Brief to the Federal-Provincial Ad Hoc Committee on Plasma Fractionation (supporting Red Cross)

1979

Joint Submission to Health Services Review with the Catholic Hospital Association, Association of Canadian Teaching Hospitals, Canadian Association of Paediatric Hospitals

1980

Recommendations to Justice Emmett Hall in response to the mandate of the Health Services Review '79

Brief to the Special Committee on the International Year of the Disabled

Submission to the House of Commons Special Committee on the Disabled and Handicapped

Submission to the House of Commons Parliamentary Task Force re: Employment Opportunities for the 80s

1981

Brief to the Senate of Canada re: Bill C-50 An Act to Amend the Customs Tariff

Submission to the Parliamentary Task Force on Federal/Provincial Fiscal Arrangements re: Development of a Health Council of Canada

1982

CHA Position on Federal/Provincial Fiscal Arrangements

Submission to the Commission of Inquiry into Part-Time Work

Submission to the Minister of National Health and Welfare re: the proposed Canada Health Act

1983

Submission to the Royal Commission on the Economic Union and Development Prospects for Canada

Submission to the Minister of Finance on the Discussion Paper "Charities and the Canadian Tax System"

1984

Submission to the Minister of National Health and Welfare on Bill C-3 – The Canada Health Act

Exploring the Future of Hospitals in Canada: A Definition Study

Joint Statement on Terminal Illness: A Protocol for Health Professionals Regarding Resuscitative Intervention for the Terminally Ill

Joint Statement on Preventing and Resolving Ethical Conflicts Involving Health Care Providers and Persons Receiving Care

Reaffirmation of 1976 resolution on smoking / Réaffirmation d'une résolution de 1976

1985

Report to the Nielson Task Force Study Group on the Canada Assistance Plan

Policy Statement re Universality /Universalité.

Policy Statement re: User fees and extra billing / Frais d'utilisation et surfacturation.

Policy Statement re: Bill C-18 Blood alcohol sampling/ Projet de loi C-18 Tests sanguins administrés aux conducteurs soupçonnés d'ivresse

Privatize Hospitals?/ Privatisé les hôpitaux?

1986

Brief to the Commission of Inquiry on Unemployment Insurance

Submission to the Legislative Committee on Bill C–96 EPF Funding Arrangements

Policy Statement re: Institutional ethics committees/ Comité d'éthiques des établissements de santé

Policy Statement re: Definition of Long Term Care/ Définition des soins de longue durée

Policy Statement re: Privatization / Privatisation

Policy Statement re: Accreditation; Quality Assurance/ L'agrément et l'appréciation de la qualité

Policy Statement re: Geriatrics/Gerontology Education for Health Professionals/ Formation en gériatrie et en gérontologie des professionnels de la santé

Joint Position Statement on Nursing Administration/ Énoncés collectif de vues sur l'administration infirmière

Joint Statement re: Long term care stream in CHA educational activities/ Composante des soins de longue durée dans les activités éducatives de l'AHC

1987

Submission to the Legislative Committee on Bill C-22 Compulsory Licensing of Pharmaceuticals: A Review of Bill C-22

Policy Statement on Hospital Medical Staff Appointments

Policy Statement on the Need for National Health Objectives

1988

Hospital Response Protocols for Child Sexual Abuse and Sexually Transmitted Diseases in Children/ Protocoles en application dans les hôpitaux qui reçoivent des enfants victimes d'agression sexuelle et qui traitent les maladies transmissibles sexuellement chez les enfants

Submission to the Federal/Provincial/Territorial Review on Liability and Compensation Issues in Health Care/ Mémoire au Groupe d'étude Fédéral-Provincial-Territorial sur les problèmes de la responsabilité et de l'indemnisation dans le secteur des soins de santé

Submission to the Standing Committee on National Health and Welfare: Issues Concerning the Canadian Health Care System and Its Funding

HIV Related Disease: Guide to Policies for Health Care Institutions/ Affections reliées au VIH : Guide relatif aux principes directeurs à l'intention des établissements de santé

Policy Statement on Organ and Tissue Donation/ Dons d'organes et de tissus

1989

Submission to the House of Commons Standing Committee on Finance: CHA recommendation on the proposed Goods and Services Tax

1990

Accessibility to Acute Care Hospital Services: Major Problems Facing Hospitals/ L'accessibilité aux services hospitaliers de soins actifs : Les grands problèmes qui confrontent les hôpitaux

Brief to the House of Commons Standing Committee on Health and Welfare, Social Affairs, Seniors and Status of Women: Health Care Human Resources/ Mémoire au Comité permanent de la Chambre des communes de Santé et Bien-Être Social, Affaires sociales, Troisième âge et condition féminine : Les ressources humaines des services de santé

Brief to the Senate Standing Committee on Banking, Trade and Commerce on Bill C–62: The Proposed Goods and Services Tax/ Mémoire au Comité sénatorial permanent des banques et du commerce sur le projet de loi C-62 : La taxe sur les produits et services

1991

Brief to the Canadian Council on Health Facilities Accreditation: Areas for Improvement in Corporate Structure, Strategic Direction and Operations/ Mémoire au Conseil canadien d'agrément des établissements de santé : Possibilités d'amélioration de la structure organisationnelle, de l'orientation stratégique et du mode de fonctionnement

Policy Statement: *Guidelines for the Appointment/Reappointment Process*

Policy Statement: on Health Service Organization Governance

Policy Statement: on Management Information Systems Guidelines for Long Term Care Facilities

1992

Response to June 1991 Draft Report of the CCHFA Ad Hoc Committee on Board Representation/ Réponse à la version préliminaire de juin 1991 du rapport du comité spécial du CCAES sur la composition du conseil d'administration

Final Report on the Evaluation of the Stress Management Program: Caring for HIV/AIDS Caregivers

Policy Statement re: Health in the Context of Constitutional Reform

1993

Brief to the Standing Senate Committee on Banking, Trade and Commerce re: Bill C-91: An Act to Amend the Patent Act (1992) / Mémoire au Comité sénatorial permanent des banques et du commerce sur le projet de loi C-91 : Loi de 1992 modifiant la loi sur les brevets

An Open Future: A Shared Vision/ Un avenir à bâtir : une vision commune

Hospital Waste Audit Manual/ Guide de vérification de la gestion des déchets dans les hôpitaux

Regionalization and Long-Term Care Issues and Recent Developments, jointly with CLS

1994

Brief on the Importance of "User" Representation in the Governance Structure of the Canadian Institute for Health Information

Brief to the Medical Research Council Task Force on Health Research/ Mémoire au Groupe de travail du conseil de recherches médicales sur la recherche en sciences de la santé

Guide to Policies for Health Care Facilities and Agencies: Bloodborne Pathogens, Especially Human HIV, HBV and HCV/ Guide des politiques à l'intention des établissements et organismes de santé : Les agents pathogènes à diffusion hématogène notamment le VIH, le VHB et le VHC

The Elimination of CFCs in Health Care Facilities (with Environment Canada)

Presentation to the Special Senate Committee on Euthanasia and Assisted Suicide

Guidelines for Health Facility Policy Development on Resuscitative Intervention: CPR/ Élaboration des politiques sur les interventions de réanimation (RCR) : Directives à l'intention des établissements de santé

1995

Brief to the House of Commons Standing Committee on Government Operations on Bill C-224: Charitable and Non-profit Organization Director Remuneration Disclosure/ Mémoire au Comité permanent des opérations gouvernementales de la Chambre des communes sur le projet de loi d'initiative parlementaire C-224 : Loi sur la divulgation de la rémunération versée aux dirigeants d'organismes de charité et d'organisation sans but lucratif

Response to the Interim Report of the Commission of Inquiry on the Blood System in Canada/ Réponse au rapport provisoire de la Commission d'enquête sur l'approvisionnement en sang au Canada

Brief to the Patented Medicine Prices Review Board re : Pharmaceutical pricing issues including patent dedication/ Mémoire au Conseil d'examen du prix des médicaments brevetés sur le prix des produits pharmaceutiques et la cession des brevets au domaine public

L'élimination des CFC dans les établissements de santé (avec Environnement Canada)

1996

Position Statement re: Canada's Health System under Challenge: Comprehensiveness and Core Insured Benefits in the Canadian Health System/ Énoncé de position : Le système de santé du Canada mis au défi : L'intégralité et les avantages assurés de base dans le système de santé du Canada

The Reuse of Single-Use Medical Devices: Guidelines for Healthcare Facilities/ La réutilisation des instruments médicaux uniservice : lignes directrices à l'intention des établissements de santé

Integrating Clinical Practice Guidelines into Canadian Healthcare Facilities (with the Canadian Medical Association)

Guidelines for the Management of Latex Allergies and Safe Latex Use in Healthcare Facilities (with Health Canada)

Regional Governance: A Resource Guide for Trustees

1997

Submission to the House of Commons Standing Committee on Industry-Review of the Patent Act Amendment Act 1992-Bill C-91/ Mémoire au Comité permanent de l'industrie de la Chambre des communes-Étude parlementaire de la loi de 1992 modifiant la loi sur les brevets-Projet de Loi C-91

1998

Response to the *Discussion Paper on Examining the Role, Function and Methods of the Patented Medicine Prices Review Board*

Submission to the House of Commons Standing Committee on Finance: "Preserving and Strengthening Our Healthcare System"

Presentation to the Standing Committee on Industry: "Year 2000 Preparedness: Healthcare Facilities and Agencies"

Response to the *Final Report of the Commission of Inquiry on the Blood System in Canada*

Response to Revenue Canada on *GST/HST Tax Policy for the Healthcare Sector*

1999

Submission to the House of Commons Standing Committee on Health: "Organ and Tissue Donation and Distribution in Canada: Need for Action on a National Strategy"

Submission to the House of Commons Standing Committee on Finance: "Creating a Sustainable Healthcare System for the New Millenium"/ Mémoire au Comité permanent des finances de la Chambre des communes : «Créer un système de soins de santé durable pour le nouveau millénaire»

Presentation to the Standing Senate Committee on Social Affairs, Science and Technology re: Bill C-6 Personal Information Protection and Electronic Documents Act

Funding Canada's Healthcare System (Policy Brief #1)

CHA's Framework for a Sustainable Healthcare System in Canada: Discussion Paper (Policy Brief #2)

2000

Presentation to the Subcommittee of the Standing Senate Committee on Social Affairs, Science and Technology: "Of Life and Death"

2000 Federal Election Primer—*Federal Government Commitments Required for a Responsive, Innovative and Accountable Canadian Health System*

2001

Towards Improved Accountability in the Health System: Getting from Here to There (Policy Brief #4)

Submission to the Romanow Commission on the Future of Health Care in Canada: *A Responsive, Sustainable, Publicly Funded Health System in Canada: The Art of the Possible*

2002

Ten-Point Plan for Moving from Discussion to Action included in: *A Responsive, Sustainable, Publicly Funded Health System in Canada: The Art of the Possible*

Response to the Standing Senate Committee on Social Affairs, Science and Technology Report (Kirby report) *Principles and Recommendations for Reform* , volume 5

The Private-Public Mix in the Funding and Delivery of Health Services in Canada: Challenges and Opportunities (Policy Brief #3)

Background document titled "Patient Safety and Quality Care: Action Required Now to Address Adverse Events"

2004

Excellence in Canada's Health System: Principles for Governance, Management, Accountability and Shared Responsibility / L'excellence dans le système de santé du Canada : Principes guidant la gouverne, la gestion, la reddition de comptes et le partage des responsabilités, joint publication with CCAF-FCVI Inc.

Stitching the Patchwork Quilt Together: Facility-Based Long-Term Care within Continuing Care — Realities and Recommendations (Policy Brief #5)

BIBLIOGRAPHY

Agnew, G. Harvey, MD. *Canadian Hospitals, 1920 to 1970: A Dramatic Half Century.* Toronto: University of Toronto Press, 1974.

— — —. "The Department of Hospital Service of the C.M.A. in Relation to Hospital Associations." *The Canadian Hospital* 6 (Jan 1929): 15-16.

— — —. "The Trend of Hospital Development in Canada." *The Canadian Hospital* 7 (Mar 1930): 27-28, 33.

— — —. "The Relationship of the Medical Profession to the Hospital." *The Canadian Hospital* 7 (Nov 1930): 15-17.

Agnew, Harvey, MD, ed. "Memorandum on Health Insurance Presented to Parliamentary Committee." *The Canadian Hospital* 20 (May 1943): 15-19, 42, 44, 46.

— — —. "Lack of Hospital Facilities Stressed in Memorandum to Dominion Council of Health." *The Canadian Hospital* 24 (Jun 1947): 25-26.

"American College of Hospital Administrators Holds Successful Meeting." *The Canadian Hospital* 11 (Nov 1934): 24.

Angus, Douglas E. *Review of Significant Health Care Commissions and Task Forces in Canada Since 1983-84.* Ottawa: Canadian Hospital Association, Canadian Medical Association, Canadian Nurses Association, 1991.

Association des hôpitaux du Canada, Caron Bélanger et Ernst & Young. *La taxe sur les produits et services : Guide des questions des résponses à l'intention du secteur de la santé.* Ottawa : Association des hôpitaux du Canada, 1990.

— — —. *Un avenir à bâtir : une vision commune.* Ottawa : Les Presses de l'AHC, 1993.

Bégin, Monique. *L'assurance santé: Plaidoyer pour le model canadien.* Montreal : Boréal, 1987.

Bezold, Dr. Clement in Ruta Kilicius. "Futures Thinking: Strategic Tool for Creating a Preferred Future." *Dimensions in Health Service* 62 (Apr 1985): 42–43.

"Brief Submitted to the Royal Commission on Federal-Provincial Relations by the Canadian Hospital Council." *The Canadian Hospital* 15 (Feb 1938): 32–33.

Brosseau, B.L.P. "A Look at the Task Force Reports on Hospital Services." *Canadian Hospital* 47 (Jan 1970): 5-6.

Burcher, Mary L. "The 'Canadian Hospital Council' Elects Its First Officers." *The Canadian Hospital* 8 (Oct 1931): 11-12.

Burnell, Robin J. "CHA: Some Thoughts upon Retirement." *CHA News* (Nov 1995): 1-10.

Cameron, Andrew. "CHA Wants to Serve You Better." *Dimensions in Health Service* 62 (Jan 1985): 4.

Cameron, G.D.W., MD. "Federal Hospital Insurance Proposals." *The Canadian Hospital* 34 (Jul 1957): 32-33, 70.

Canada. National Health and Welfare. *Mental Health for Canadians: Striking a Balance.* Cat. H39-128/1988E. Ottawa: National Health and Welfare, 1988.

CCAF-FCYI and Canadian Healthcare Association (CHA). *Excellence in Canada's Health System: Principles for Governance, Management, Accountability and Shared Responsibility.* Ottawa: CCAF-FCYI Inc. and CHA, 2004.

"C.H.A.-Canada's National Hospital Association." *HospitAlta* (n.d.): 1-6.

"A Change of Name." *The Canadian Hospital* 1 (Nov 1924): 11.

Canadian Healthcare Association. "Memorandum." 30 April 1996a, Ottawa [3 pages].

_ _ _. "Review Mission and Association Services: Final Report." September 1996b, Ottawa.

_ _ _. "Board of Directors' Meeting Minutes." 7 March 1997, Ottawa. In "Briefing Documents," June 1997.

_ _ _. "Highlights from the CHA Board Meeting of November 5 -7, 1998a." Ottawa.

_ _ _. "Briefing Documents: Board of Directors Meeting." 5-7 November 1998b, Ottawa.

_ _ _. "Briefing Documents for the Board of Directors Meeting." June 1999, Quebec City.

_ _ _. *CHA's Framework for a Sustainable Healthcare System in Canada: A Discussion Paper.* Ottawa: CHA Press, 2000.

_ _ _. "Briefing Documents: Board of Directors Meeting." 9-10 November 2001a, Ottawa.

_ _ _. *A Responsive, Sustainable, Publicly Funded Health System: The Art of the Possible.* Submission to the Romanow Commission on the Future of Health Care in Canada. Ottawa: Canadian Healthcare Association, 2001b.

_ _ _. "Briefing Document Board of Directors Meeting." 22-23 February 2002, Ottawa.

_ _ _. "CHA Supports Federal Budget Directions But Remains Concerned about Health System Funding [press release]. 18 February 2003a, Ottawa.

_ _ _. "Minutes of the Board of Directors Meeting." 7 June 2003b, Edmonton.

_ _ _. "Briefing Documents: Board of Directors Meeting." Section 11 Policy and Public Affairs Update, 14-15 November 2003c, Ottawa.

_ _ _. "Briefing Documents: Board of Directors Meeting." 29-30 May 2004, Quebec City.

Canadian Hospital Association. "Draft Copy of Constitution and By-Laws." Constitution. Article 2.

_ _ _. "Minutes of the Canadian Hospital Association." 20-21 April 1908, Toronto.

_ _ _. "Minutes of the Executive Committee." 18 January 1909, Toronto.

_ _ _. "Minutes of the Fifth Annual Meeting of the Canadian Hospital Association." 23-24 May 1911, Niagara Falls, Ontario.

_ _ _. "Minutes of the 6th Annual Meeting of the C.H.A." 4-5 April 1912, Toronto.

___ ___ ___. "Minutes of the Executive Committee." 20 February 1914, Toronto.

___ ___ ___. "Minutes of the Board of Directors Meeting." 15–16 May 1953a, Ottawa.

___ ___ ___. "Minutes of the Board of Directors Meeting." 20 May 1953b, Ottawa.

___ ___ ___. "Minutes of the Board of Directors Meeting." 25-26 June 1954, Toronto.

___ ___ ___. "Minutes of the Board of Directors Meeting." 6-7 May 1958, Toronto.

___ ___ ___. "Minutes of the Executive Committee." 17 March 1961a, Toronto.

___ ___ ___. "Minutes of the Board of Directors' Meeting." 18 March 1961b, Toronto.

___ ___ ___. "A Guide to Hospital-Government Relations." September 1961c, Toronto.

___ ___ ___. "Memorandum to Board of Directors." 8 December 1962, Toronto.

___ ___ ___. "Minutes of the Executive Committee." 14 February 1964a, Toronto.

___ ___ ___. "Constitution and By-Laws." Adopted by the Board of Directors, 26 March 1964b. (Amended by the Assembly 1968.)

___ ___ ___. "Resolutions of the 23rd Assembly Meeting." 27 May 1966, Halifax.

___ ___ ___. "Assembly Report of the Resolutions Committee." 12 May 1967, Montreal.

___ ___ ___. "Minutes of the Executive Committee." 24 January 1968a, Toronto.

___ ___ ___. "Executive Director's Report to the Meeting of the Board of Directors." 26 February 1968b, Toronto.

"Canadian Hospital Association's 2nd National Convention." *The Canadian Hospital* 46 (7 Jul 1969a): 22.

___ ___ ___. "Report of Executive Director to the Meeting of the Board of Directors." 3 November 1969b, Toronto.

___ ___ ___. "Minutes of the Board of Directors." 29 October 1970, Toronto.

___ ___ ___. "Minutes of the Meeting of the Board of Directors." 27 March 1972a, Ottawa.

___ ___ ___. "The Voluntary Trustee System." *The Canadian Hospital* 41 (May 1972b): 30–31.

___ ___ ___. "Report of the Study Committee on the Role of the Association and Sources of Finance." Toronto, 1973a.

___ ___ ___. "Minutes of the Board of Directors Meeting." 11-12 March 1973b, Ottawa.

"Canadian Hospital Association/Association des hôpitaux du Canada. By-Law 1." As Amended by the Annual General Meeting, 6 June 1975a, Saskatoon.

___ ___ ___. "Minutes of the Board of Directors." 30 October 1975b, Toronto.

___ ___ ___. "Committee on By-Laws and Regulations: Terms of Reference." 1976a, Toronto.

___ ___ ___. "Minutes of the Board of Directors." 4-5 March 1976b, Toronto.

___ ___ ___. "Minutes of the Publications Committee." 15 June 1976c, Toronto.

___ ___ ___. "Report of the 33rd Annual General Meeting." 16 June 1976d, Ottawa.

___ ___ ___. "1975 Annual General Meeting Resolutions." in "Report of the 33rd Annual General Meeting." 16-18 June 1976e, Ottawa.

___ ___ ___. "Minutes of the Meeting of the Executive Committee." 8 October 1976f, Toronto, as spoken by Gordon Frith, Chair of the Search Committee-Executive Director.

___ ___ ___. "Minutes of the Committee on By-Laws and Regulations." 14 January 1977a, Toronto.

___ ___ ___. "Minutes of the Publications Committee." 18 February 1977b, Toronto.

___ ___ ___. "Minutes of the Meeting of the Board of Directors." 10-11 March 1977c, Ottawa.

_ _ _. "Minutes of the Board of Directors Meeting." 4 June 1978, Calgary.

_ _ _. "Minutes of the Board of Directors." 21 March 1979, Ottawa.

_ _ _. "Minutes of the Research and Statistics Committee." 5 March 1980, Ottawa.

_ _ _. "Minutes of the Meeting of the Board of Directors." 15 September 1981a, Ottawa.

_ _ _. "By-Law No. 1." Approved by Special Assembly Meeting, 15 December 1981b, Ottawa.

_ _ _. "Minutes of the Board of Directors." 30 March 1982, Ottawa.

_ _ _. "Minutes of the Board of Directors Meeting." 11 September 1983a, Ottawa.

_ _ _. "Report of the Long Range Planning Committee to the Board of Directors." 4 November 1983b, Ottawa.

_ _ _. *Exploring the Future of Hospitals in Canada: A Definition Study.* Ottawa: Canadian Hospital Association, 1984a.

_ _ _. "Minutes of the Board of Directors." 19 November 1984b, Ottawa.

_ _ _. "Annual Conference." [Committee Terms of Reference]. 17 March 1986a, Ottawa.

_ _ _. "InfoHealth Helps Find Answers." *Dimensions in Health Service* 63 (Apr 1986b): 4.

_ _ _. *Health Promotion in Canadian Hospitals.* Ottawa: Canadian Hospital Association, 1987a.

_ _ _. "Index to Strategic Information Canadian Hospital Association." January 1987b, Ottawa.

_ _ _. "Minutes of the Meeting of the Board of Directors." 20 November 1987c, Ottawa.

_ _ _. "Minutes of the Meeting of the Board." 13 March 1989a, Ottawa.

_ _ _. "Strategic Plan 1989." June 1989b.

_ _ _. "Minutes of the Board of Directors." 17 June 1991, Toronto.

_ _ _. *Annual Report 1992.* Ottawa: Canadian Hospital Association, 1993a.

_ _ _. *An Open Future: A Shared Vision.* Report of the National Health Reform Policy Project. Ottawa: CHA Press, 1993b.

_ _ _. *Briefing Report for the National Health Policy Reform Project.* Ottawa: CHA Press, 1993c.

_ _ _. "Partnership Guarantees Best Conference Ever." *Leadership in Health Services* 3 (Feb 1994a): 6.

_ _ _. *Annual Report 1993.* Ottawa: Canadian Hospital Association, 1994b.

Canadian Hospital Association. *Canadian Hospital Accounting Manual.* Toronto: Canadian Hospital Association, 1968.

Canadian Hospital Association and Ernst & Young. *The Goods and Services Tax: A Question and Answer Guide for the Health Care Sector.* Ottawa: Canadian Hospital Association, 1990.

Canadian Hospital Council. "Letters Patent." 7 August 1936, Ottawa.

_ _ _. "Transactions of the 4th Biennial Convention, 8-9 September 1937, Toronto.

_ _ _. "Transactions of the Fifth Biennial Convention." 22-23 September 1939, Toronto.

_ _ _. "Transactions of the Sixth Biennial Convention." 10-11 September 1941, Montreal.

_ _ _. "Transactions of the Seventh Biennial Convention." 9-10 September 1943, Ottawa.

_ _ _. "Transactions of the Eighth Biennial Convention." 19-21 September 1945, Hamilton, Ontario.

_ _ _. "Transactions of the Ninth Biennial Convention. 16-18 October 1947, Winnipeg.

_ _ _. "Minutes of the Executive Committee Meeting." 25 May 1949a, Quebec City.

_ _ _. "Transactions of the Tenth Biennial Meeting." 26-28 May 1949b, Quebec City.

_ _ _. "Minutes of the Executive Meeting." 13-14 September 1950, Toronto.

_ _ _. "Minutes of First Meeting of the Committee on Education." 27 May 1951, Ottawa.

_ _ _. "Constitution and Bylaws 1953." Amended by the 12th Biennial Meeting of the Canadian Hospital Council, 18 May 1953a, Ottawa.

_ _ _. "Minutes of Board of Directors' Meeting." 20 May 1953b, Ottawa.

"Canadian Hospital Council to Meet in Winnipeg," *The Canadian Hospital* 10 (Apr 1933): 26-27.

"Canadian Hospital Council Resolutions Ottawa Meeting, 1935." *The Canadian Hospital* 12 (Dec 1935): 5-6, 11.

CHA News. "Information Shared." (Nov 1995): 1-10.

"C.H.C. Biennial Meeting Held in the Nation's Capital." *The Canadian Hospital* 28 (June 1951): 40-41, 44, 80, 90, 96, 106, 108.

Chown, Ed. "Publishing Crisis—A Lament for Literature." *Dimensions in Health Service* 61 (Apr 1984): 4.

"CHST Cash Floor Increased to $12.5 Billion for 1997-98" [press release]. Finance Canada, Federal Provincial Relations Division, 8 December 1997, Ottawa.

Clemmer, Jim. *Growing the Distance: Timeless Principles for Personal, Career and Family Success.* Kitchener, ON: TCG Press, 1999.

Committee on Training of Hospital Executives. "Training Hospital Executives." *The Canadian Hospital* 2 (Dec 1925): 11-12, 28.

Crichton, Anne, and David Hsu, with Stella Tsang. *Canada's Health Care System: Its Funding and Organization.* Rev. Ed. Ottawa: CHA Press, 1994.

"Crowded Hospitals and Waiting Lists." *The Canadian Hospital* 2 (Mar 1925): 11.

Crysler, John. "Future Options for Research and Statistics" [memo]. 21 April 1977, Toronto.

Editorial. "The Education Jungle in the Hospital Field." *The Canadian Hospital* 46 (Jul 1969): 7–8.

Epp, Jake. *Achieving Health for All: A Framework for Health Promotion.* Cat. No. H39-102/1986. Ottawa: Health and Welfare Canada, 1986.

Fifield, Clark, ed. *American and Canadian Hospitals.* Minneapolis, MN: Midwest Publishers Company, 1933.

"First Canadian Conference on Hospital-Medical Staff Relations." *The Canadian Hospital* 44 (Jul 1967): 28-D-29.

"Focus on Computers in the Health Field." *The Canadian Hospital* 47 (May 1970): 30-31.

Foley, Matthew O. "History of the Hospital Day Movement in Canada." *The Canadian Hospital* 8 (Apr 1931): 16.

Fraser, Jessie. "Canadian Hospital Council Considers Topics of Timely Concern." *The Canadian Hospital* 26 (Jun 1949): 40-41, 70, 94.

_ _ _. "Canadian Hospital Council Adopts a New Name." *The Canadian Hospital* 30 (Jun 1953): 44-48, 50, 62, 64.

_ _ _. "Convention Round-Up." *The Canadian Hospital* 34 (Jul 1957): 39-55.

"Further Tariff Exemptions Will Benefit Hospitals." *The Canadian Hospital* 7 (Jun 1930): 18-19, 42.

"Future Role Report Approved." *Dimensions in Health Service* 51 (Aug 1974): 15, 18-19.

Hall, Emmett M. *Canada's National-Provincial Health Program for the 1980's: A Commitment for Renewal.* Saskatoon: Health Services Review '79, 1980.

Health Association of BC. "Canadian Healthcare Association Releases Sustainability Plan." *Bulletin* (30 Nov 2001): 1–4.

Hesselbein, Frances, Marshall Goldsmith and Iain Somerville, eds. *Leading Beyond the Wall.* San Francisco: Jossey-Bass Publishers, 1999.

"Hospital Construction in 1923 about Even with 1922." *Hospital Buying* 1 (Feb 1924): 7.

"Hospitals Handicapped by Meagre Grants: Ontario Hospital Association Makes Appeal for Adequate Financial Support." *The Canadian Hospital* 4 (Nov 1927): 11-12.

Hughes, Judge E.N. "A Milestone for the CHA." *Dimensions in Health Service* 51 (Jan 1974): 6.

"Incorporation of Canadian Hospital Council Accompanied with Changes in Constitution." *The Canadian Hospital* 14 (Jul 1937): 11-13.

Institute for Health Care Facilities of the Future. *Future Health: A View of the Horizon.* Ottawa: Institute for Health Care Facilities of the Future, 1988.

_ _ _. *Future Health: A View of the Horizon, Regional Trends.* Ottawa: Institute for Health Care Facilities of the Future, 1990.

"Introducing Hospital Buying." *Hospital Buying* 1 (Feb 1924): 7.

Keith, J. Clark. "A Trustee's Conception of His Responsibility." *The Canadian Hospital* 24 (Jun 1947): 29–30, 76.

Lalonde, Marc. *A New Perspective on the Health of Canadians: A Working Document.* Cat. No. H31–1374. Ottawa: Health and Welfare Canada, 1974.

MacEachern, Malcolm T., MD. "Institutes for Hospital Administrators." *The Canadian Hospital* 14 (Dec 1932): 15-18.

"A Major Event in Health Progress." *The Canadian Hospital* 36 (Feb 1959): 48-49, 108-109.

Martin, Jean-Claude. "The Need for a National Framework for Hospital Management Information Systems." *Dimensions in Health Service* 56 (Mar 1979): 6.

_ _ _. "Is There an Energy Crisis?" *Energy Conservation for Health Care Institutions Supplement Dimensions in Health Service* 57 (Feb 1980): E2.

_ _ _. "Liability Insurance: What Can We Do?" *Dimensions in Health Service* 62 (Apr 1985): 6.

_ _ _. "A Year of Decision." *Dimensions in Health Services* 66 (Oct 1989): 5.

Martin, Stanley W. "The Sixties: A Period of Honest Questioning." *The Canadian Hospital* 38 (July 1961): 36-37, 86-87.

McGugan, A.C., MD. "Presidential Address to the Canadian Hospital Association." *The Canadian Hospital* 32 (Jun 1955): 33–34.

_ _ _. "Gleanings from History." *The Canadian Hospital* 37 (Dec 1960): 33, 74.

Monteith, J. Waldo. "Progress Report on Canada's Hospital Insurance Program." *The Canadian Hospital* 36 (Jun 1959): 36–37, 86, 88.

"National Symposium on Computer Applications in the Health Care Field Slated for March 18 to 20, 1970." *The Canadian Hospital* 46 (12 Dec 1969): 26.

Ostry, Aleck, PhD. *Change and Continuity in Canada's Health System.* Ottawa: CHA Press, 2006.

Parry, B. Evan. "The Report of the Sub-Committee of the Canadian Hospital Council on 'General Problems on Construction and Equipment.' " *The Canadian Hospital* 9 (Dec 1932): 8-9, 26-27.

Piercey, W. Douglas, MD. "*Canadian Hospital* Belongs to You." *The Canadian Hospital* 36 (Aug 1959): 31.

_ _ _. "Executive Director's Report to the Executive Committee." 8 May 1959, Montreal.

Porter, D.F.W., MD. "Your President Reports to the 15th Biennial Meeting of the Canadian Hospital Association." *The Canadian Hospital* 36 (Jan 1959): 41-42, 100,102.

"A Quarter Century: HOM" [booklet.] Canadian Hospital Association, Ottawa, 1978.

Quebec. Commission on Fiscal Imbalance. *Fiscal Imbalance in Canada: Historical Background.* Quebec: Government of Quebec, 2002.

"Recent Canadian Hospital Statistics Are Interesting." *The Canadian Hospital* 12 (Apr 1935): 14.

"Report of the Secretary to the Canadian Hospital Council." *The Canadian Hospital* 16 (Oct 1939): 15-19.

"Resolutions." *The Canadian Hospital* 34 (July 1957): 57, 80.

"Resolutions Adopted at Quebec by the Canadian Hospital Council." *The Canadian Hospital* 26 (Jun 1949): 44–45, 64–65, 104.

Romanow, Roy J., QC. *Building on Values: The Future of Health Care in Canada.* Report of the Commission on the Future of Health Care in Canada. Cat. No. CP32-85/2002E. Saskatoon: Commission on the Future of Health Care in Canada, 2002.

"Should Hospital Employees Form Unions?" *The Canadian Hospital* 11 (Dec 1932): 20.

Stephens, George F., MD. "Presidential Address Biennial Meeting Canadian Hospital Council." *The Canadian Hospital* 20 (Oct 1943): 29-31, 72.

"Stephens Memorial Award to be Presented at C.H.C. Biennial Meeting." *The Canadian Hospital* 30 (Apr 1953): 41-42.

Stevens, Edward F. "The Trend in Hospital Construction on the North American Continent." *The Canadian Hospital* 9 (Jan 1932): 24, 26, 32.

Swanson, A.L., MD. "Obiter Dicta." *The Canadian Hospital* 30 (Jan 1953): 31.

Swanson, Arnold, MD. "Opening a Door." *The Canadian Hospital* 29 (Dec 1952): 35.

Swanson, Arnold L., MD. "Accreditation Service." *The Canadian Hospital* 30 (Jun 1953): 37-38, 60.

Taylor, Malcolm G. *Health Insurance and Canadian Public Policy: The Seven Decisions That Created the Canadian Health Insurance System.* Montreal: McGill-Queen's University Press, 1978.

Trainor, O.C., MD. "Presidential Address to the Canadian Hospital Council." *The Canadian Hospital* 30 (Jun 1953): 33-34, 116-117.

Turner, J. Gilbert, MD, FACHA. "Presidential Address." (Jul 1957): 34–36, 88.

"Uniformity in Hospital Statistical Reports Is Desirable." *The Canadian Hospital* 12 (Dec 1935): 20-21.

"With the Auxiliaries." *The Canadian Hospital* 28 (Jul 1951): 62.

Working Party of the Department of National Health and Welfare. *Canadian Hospital Terminology and Definitions.* Toronto: Canadian Hospital Association, 1972.

"Your Cooperation Is Required in Nation-Wide Survey." *The Canadian Hospital* 8 (Apr 1931): 11–12.

INDEX